Fleck

Surface Acoustic Waves and Signal Processing

Michel Feldmann and Jeannine Hénaff

The Artech House Acoustics Library

Surface Acoustic Waves for Signal Processing

Michel Feldmann and Jeannine Hénaff

Centre National d'Etudes des Télécommunications
FRANCE TELECOM

translated by S. Chomet

Preface by Professor Eric A. ASH

ARTECH HOUSE
Boston and London

Library of Congress Cataloging-in-Publication Data
Feldmann, Michel.
    [Traitement du signal par ondes élastiques de surface. English]
    Surface acoustic waves for signal processing / Michel Feldmann,
Jeannine Hénaff ; translated and edited by Severin Chomet.
      p.   cm.
Translation of: Traitement du signal par ondes élastiques de
surface.
    Bibliography: p.
    ISBN 0-89006-308-7
    1. Acoustic surface waves. 2. Solids. 3. Elastic waves.
4. Signal processing.   I. Hénaff. Jeannine, 1936–   II. Title.
QC176.8.A3F4413   1989
621.38'043--dc19   89-162
                                                   CIP

British Library Cataloguing in Publication Data
Feldmann, Michel
    Surface acoustic waves for signal processing
    1. Signals. Processing
    I. Title II. Hénaff, Jeannine III.
    Traitement du signal par ondes élastiques de
    surface. *English*
    621.38'043

    ISBN 0-89006-308-7

Original French language edition (Traitement du signal par ondes
élastiques de surface) published by Masson, 120 Bd Saint Germain,
75280 Paris Cedex 06

© Masson et CNET, Paris, 1986

English translation © Artech House, 1989

ARTECH HOUSE
685 Canton Street
Norwood
MA02062

International Standard Book Number: 0-89006-308-7
Library of Congress Catalog Card Number: 89-162

10 9 8 7 6 5 4 3 2 1

Contents

Foreword

The dominant trend in the development of electronics over the last two decades has been towards the implementation of digital techniques. Yet the history of technology is replete with surprises and contradictions. This same period has seen the emergence of a radically new approach to a class of signal processing problems—and one which lies firmly in the realm of analog methods. It is an exhilarating example of progress in applied science, swimming against the stream.

Rayleigh discovered the existence of surface acoustic waves just 100 years ago. There is evidence that he himself did not regard this particular solution of a differential equation as a matter of great importance. Indeed it was not until the early years of this century that Rayleigh waves were observed as a component of the seismic signals recorded in connection with earthquakes. It is an unlikely beginning to a new departure in electronics —with a time delay of over half a century—but that is what happened.

Acoustic surface waves are useful because they are slow—which leads to the associated components being small; because the transduction from electronic signals to acoustic signals has turned out to be capable of realization with exceedingly low losses; because the waves propagate along a surface where they are accessible to the influence of external electrodes; because the overall technology, based largely on single level lithography turns out to be inherently simple. The result is that surface wave devices are now finding application in many diverse electronic products. Every modern television receiver contains at least one SAW filter; many telecommunication systems —in particular satellite systems—are dependent on extremely high performance SAW filters; large, and to an increasing extent smaller radar systems utilize pulse compression SAW filters; one finds high frequency SAW oscillators penetrating electronic systems where previously one was forced to start with a low frequency quartz crystal source followed by a frequency multiplier chain. The nonlinear properties of SAW materials form the basis of signal multiplication, which has opened up a much wider range of signal processing capabilities. Surface acoustic wave devices are here to stay. Prediction is a dangerous hobby; but there is little risk in the assertion that SAW devices will play an increasing role in electronic systems; that they will survive well into the 21st century.

The authors of this book have contributed some of the high points in the SAW scenario, both on the fundamentals of the subject as on applications. Working from their vantage point in CNET they have been exposed to the range of needs of modern development telecommunication systems, and this has in turn inspired some of their most exciting work. Now it is not inevitable that those who make brilliant contributions to research, are also able to demonstrate the capability of conveying to others the entirety of their field of endeavor. It is therefore with great pleasure that one reads this volume, which is a true synthesis, and one which will make the field accessible to a wide range of suitably qualified readers. It presumes no prior knowledge in acoustics; yet it proceeds from fundamentals to their implementation towards applications in a manner which makes the learning process a joy. The exposition progresses to the point of detailed application. Here a particularly valuable feature is the inclusion of a series of computer programs, which can give a great impetus to the speed with which a new group could arrive at viable designs.

Professor Eric A. Ash
Imperial College
London

Introduction

Alongside the development of microelectronic circuits, new components—perhaps more esoteric—have appeared, which exploit other physical phenomena. The science of microacoustics, born at the end of the 1960's from the union of piezoelectricity and microelectronics, is one of the technologies which have led to an improvement in transmission of wideband signals. In fact, we have to look back to the last century to find the roots of this technique, which lie in the discovery of piezoelectricity by the brothers Curie in 1880 and of surface waves by Lord Rayleigh in 1885. In consequence of the work of the famous English scientist, it was observed at the beginning of the twentieth century that an earthquake could be detected at a great distance by means of three types of tremor: the first two correspond to modes of volume propagation well understood at the time, namely the transverse and the longitudinal modes; the third, which arrived later, corresponds to surface propagation on the earth's crust in the form of an 'acoustic wave'.

Piezoelectricity, which can be used to generate electrically microscopic disturbances in crystals, was not exploited in the technical world until much later, between the two wars in fact. Only the volume modes were exploited at that time, essentially in quartz resonators which could be used to obtain extraordinarily stable frequencies for radio transmitters, and subsequently in multiquartz filters. Complex modes corresponding to vibrations of plates (Lamb waves [Vlk 67]) or of multilayer structures (Love or Stoneley waves [FAR 72]) were studied and used in the 50's, essentially to realize dispersive delay lines for military applications (radar, sonar).

The application of surface acoustic waves (SAW), nowadays called Rayleigh waves, dates from just before 1965 with the invention of an effective piezoelectric transducer, in the form of an interdigital comb, by White and Voltmer. This transducer, deposited on a substrate by photolithographic methods using techniques of microelectronics, offers a method—at once reproducible and stable—of producing vibrations on the surface of crystals. From then on things moved very rapidly—mastery of the phenomena of propagation, development of various types of transducers, research on amplification and nonlinear effects, determination of fields of application, appearance of the first commercial components . . . Although at present numerous developments in 'piezoelectrics' are in progress, the subject has now attained sufficient maturity to justify the production of this work of synthesis.

The importance of SAW in signal processing is due to three specific properties of these devices.

First of all, the technology of SAW devices from techniques of micro-electronics. There are similar advantages in the two areas: low marginal cost, excellent reproducibility, robustness both electrical and mechanical.

In the second place, SAW devices function over frequency ranges hitherto almost inaccessible, for want of an adequate technology—namely, the frequency band stretching in practice from 100 MHz to 2 GHz. Now the development of telecommunications involves the processing of larger and larger quantities of information. Increasingly greater output and higher intermediate frequencies are required and force us to contemplate signal processing devices in the VHF and UHF ranges.

Finally, SAW allow a very flexible approach. The product BT (of the frequency band passing by the time of processing) characterizes the complexity of signal processing. Its maximum is in the neighbourhood of 10 000 but is attained, depending on applications, for widely different values of B and T. In the case of SAW oscillators, the peak voltage can be adapted to the desired function—an oscillator tunable over a wide frequency-band, a frequency-modulated oscillator, or a very stable frequency generator. The accessibility of the surface allows us to deploy over one and the same substrate multifunctional systems in which several processes can be carried out simultaneously or in succession. Moreover, the acoustic wave can interact with an external wave —a light wave, a wave in the space charge associated with a movement of electrons, a magnetic wave, etc. Finally, the association of microacoustic and microelectronic devices—such as devices for transfer of charge (CCD)—makes possible the construction of programmable filters, of convolvers and correlators of various types, whose feasibility has already been established in the laboratory.

Alongside other researchers, the authors of the present work have been among the few workers in France who have opened up this area of technology. This pioneering position has had a large effect on the writing of the book: many of the results are unpublished and the authors have chosen original methods of exposition and of presentation. Conversely, certain subjects which have not been studied directly by the authors have been deliberately treated in a very succinct manner. Finally, some research topics which have not been successfully completed have nevertheless been indicated, perhaps because of the authors' excessive enthusiasm for these subjects.

As in much of the most up-to-date technology, it is primarily military applications which have inspired research in the years 1965-70. The first applications were in fact developed in the area of modern radars and sonars using pulse compression. This technique improves by several orders of magnitude—at constant output power—the resolution capability of the radar, for a given range; for this it requires dispersive filters adapted to the signal to be processed. In this operation, the essential quantity is the pulse compression rate, which is equal to the product BT of the intervals, where B is in the spectral domain and T is in the time domain. Radar signals are processed by means of devices with large bandwidth B, whereas sonar signals are processed through lines with long delay T; but in both cases we can easily obtain a compression rate of 10^3, and even exceptionally 10^4.

In the most recent and most extensive applications, the primary object of telecommunications has been the transmission of signals over different media. For many decades, speech transmission—the telephone—has been the principal objective, even although its importance for telex or facsimile has already declined. More recently, image transmission over distances has become necessary, and the quantity of information to be processed and to be transmitted has therefore been considerably increased. Finally, the advent of 'multiservice' integrated networks, involving the transmission of a great variety of numerical signals, perhaps of very different magnitudes, has opened the era of 'telematics' and of 'videocommunications' in which every subscriber can communicate with data banks, can obtain graphics and fixed images, and finally can transmit and receive moving images.

To meet these objectives, numerous signal-processing devices are necessary, and SAW present, in comparison with traditional technologies, appreciable advantages; and even give rise to possibilities hitherto ruled out. This originality is due to their preference for a frequency range in which few other phenomena can operate, as well as to their flexibility of use in terms of bandwidth and time of integration. The studies carried out at CNET are based on fundamental concepts in the theory of frequency filters, delay lines, and oscillators.

Chronologically, the first specific applications were aimed at image processing for development of the videophone. It was for this reason that research was initiated into image transformers with the purpose of condensing the spatial information of a videophone picture. In the same spirit, temporal compression of the videophone signal required the construction of a large-capacity delay line capable of containing a complete picture. This subject led to work on acoustoelectric amplification and alignment of beams.

This research, moreover, had exposed a weak point in this technology, namely the absence of an ideal material, characterized by considerable piezo-electric coupling, good temperature stability, and convenient propagation parameters. Work has therefore been aimed at research in new sections for quartz and other piezoelectric materials, in the first instance on the theoretical level by the calculation of different propagation constants; and this work has resulted in the discovery of new sections in new (and even in old) materials. At the moment, principally as a result of these studies, berlinite promises to be a material of very great potential. A byproduct of these researches on materials has concerned the study of nonlinear effects. In fact, new properties relating to the interaction of noncolinear acoustic waves have been discovered, and signal processing devices have been proposed and tested; certain correlation and convolution devices, even solid state image analysers could be of interest in the future.

Apart from these relatively complex functions, other apparently simple processes constitute important prospects on the economic level, for example frequency filters and oscillators. Being able to operate in frequency ranges seldom used up to now, SAW devices offer new, and often simple, solutions to numerous problems. As regards filters, a new structure for selective couplers has been proposed. It has turned out to be extremely useful for deploying, on one and the same substrate, a whole battery of filters. Also, the technique of minimal phase synthesis has been applied for the first time to SAW filters to meet particular specifications while improving sensitivity. Moreover, an ensemble of specialized devices has been inserted into digital transition equipment. This development has turned out to be one of the major applications of SAW in telecommunications at present.

In telecommunications centres, SAW filters have been used for the extraction of carriers of quaternary groups from analogue multiplexes for 10 800 telephone lines. Many thousands of these filters have been constructed and installed in equipment over the years. But it is principally in the domain of satellite telecommunications and digital beams that essential openings have been found for SAW devices: linear or minimal phase intermediate-frequency filters, differential demodulators, oscillators with fixed or electronically tunable frequency which allow the generation of high-frequency waves or the recovery of a frequency-rhythm or of a carrier frequency, analog-digital converters etc. In the immediate future, it will be communications with elements of frequency principally in the region of 900 MHz and optical communication opening the way for videocommunications which will benefit decisively from this new technology.

The development of these techniques represents an appreciable body of research and of experiment which the authors propose to describe in this work.

The book is composed of two parts: the first, which is more theoretical, begins with elementary motions of acoustics, to set up a model of the propagation of SAW in an original formulation which makes use of the idea of 'surface permittivity'. This concept, defined by K. A. Ingebristen in 1969, had never been used for the modeling of acoustic microcircuits. The authors of this book, however, use it as a powerful instrument leading to the notion of 'depolarization waves', tremors on the surface of piezoelectric materials. The systematic use of this idea leads to a remarkably simple formalism, which frees us completely from analog 'equivalent schemes', in which there is an enormous technical literature but which are of such an arbitrary nature as to render the results uncertain, if not problematical. This formalism is used further to model the devices used in signal processing filters, oscillators and various components.

The same idea is used to calculate propagation parameters of waves in different materials. It leads to clarification of the rather complex idea of 'surface pseudo waves' as well as to 'pathological' modes of propagation such as Bleustein–Gulyaev waves or the waves called Surface Skimming Bulk Waves (SSBW). Modeling of these 'pathological' modes allows us, moreover, to predict their behavior in practical devices.

Finally, still on the theoretical level, the important work carried out by the authors in their research into temperature-stable materials leads to numerous diagrams and multiple tables, sometimes unpublished, concerning original propagation configurations in various materials.

The second part of the work is concerned with applications. On this level, two chapters deal respectively with filters and oscillators. The chapter on filtering recapitulates the theory necessary for synthesis at various levels: surface-wave filters approximate in concept to finite impulse-response digital filters, and an account is given of methods of calculation suitable for this technology. The practical point of view, particularly the close attention to 'parasite' modes, is underlined, and if the reader is equipped with the most elaborate theoretical apparatus, a certain number of cautious and of commonsense rules are indicated. Other methods and principles used in this technology (resonators, gratings, multiphase transducers, etc) are also described. Finally, a series of concrete examples of actual filters enables the reader to appreciate the true range of use of these devices.

The chapter on oscillators presents first a theoretical clarification of concepts of time and of frequency stability, so as to identify aspects of the performance of surface wave oscillators: 'honorable' time stability but very great spectral 'purity' round the carrier frequency. The conception and realization of these components are then fully described, and as with the filters, a series of concrete examples is provided. A final chapter on materials, technology and implementation recapitulates in detail the complete conception of a surface-wave device from the very practical point of view of the technician responsible for constructing such a circuit. He will also find at numerous points, full digital documentation of computer programs used at different stages: calculation of velocities, conception of devices, synthesis of filters, simulation of subsets, realization of masks, etc.

To sum up, this work represents a general survey of research as well as a guide and a basic presentation. The hope of the authors is that it will be of use to the researcher as well as to the practical man, and trust that it will contribute to the recognition of the important work stimulated by the development of this new technology.

Organization of the book

Chapters 1 to 3 constitute the physical basis of a model of piezoelectricity which enables us to treat SAW as electric circuits without making explicit reference to acoustics.

The engineer who wishes to pass rapidly to applications can ignore these chapters at a first reading provided that he learns a few definitions and accepts a few results.

Piezoelectricity is a coupling between elastic deformation and electric polarization which exists in certain crystals such as quartz.

Surface waves are piezoelectric microwaves which can be propagated over the surface of these crystals at a velocity of the order of 3500 m/s (or 3 μs per cm). This velocity, denoted by v_∞, applies to the case where the surface is free and isolated. If the surface is short-circuited, the velocity of propagation is very slightly reduced to a value v_0 and we can characterize the intensity of piezoelectric coupling precisely by a parameter k^2 (of the order 0.1% to 5%) which measures this reduction in velocity.

There are several modes of propagation. The ones used most frequently (we might say almost always) are called Rayleigh modes (or 'Rayleigh-type' modes, the difference being unimportant from the point of view of circuit theory).

For Rayleigh modes, we have:

$$\frac{v_\infty^2 - v_0^2}{v_\infty^2} = k^2$$

(There are other modes: *pseudo-modes* which are propagated with attenuation, *Bleustein–Gulyaev* modes which have a special behavior, and even the so-called SSBW [Surface Skimming Bulk Waves] whose behavior is almost 'pathological'. Except insofar as they concern oscillators, these modes can be ignored at first reading).

In view of these ideas, a surface-wave device is essentially a series of *delay lines* to which access can be obtained electrically only across a capacitance.

Chapter 4 deals with *transducers*: it describes in simple language more or less ingenious circuits which allow access to this delay line across an irreducible input capacitance for signals of given characteristics (bandwidth, frequency, duration . . .)

From the point of view of circuit theory there are really two delay lines (one in each direction) which are connected to the capacitance. This implies a number of difficulties, the least of which is the splitting of the incident energy into two parts. Two points of access constitute a two-post network which will be, in general, the cononical structure for processing signals whose input and output are both electrical.

Chapter 5 deals with the fundamental application, *frequency filtering*.

Chapter 6 is concerned with the use of surface waves in the construction of *oscillators* and frequency generators.

Chapter 7 is very specialized and concerns nonlinear applications: it can be ignored at a first reading.

Chapter 8, on the other hand, is a fundamental one for applications. It describes materials (see also a resumé in Chapter 1) and the technology for actual implementation (microlithography), and also describes in detail the development of a device. The engineer concerned with concrete applications could actually begin by running through this chapter.

In conclusion, if the book is to be read in the order of the chapters, the physicist will be interested mainly in Chapters 1, 2, 3 and 7; the engineer can run quickly through the first three chapters, start effectively at Chapter 4 and jump immediately to Chapter 8 to construct his first device!

Notes on the references

A list of references is given at the end of the book. Each item is referred to in the text by the first three letters of the author's name and the year of publication, followed, if need be, by an index. The following general works can be consulted:

[BRI 56] and [BRI 60]: fundamental works, in French, giving a clear explanation of phenomena at microscopic tensor formulation which has now become classical.

[LAN 67]: a classical work, in French (translated from Russian), very compact and concise, providing a link between acoustic theory and the different disciplines of physics.

[AUL 73]: basic theoretical work, in English, on acoustic fields and waves in solids, dealing largely with surface waves.

[DIE 74]: basic work, in French, on acoustics and piezoelectricity, including a chapter on applications of signal processing.

[MAS 64 to 84]: a series of works, in English, on physical acoustics, consisting of monographs giving the state, from time to time, of the various disciplines in this area. Of particular importance are Vols. I, part A; IV, part A; VI; IX; XI; XIII, XV.

[OLI 78]: a work in English entirely devoted to surface waves; the various chapters are edited by well-known specialists.

Chapter 1

Generalities: Piezoelectric Models

The phenomenon of elastic vibration of the surface of solids was demonstrated by Lord Rayleigh in 1885 (Rayleigh 1885). Shortly before this (in 1880), piezoelectricity was discovered by the Curie brothers (Curie and Curie 1880), but it was not until 1965 that these two discoveries were applied to signal processing, following the invention, by White and Voltmer (1965), of the surface acoustic waves (SAW) interdigital transducer. In the interval, the study of acoustic vibrations had progressed considerably, mainly as a consequence of the work of Brillouin (Brillouin and Parodi 1956) and the development of tensor calculus (Brillouin 1960). At the same time, the microscopic point of view, which provides the physical basis for the phenomena, helps us to understand the macroscopic concepts used in precise calculations.

1.1   The Microscopic field

Macroscopic acoustics is, of course, the outcome of microscopic motion in the interior of solids.

1.1.1   Simple purely acoustic model

Let us imagine ourselves going into the interior of a solid at rest, and consider a particular atom in a state of stable equilibrium. If we try to displace it to a distance x, we find that the other atoms produce a force $-Ax$ tending to restore it to its equilibrium position. Newton's second law then shows that the position of the atom in question is governed by the equation (Fig. 1.1a)

$$m \frac{d^2 x}{dt^2} = -Ax$$

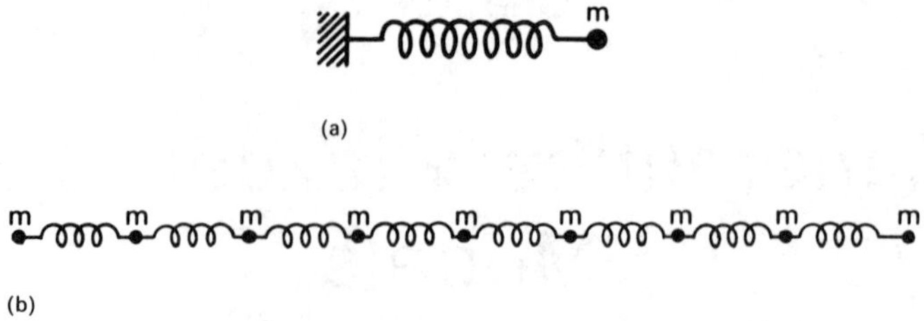

(a)

(b)

Fig. 1.1 (a) Model of an atom in equilibrium; (b) chain of atoms in equilibrium.

where m is the mass of the atom and A is a positive constant that depends on the environment of the atom. The atom oscillates about its equilibrium position with the natural frequency $(A/m)^{1/2}$.

The problem is complicated by the fact that the oscillation of the atom cannot take place in isolation, i.e. the neighboring atoms also begin to oscillate. Suppose, for simplicity, that all the atoms are identical and are arranged in a straight line (one-dimensional model of a crystal). Let us also suppose that the restoring force between two adjacent atoms is proportional to the difference between their current separation and the equilibrium separation.

When atom number n is displaced from its equilibrium position to a distance x_n, it experiences a restoring force that is no longer proportional simply to x_n but to $(x_n - x_{n+1}) + (x_n - x_{n-1})$, where x_{n-1} and x_{n+1} are, respectively, the displacements of atoms $n - 1$ and $n + 1$ from their equilibrium positions.

The equation of motion of atom number n is now (Fig. 1.1b)

$$m \frac{d^2 x_n}{dt^2} = -A(2x_n - x_{n+1} - x_{n-1})$$

and there is, in fact, an infinite number of such equations that we have to solve (for each value of n). Fortunately, the solution is very easy. We substitute

$$x_n = \text{Re}\{\exp[+i(n\psi + \omega t)]\}$$

where Re signifies the real part, ψ is a parameter to be adjusted, and ω is the angular frequency of the vibration. This yields

$$-m\omega^2 = -A(2 - 2\cos\psi)$$

and

$$\omega = 2\left(\frac{A}{n}\right)^{1/2}\left|\sin\frac{\psi}{2}\right| \qquad (1.1)$$

Thus, instead of the natural vibration obtained as a first approximation, we have a resonant angular frequency of the chain of atoms for each value of ψ. We can confine ourselves to values of ψ between $-\pi$ and $+\pi$, and the set of corresponding resonances is called a *vibration branch*.

First, we must give an interpretation of the angle ψ. If the equilibrium separation between the atoms is a, and the position of the nth atom at rest is $X_n = na$, the differences x_n are given by

$$x_n = \mathrm{Re}\{\exp[-i(KX_n - \omega t)]\}$$

where

$$K = \frac{\psi}{a} \tag{1.2}$$

Thus, each value of ψ can be associated with a traveling wave of *wave number* $K = \psi/a$. As an indication of the orders of magnitude that are involved here, we note that $\psi = \pi$ corresponds to infrared waves in eqn (1.1). For radio frequencies, the dispersion relation

$$\omega = 2\left(\frac{A}{m}\right)^{1/2}\left|\sin\frac{\psi}{2}\right|$$

can be simplified to

$$\frac{\omega}{K} = \left(\frac{A}{m}\right)^{1/2} a$$

i.e. the phase velocity of acoustic waves is *constant* (independent of the frequency). The order of magnitude of this velocity is $1-10\,\mathrm{km\,s^{-1}}$ for the most commonly used crystals.

Finally, it is customary to represent the dispersion relation on the (ω, K) plane rather than the (ω, ψ) plane. The interval of ψ between $-\pi$ and $+\pi$, or that of K between $-\pi/a$ and $+\pi/a$ is called the first *Brillouin zone* (Fig. 1.2a).

1.1.2 More elaborate models: piezoelectricity and nonlinearity

The approximations made in the preceding model can be classified as follows.

One-dimensional model

A real crystal is three-dimensional and each of its atoms can be displaced from its equilibrium position in three possible directions. We can show from this that there are three vibration branches, corresponding to the three acoustic polarizations (one longitudinal and two transverse).

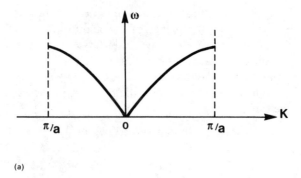

(a)

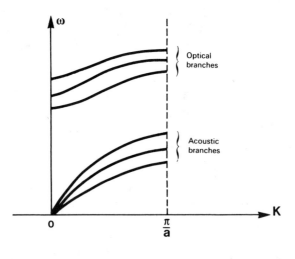

(b)

Fig. 1.2   Crystal vibration branches: (a) one-dimensional model; (b) three-dimensional model with a two-atom unit cell.

Identical atoms

There is usually more than one type of atom in a crystal lattice. When there are several different such atoms, the preceding analysis applies not to a single atom but to the center of gravity of the chain, and the above conclusions remain valid. If there are s atoms in the chain, we can show that there are $3s$ vibration branches in the crystal. The $3s - 3$ branches other than those corresponding to the center of gravity have a very different appearance (Fig. 1.2b): they do not pass through zero frequency and, in general, they lie in the infrared. They are called *optical branches* and they do not concern us in microacoustics.

Short-range restoring forces

The restoring force acting on an atom displaced from its equilibrium position depends not only on its distance from its nearest neighbors (short-range forces) but, more generally, on all the interatomic distances. These long-range forces include the electromagnetic forces that are of particular interest to us here. Consider an atomic cell at rest; the center of gravity of the positive electric charges will, in general, coincide with that of the negative charges. When this is not the case, the crystal is called pyroelectric, and has a permanent dipole moment. Nevertheless, even if the crystal is not pyroelectric, it is possible that, during the vibration, the centers of gravity of the positive and negative electric charges will no longer coincide. There is then an oscillating dipole moment and, consequently, electromagnetic radiation that acts even on distant chains is produced. This is precisely the phenomenon of *piezoelectricity*.

We note that this phenomenon is still unusual for acoustic branches (we shall return to this in Section 1.2), but it is common for the optical branches, where the center of gravity of the chain is fixed and where the atoms of a chain vibrate about this center of gravity. In this sense, we sometimes say that piezoelectricity corresponds to a coupling between acoustic and optical branches.

Harmonic restoring forces

The simple linear expression $F = -Ax$ is valid only for small displacements. In fact, there are good reasons for taking a series expansion, i.e. for adding anharmonic terms, which introduces *nonlinearities* into the model.

This short account of phenomena at the microscopic level should suffice as an introduction to the macroscopic problem of vibrations. Readers interested in optical vibration modes may consult specialist publications (Brillouin and Parodi 1956; Kittel 1958; Born and Huang 1954; Feldmann 1973a).

1.2 Macroscopic description

We now confine our attention to acoustic branches at radio frequencies. This will enable us to give a description within the framework of the mechanics of continuous media (Brillouin 1960; Landau and Lifchitz 1967; Auld 1973; Dieulesaint and Royer 1974).

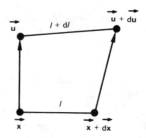

Fig. 1.3 The displacement vector $u(x)$ is defined at each point x.

1.2.1 Displacement and strain

The displacement of the center of gravity of a unit cell can be represented by a continuous displacement field vector $u(x)$.

Consider a point with position coordinate x in a solid in equilibrium. After displacement, the position of the point becomes $x + u(x)$. The possible displacement fields include the displacement of the solid as a whole, but we are more interested in the *deformation* of the solid. To define this, we measure the distance l between two neighboring points x and $x + dx$ before and after the application of the displacement field. In three dimensions, we take vectors u and x (Fig. 1.3) and obtain, before displacement,

$$l^2 = dx^2$$

and, after displacement,

$$(l + \delta l)^2 = (dx + du)^2 = dx^2 + 2dx \cdot du + du^2$$

Neglecting the second-order quantities $(du)^2$ and $(\delta l)^2$, we obtain, for small deformations,

$$l\delta l = dx \cdot du$$

To introduce the notion of deformation, or strain, in a general form, it is essential to employ a less condensed notation.

Let us put

$$du = \sum_{i=1}^{3} \frac{\partial u}{\partial x_i} dx_i \tag{1.3}$$

where we suppose that the space is specified by the three orthonormal coordinates x_1, x_2, x_3. Similarly, we specify the displacement vector u by its three components u_1, u_2, u_3, so that, finally,

$$l\delta l = \sum_{i=1}^{3} \sum_{j=1}^{3} \frac{\partial u_j}{\partial x_i} dx_i dx_j$$

is the product $l\delta l$ expressed as a quadratic form in terms of the infinitesimal displacements dx_1, dx_2, dx_3. The matrix of coefficients S_{ij} of a quadratic form of this type constitutes a tensor, called the *strain tensor*.

We can verify that

$$S_{11} = \frac{\partial u_1}{\partial x_1} \qquad S_{12} = \frac{1}{2}\left(\frac{\partial u_1}{\partial x_2} + \frac{\partial u_2}{\partial x_1}\right) \text{ etc.} \qquad (1.4)$$

By definition, this tensor is symmetric: $S_{12} = S_{21}$. Terms like S_{11} correspond to extension or compression, whereas terms like S_{12} describe shearing of the medium in the chosen coordinate system. Note that *strain* is a pure number, i.e. it is dimensionless.

1.2.2 Surface forces and stresses

We must now describe, at the macroscopic level, the restoring forces that bring the centers of gravity of the unit cells to their equilibrium positions. This problem is the equivalent in three dimensions to that of describing the tension of a one-dimensional string. We can proceed as follows. Imagine that we extract a portion of the solid from the interior of the crystal. To re-establish equilibrium, we must introduce forces on the surface of the imaginary cavity thus created. These forces depend only on the shape of the surface σ. Let their resultant be $F(\sigma)$. For a surface element $d\sigma$, at a point x in the solid, we can then introduce the restoring force $dF = F(d\sigma)$.

In three dimensions, the force dF has three components, dF_1, dF_2, dF_3, and the surface element also has three components $d\sigma_1$, $d\sigma_2$, $d\sigma_3$, which specify the normal to it.

We can write

$$dF_i = \sum_{j=1}^{3} T_{ij}d\sigma_j \qquad i = 1, 2, 3 \qquad (1.5)$$

where $T_{ij} = \partial F_i/\partial \sigma_j$ is the partial derivative of the force with respect to the surface element. A constraint is then equivalent to a pressure.

The components T_{ij} form a tensor called a *stress tensor*. The following remarks may be useful to the reader especially interested in the various types of tensor:

(i) The surface element $d\sigma_j$ should actually be written as $d\sigma_{kl}$ (two antisymmetric indices), so that the rigorous expression is $F_1 = T_{lki}d\sigma_{ki}$, i.e. the stress tensor is a three-index tensor, antisymmetric in the last two. With two indices, we have the "pseudotensor" T_{lj}.

(ii) The orientation of the surface element is specified with respect to the solid and not to the frame of reference; the three-index tensor is therefore an "odd" or "left" tensor.

(iii) By definition, the stress tensor is an odd pseudotensor that behaves like a true tensor under the orthonormal coordinate transformation (cf. Appendix 1.1).

To define the stress tensor uniquely, we must ensure that the surface element points toward the exterior of the solid (or the interior of the cavity).

We can calculate the resultant of the initial forces due to the rest of the solid on the element replaced by the cavity. It is given by

$$F = \iint_{\sigma} dF$$

where the integrals are evaluated over the cavity surface.

This relation can be transformed into a volume integral by the well-known divergence formula

$$F = \iiint f \, d\tau$$

where the "force density" is defined by

$$f_i = \sum_{j=1}^{3} \frac{\partial T_{ij}}{\partial x_j} \qquad i = 1, 2, 3 \tag{1.6}$$

We can also show that, in order that the macroscopic tensor T_{ij} should not involve a density couple, we must have $T_{ij} = T_{ji}$, i.e. the stress tensor must be symmetric.

The work done by the force f_i in a virtual displacement δu_i may, of course, be expressed by the scalar product

$$\delta W = f \cdot \delta u \tag{1.7}$$

Conservation of energy implies that this work corresponds to the flux of energy over the surface of the elastic volume. Its value per unit of surface area (from eqn 1.5) is

$$dF \cdot \delta u = \sum_{i=1}^{3} \sum_{j=1}^{3} T_{ij} \delta u_i \, d\sigma_j$$

This equation defines the (inward) energy flux vector P whose value in an actual displacement $\delta u_i = \dot{u}_i dt$ is

$$P_j = \sum_{i=1}^{3} T_{ij} \dot{u}_i \tag{1.8}$$

where $\dot{u}_i$ indicates the time derivative. Finally, the rate of change of the energy stored in an elastic solid is given by the surface integral

$$\frac{dW}{dt} = \int\int \sum_{j=1}^{3} P_j d\sigma_j \tag{1.9}$$

The elastic flux vector $\boldsymbol{P}$ is thus the equivalent of the Poynting vector in electromagnetism. The elastic energy density can be calculated by transforming to a volume integral as in eqn (1.7).

1.2.3 Short-range forces and elasticity

We must now assume that the restoring forces are proportional to the distances of the centers of gravity of the unit cells from their equilibrium positions. On the macroscopic scale, it is sufficient to use the empirical linear stress/strain relation, i.e. Hooke's law

$$\boldsymbol{T} = \boldsymbol{CS} \tag{1.10}$$

The reader who is allergic to tensor notation must be patient. In three dimensions, this relation may be written in the form

$$T_{ij} = C_{ijkl}S_{kl} \tag{1.11}$$

where we have introduced the tensor C_{ijkl} with the four indices i, j, k, l that can take the values 1, 2 or 3. Moreover, for the indices k and l in this formula, we use the implicit summation convention. (This so-called Einstein convention, of implicit summation over repeated dummy indices, is henceforth used systematically.) The above sum thus contains nine terms, and there are nine equations of this type (of which six are distinct when symmetries are taken into account).

The tensor thus introduced is called the elasticity tensor. We can see that, by definition,

$$C_{ijkl} = C_{jikl} = C_{ijlk} \tag{1.12}$$

We can shown from thermodynamic considerations that $C_{ijkl} = C_{klij}$ (cf. Section 1.3.2).

Let us leave on one side this three-dimensional case, in order to see what form the fundamental law of mechanics takes in a single dimension: the problem is then equivalent to that of a stretched string. We have, in fact, for a volume element,

$$S = S_{11} = \frac{\partial u}{\partial x}$$

and the force density is (eqn 1.5)

$$f = \frac{\partial T}{\partial x}$$

The acceleration of this volume element is

$$\gamma = \frac{d^2 u}{dt^2} \approx \frac{\partial^2 u}{\partial t^2}$$

(assuming small displacements, which amounts to neglecting infinitesimals of the second order). This means that the equation

$$f = m\gamma$$

can be written as

$$\frac{\partial T}{\partial x} = \rho \frac{\partial^2 u}{\partial t^2} \tag{1.13}$$

where ρ is the density of the medium.

Using Hooke's law

$$T = C \frac{\partial u}{\partial x}$$

we then obtain

$$C \frac{\partial^2 u}{\partial x^2} - \rho \frac{\partial^2 u}{\partial t^2} = 0$$

This is the equation of a vibrating string, which shows that elastic waves propagate at the constant velocity

$$v = \left(\frac{C}{\rho} \right)^{1/2}$$

In practice, v is of the order of several kilometres per second. Equation (1.13) can be written in tensor form:

$$\partial_i T_{ij} = \rho \ddot{u}_j \tag{1.14}$$

where ∂_i is written for $\partial/\partial x_i$ and $\dot{u}_j$ indicates derivative with respect to time (moreover we are using the Einstein summation convention for the dummy indices). Using eqn (1.7) (cf. Appendix 1.1) we find that the problem in three dimensions is very similar: there are simply three types of wave, or of acoustic polarization, that can propagate: two transverse modes (i.e. waves whose displacement vector u is perpendicular to the direction of propagation) and a longitudinal mode (which, as is well known, is the only wave in liquids).

In fact, in an anisotropic crystal, these acoustic polarizations turn out to be only approximations. They are therefore referred to as quasi-transverse or quasi-longitudinal, to remind us that the displacement is not strictly perpendicular or parallel to the direction of propagation.

1.2.4 Long-range forces and piezoelectricity

To take account of the long-range forces due to a dipole, we must define the macroscopic electric polarization of the medium, which is related to strain. Since these effects are small, we have as a first approximation the linear relation

$$P \ = \ eS$$

where P is the piezoelectric contribution to the polarization vector and S is the strain tensor. The quantity e represents the piezoelectricity. It is of the order of a coulomb per square meter.

In fact, we usually prefer to take the variables to be the electric displacement D and the electric field E, where

$$D \ = \ eS + \varepsilon E$$

and ε is the permittivity of the medium. The field E is presumed to be the derivative of a potential:

$$E \ = \ -\operatorname{grad} V \qquad (1.15)$$

Electrostatic equilibrium then requires that Poisson's equation be satisfied, i.e.

$$\operatorname{div} D \ = \ \mu \qquad (1.16)$$

where μ is the electric charge density, usually equal to zero when the medium is an insulator.

The dielectric polarization of the medium under the influence of strain implies also the creation of stresses under the influence of an external electric field.

As we shall see in Section 1.3 below, thermodynamics requires that the constitutive relations must be written, finally, in the form

$$T \ = \ CS - eE$$
$$D \ = \ eS + \varepsilon E$$

and it is the same piezoelectric tensor e that occurs in both relations.

The formulae are homogeneous because E and D are vectors, T and S are second-order tensors, and e is the three-index tensor e_{lij} that is symmetric, by construction, in the indices i and j. Hence, finally,

$$T_{ij} = C_{ijkl}S_{kl} - e_{lij}E_l \qquad (1.17)$$

$$D_i = e_{ikl}S_{kl} + \varepsilon_{il}E_l \qquad (1.18)$$

Taking account of the symmetry in the last two indices of the strain tensor, the elasticity tensor and the piezoelectricity tensor, we can replace S_{kl} with $\partial_k u_l$ in these formulae and, similarly, E_l with $-\partial_l V$ (by eqn 1.15).

The introduction of electromagnetism must now be represented by an electric contribution to the energy flux (eqn 1.9). In practice, the electromagnetic Poynting vector $\boldsymbol{E} \times \boldsymbol{H}$ can be simplified (on the assumption of slowly varying fields) to $-V\dot{\boldsymbol{D}}_i$ (where V is the potential from which the electric field is derived and $\dot{\boldsymbol{D}}_i$ is the derivative of the electric induction with respect to time). If we use (eqn 1.8) for the elastic energy flux, we see that the total energy flux associated with the *piezoelectric flux vector* is

$$P_i = T_{ij}\dot{u}_i - V\dot{D}_i \qquad (1.19)$$

Thus, the total energy entering a given volume per unit time is equal to the flux of P_i across its surface (cf. eqn 1.9)

$$\frac{\mathrm{d}W}{\mathrm{d}t} = \iint P_i \mathrm{d}\sigma_i$$

When this integral is transformed into a volume integral, it shows that there is a piezoelectric energy density, given by

$$\dot{w} = \partial_i P_i \qquad (1.20)$$

Taking account of eqn (1.14), we find that, for an insulator,

$$\dot{w} = \rho\ddot{u}_j\dot{u}_j + T_{jk}\,\partial_j\dot{u}_k + E_i\dot{D}_i \qquad (1.21)$$

1.3 Geometric and thermodynamic symmetries

1.3.1 Geometric symmetries

The equations of piezoelectricity can be written in tensor form. For the reader unfamiliar with this formalism, we recall that a tensor represents an intrinsic physical quantity (independent of any particular frame of reference) in terms of its components in a particular frame that, in general, is chosen to be orthonormal (cf. Appendix 1.1). When the frame changes, which is allowed, the components change accordingly. By way of an example, consider a crystal with trigonal symmetry that is globally invariant under a 120° rotation about the z-axis. This operation implies a change in the components of tensors associated with the crystal. Global invariance of the crystal requires that the new tensor components be identical with the old ones, which in turn implies a restriction on the form of the tensor: some of its components must vanish. In general, we must take into account the (macroscopic) symmetries of the crystal, i.e. its *point group* of symmetries. It is shown in crystallography that there are 32 possible point groups (e.g. quartz belongs to group 32, and lithium niobate to group 3m).

These geometric symmetries are tabulated for the 32 point groups in Nye's book (Nye 1961). The principal results are reproduced in Appendix 1.2.

In addition to the partial results concerning one or other of the point groups, it is important to note that three-index tensors like e_{ijk} vanish identically in groups that have *a center of symmetry*: only 20 point groups (out of the 32) are compatible with the existence of the phenomenon of linear piezoelectricity.

1.3.2 Thermodynamic relations

In Section 1.2.4 we invoked thermodynamics in order to write the piezoelectric equations in the form

$$\boldsymbol{T} = \boldsymbol{CS} - \boldsymbol{eE}$$

$$\boldsymbol{D} = \boldsymbol{eS} + \boldsymbol{\varepsilon E}$$

with the same tensor $\boldsymbol{e}$ in both equations. This relies on the assumption that the medium is reciprocal, and is rigorously established from considerations discovered by Onsager (1931) for nonequilibrium media. For a medium that may not be reciprocal, but is *nondissipative*, we can deduce this property from the *first law of thermodynamics* (we shall do this in this section). Suppose, first, that two distinct tensors $\boldsymbol{e}$ and $\boldsymbol{e}'$ are involved. We can then write eqns (1.17) and (1.18) in the form

$$T_{jk} = C_{jkil}\partial_i u_l + e_{ijk}\partial_i V \qquad (1.22)$$

$$D_i = e'_{ijk}\partial_j u_k - \varepsilon_{ij}\partial_j V \qquad (1.23)$$

In *isentropic* transformations, which alone interest us here, the internal energy density in a lossless medium follows uniquely from the *inward piezoelectrical energy flux*, and is therefore given by eqn (1.21).

Taking account of eqns (1.15), (1.22) and (1.23), we obtain

$$\frac{dw}{dt} = \frac{1}{2}\frac{d}{dt}(\rho\dot{u}_j\dot{u}_j) + C_{jkil}\partial_i u_l\partial_j\dot{u}_k + \varepsilon_{ij}\partial_i V\partial_j\dot{V} + (e_{ijk} - e'_{ijk})\partial_j\dot{u}_k\partial_i V$$

The first term represents the *kinetic energy*, so that the others represent the variation δw_p of piezoelectric energy, which must therefore be a total differential. Using the *strain field formulation*, we find for virtual displacements

$$\delta w_p = C_{jkil} S_{il} \delta S_{jk} + \varepsilon_{ij} E_i \delta E_j - (e_{ijk} - e'_{ijk}) E_i \delta S_{jk}$$

Hence we deduce that

$$\frac{\partial w_p}{\partial S_{jk}} = C_{jkil} S_{il} - (e_{ijk} - e'_{ijk}) E_i$$

$$\frac{\partial w_p}{\partial E_j} = \varepsilon_{ij} E_i$$

and

$$\frac{\partial^2 w_p}{\partial S_{jk} \partial S_{il}} = C_{jkil} \qquad \frac{\partial^2 w_p}{\partial S_{il} \partial S_{jk}} = C_{iljk}$$

$$\frac{\partial^2 w_p}{\partial E_j \partial E_i} = \varepsilon_{ij} \qquad \frac{\partial^2 w_p}{\partial E_i \partial E_j} = \varepsilon_{ji}$$

$$\frac{\partial^2 w_p}{\partial S_{jk} \partial E_i} = e'_{ijk} - e_{ijk} \qquad \frac{\partial^2 w_p}{\partial E_i \partial S_{jk}} = 0$$

From Schwarz's theorem we know that the order of differentiation of the function w_p does not affect the result.

These different relations thus show that

$$\varepsilon_{ij} = \varepsilon_{ji} \tag{1.24}$$

$$C_{jkil} = C_{iljk} \tag{1.25}$$

$$e'_{ijk} = e_{ijk} \tag{1.26}$$

Relation (1.24) is the classical result in electromagnetism. Relation (1.25) completes relations (eqn 1.12). Finally, relation (1.26) is now proved. The piezoelectric energy density can therefore be put in the form

$$w_p = \tfrac{1}{2}(C_{jkil} S_{jk} S_{il} + \varepsilon_{ij} E_i E_j) \tag{1.27}$$

Reciprocity and symmetry of Onsager

Let us take eqns (1.24) to (1.26) as axiomatic. *Time reversal* is the operation whereby the constants of a crystal are transformed as follows:

$$\varepsilon_{ij} \to \varepsilon_{ji} \qquad C_{jkil} \to C_{iljk} \qquad e'_{ijk} \to e_{ijk}$$

It can be shown (Onsager 1931; Casimir 1945; Feldmann 1981) that this operation amounts to the reversal of the direction of internal microscopic motion in the crystal. Relations (1.24) to (1.26) indicate that the equations of piezoelectricity are invariant under this transformation. This can also be expressed by saying that *piezoelectricity is a reciprocal phenomenon*. It does not hold for materials that are both magnetic and dissipative.

1.3.3 Other formulations and conventions

We have given the piezoelectric equations in terms of S and E as independent variables:

$$\begin{cases} T = CS - eE \\ D = eS + \varepsilon E \end{cases}$$

It is clear that there are other possibilities. For example, we can choose S and D or T and E or T and D. The quantities T and E are often used. We then obtain

$$\begin{cases} S = sT + dE \\ D = dT + \varepsilon^T E \end{cases}$$

where we have taken ε^T, and not ε, because these two tensors are distinct in a piezoelectric medium.

Thermodynamics again implies that the same tensor d appears in both equations (cf. Table 1.1). In the expression for the different tensors, it is convenient to number the pairs of indices according to the so-called Voigt convention (Table 1.2), which takes symmetries into account.

We can verify by explicit calculation that eqns (1.22) and (1.23), on the one hand, and (1.28) and (1.29), on the other, are still consistent if we

Table 1.1 Symmetries of constitutive tensors

C_{ijkl}	$\begin{aligned} C_{ijkl} &= C_{klij} \\ &= C_{jikl} \end{aligned}$	Elastic rigidity with constant electric field
s_{ijkl}	$s_{ijkl} = s_{klij} = s_{jikl}$	Flexibility with constant electric field
ε_{ij}	$\varepsilon_{ij} = \varepsilon_{ji}$	Permittivity with constant strains
ε_{ij}^T	$\varepsilon_{ij}^T = \varepsilon_{ji}^T$	Permittivity with constant stresses
e_{ijk}	$e_{ijk} = e_{ikj}$	Piezoelectricity
d_{ijk}	$d_{ijk} = d_{ikj}$	Inverse piezoelectricity

Table 1.2   Voigt convention

Pair of indices (i, j)	Global index I
(1, 1)	1
(2, 2)	2
(3, 3)	3
(2, 3) or (3, 2)	4
(3, 1) or (1, 3)	5
(1, 2) or (2, 1)	6

consider the global index (varying from 1 to 6) as a dummy index for the implicit summation, provided we take

$$t_I = t_{ij} \quad (I = 1, 2, \ldots 6)$$

$$S_I = S_{ij} \quad (I = 1, 2, 3)$$

$$S_I = 2S_{ij} \quad (I = 4, 5, 6)$$

$$C_{IJ} = C_{ijkl} \quad (I, J = 1, 2, \ldots 6)$$

$$e_{kI} = e_{kij} \quad (I = 1, 2, \ldots 6)$$

For example,

$$T_I = C_{IJ}S_J - e_{kI}E_k \qquad (1.28)$$

$$D_k = e_{kI}S_I + \varepsilon_{kl}E_l \qquad (1.29)$$

However, the global consistency of the formulae requires that more complex correspondences be established between s_{ijkl} and s_{IJ} if we use simultaneously several series of independent parameters (cf. Nye 1961). We shall not linger any further over these rather artificial difficulties, because from now on we shall use only the single set of independent variables S, E.

1.4   Brief survey of piezoelectric materials

Chapter 8 is devoted to a detailed study of the properties of piezoelectric materials, and to considerations underlying the choice of a given material and its orientation (cut, propagation) according to the application envisaged. It is useful, however, to describe at this point the principal piezoelectric crystals so as to fix the reader's ideas. The criteria of choice are principally the velocity v, the piezoelectric coefficient e or, better still, the dimensionless number $k^2 = e^2/\varepsilon C$, which we shall identify later as the coefficient of electromechanical coupling, the relative permittivity ε_r and the temperature behavior.

To describe this behavior, we shall initially content ourselves in a first approach with the first-order temperature coefficient that corresponds to the natural frequency of the device and is listed in FTC (frequency temperature coefficient) tables. We shall see that the velocity v defines the geometry of a device whereas the coefficient k^2 limits its maximum bandwidth: strong coupling allows large relative bandwidths, high velocity allows higher central frequencies but shorter delays. Moreover, the characteristics of propagation (attenuation and anisotropy), diffraction and nonlinear effects can also influence the performance of signal-processing devices.

Most of these devices use materials like quartz, lithium niobate ($LiNbO_3$) and lithium tantalate ($LiTaO_3$). The situation in this field can be summarized as follows. There are good piezoelectric materials, i.e. those with strong electromechanical coupling, like lithium tantalate and, especially, lithium niobate, but their known cuts are very temperature sensitive (of the order of $90 \, ppm \, K^{-1}$), which excludes them from certain functions. However, quartz exhibits moderate coupling, and has the advantage of the ST cut whose temperature coefficient is zero to the first order. Less commonly used materials include Berlinite ($AlPO_4$) which also has an ST cut that is more sensitive to the second order than that of quartz, but offers slightly higher coupling. The double oxide of bismuth and germanium ($Bi_{12}GeO_{20}$) is interesting for the realization of long delays because the corresponding velocity is lower by a factor of 2 as compared with the other materials.

Table 1.3 lists the essential characteristics of these crystals as well as those of gallium arsenide (GaAs) which has the double advantage of being piezoelectric and semiconducting, thus allowing the realization of integrated acoustic and microelectronic devices.

Table 1.3 Principal characteristics of some piezoelectric materials. The materials most commonly used at present are quartz, lithium niobate and lithium tantalate

Crystal	Orientation		Velocity v (m/s)	Coupling k^2 (%)	Permittivity ε_r	Temperature coefficient FTC (ppm °C^{-1})
	Cut	Direction of propagation				
$LiNbO_3$	Y	Z	3 490	5	46	90
$LiTaO_3$	Y	Z	3 230	0.9	47	38
Quartz	ST	X	3 158	0.16	4.5	0
$Bi_{12}GeO_{20}$	$\langle 100 \rangle$	(011)	1 681	1.4	40	140
$AlPO_4$	ST	X	2 736	0.56	6.1	0
GaAs	$\langle 100 \rangle$	(011)	2 863	0.09	11	45

ppm $= 10^{-6}$ (parts per million).

Appendix 1.1   Brief review of tensors with orthonormal frames of reference

The equations of physics describe the relations between physical quantities. When these equations are linear and the quantities are scalars, the relation of, say, proportionality between x and y is indicated simply by the equation

$$y = ax \qquad (1.30)$$

where a is the proportionality factor. The implication is that the coefficient a is *intrinsic* and depends only on the physical system. The question is: what does this mean when x and y are now vectors (x, y)?

First, the expression

$$y = ax \qquad (1.31)$$

can be written (in three-dimensional space) in the form

$$y_i = \sum_{j=1}^{3} a_{ij} x_j \qquad (1.32)$$

i.e. the vector equation can be resolved into three scalar equations $(i = 1, 2, 3)$ and the "coefficient" a is now a matrix of nine coefficients $(i, j = 1, 2, 3)$.

It is clear that the coefficients x_i and y_i in eqn (1.32) are not independent of the coordinate axes even when the vectors x and y are themselves completely intrinsic. It follows that the matrix (a_{ij}), even though it is supposed to establish an intrinsic relation between intrinsic quantities, will change when the set of coordinates is changed. The intrinsic character of the matrix is indicated by the fact that its law of variation must be such that the three equations in eqn (1.32) remain valid when the vectors x and y are given in a new coordinate frame, i.e. the coefficients in the matrix have to be modified accordingly. Thereafter, when the law of variation of a vector due to a change of the frame of reference is known, the corresponding law of variation of the two-index matrix (a_{ij}) can be deduced from it. If we confine ourselves to orthonormal frames of reference for which

$$x_i \rightarrow X_k = \sum_{i=1}^{3} R_{ki} x_i$$

where R_{ki} is an orthogonal matrix, we can verify that

$$a_{ij} \rightarrow A_{kl} = \sum_{i=1}^{3} \sum_{j=1}^{3} R_{ki} R_{lj} a_{ij}$$

An intrinsic matrix of this kind (in the sense that its parameters vary in accordance with those of a vector under a change of coordinates), is called a *tensor*. Clearly the tensor (a_{ij}) must have two indices.

A tensor is thus an *intrinsic* entity that possesses a number of indices: a scalar can be considered to be a tensor with zero index, and a vector to be a tensor with one index. An intrinsic *proportionality* between a vector and a two-index tensor can be described by a three-index tensor, and so on. For example, the law of transformation of a three-index tensor under a transformation of the frame of reference is

$$e_{ijk} \rightarrow E_{lmn} = R_{li}R_{mj}R_{nk}e_{ijk}$$

where we have used the summation convention for the three indices (i, j, k).

Examples of one-index tensors: electric field, dielectric polarization.
Examples of two-index tensors: stress tensor, strain tensor, dielectric permittivity tensor.
Example of three-index tensor: piezoelectric tensor.
Example of four-index tensor: elastic tensor.

REMARK 1. Note that there are tensors that represent a physical field (electric field, stress field etc.) and tensors that represent a property of the medium (permittivity tensor, elasticity tensor). These physical differences have no effect on the mathematical nature of a tensor.

REMARK 2. When a two-index tensor is antisymmetric (in three-dimensional space), it is customary to represent it by its three independent components which, by definition, constitute an *axial vector* or *pseudovector*. We can define more generally an n-index *pseudotensor* by "contracting" two antisymmetric indices of an $(n + 1)$-index tensor. A *pseudoscalar* is a completely antisymmetric nonzero component of a three-index tensor. A pseudotensor can be transformed like a true tensor under a *right* orthonormal change of coordinates, but changes sign when the direction of the frame of reference is inverted. In mathematics, the orientation of a surface is normally set by the choice of the local coordinate system as a function of the space frame of reference. In physics, the orientation of a surface is often intrinsic. If the space framework changes direction, the mathematical orientation changes, whereas the physical orientation remains unaltered. When a quantity is assigned to the physical orientation of a surface, it will in general be necessary to change the mathematical orientation when the orientation of the space frame is changed. A tensor obeying this transformation is called an *odd* tensor. Under orthonormal coordinate changes, an odd tensor behaves like a pseudotensor; an odd pseudotensor behaves like a true tensor.

Appendix 1.2   Symmetry of dielectric, elastic and piezoelectric coefficients

For further information, readers may consult Auld (1973) and Nye (1961).

Triclinic system

Class 1
No symmetry[†].

Class $\bar{1}$
(Piezoelectricity zero $e_{ij} = 0$ (all i and j).

Monoclinic system

Class 2
(a) permittivity $\varepsilon_{12} = \varepsilon_{23} = 0$

(b) elasticity $C_{14} = C_{16} = 0$
$C_{24} = C_{26} = 0$
$C_{34} = C_{36} = 0$
$C_{45} = C_{56} = 0$

(c) piezoelectricity $e_{11} = e_{12} = e_{13} = e_{15} = 0$
$e_{24} = e_{26} = 0$
$e_{31} = e_{32} = e_{33} = e_{35} = 0$

Class m
(a) permittivity $\varepsilon_{12} = \varepsilon_{23} = 0$

(b) elasticity $C_{14} = C_{16} = 0$
$C_{24} = C_{26} = 0$
$C_{34} = C_{36} = 0$
$C_{45} = C_{56} = 0$

(c) piezoelectricity $e_{14} = e_{16} = 0$
$e_{21} = e_{22} = e_{23} = e_{25} = 0$
$e_{34} = e_{36} = 0$

[†]We have, throughout, $\varepsilon_{ij} = \varepsilon_{ji}$ and $C_{IJ} = C_{JI}$ from the Onsager relations.

Class 2/m
No piezoelectricity, $e_{ij} = 0$ (all i and j).

Orthorhombic system

Class 222
(a) permittivity $\quad \varepsilon_{12} = \varepsilon_{13} = \varepsilon_{23} = 0$

(b) elasticity
$$C_{14} = C_{15} = C_{16} = 0$$
$$C_{24} = C_{25} = C_{26} = 0$$
$$C_{34} = C_{35} = C_{36} = 0$$
$$C_{45} = C_{46} = C_{56} = 0$$

(c) piezoelectricity
$$e_{11} = e_{12} = e_{13} = e_{15} = e_{16} = 0$$
$$e_{21} = e_{22} = e_{23} = e_{24} = e_{26} = 0$$
$$e_{31} = e_{32} = e_{33} = e_{34} = e_{35} = 0$$

Class mm2
(a) permittivity $\quad \varepsilon_{12} = \varepsilon_{13} = \varepsilon_{23} = 0$

(b) elasticity
$$C_{14} = C_{15} = C_{16} = 0$$
$$C_{24} = C_{25} = C_{26} = 0$$
$$C_{34} = C_{35} = C_{36} = 0$$
$$C_{45} = C_{46} = C_{56} = 0$$

(c) piezoelectricity
$$e_{11} = e_{12} = e_{13} = e_{14} = e_{16} = 0$$
$$e_{21} = e_{22} = e_{23} = e_{25} = e_{26} = 0$$
$$e_{34} = e_{35} = e_{36} = 0$$

Class mmm
No piezoelectricity, $e_{ij} = 0$ (all i and j).

Quadratic system

Class 4
(a) permittivity
$$\varepsilon_{12} = \varepsilon_{13} = \varepsilon_{23} = 0$$
$$\varepsilon_{11} = \varepsilon_{22}$$

(b) elasticity
$$C_{14} = C_{15} = C_{24} = C_{25} = 0$$
$$C_{34} = C_{35} = C_{36} = 0$$
$$C_{45} = C_{46} = C_{56} = 0$$
$$C_{11} = C_{22}$$
$$C_{13} = C_{23}$$
$$C_{16} = -C_{26}$$
$$C_{44} = C_{55}$$

(c) piezoelectricity

$$e_{11} = e_{12} = e_{13} = e_{16} = 0$$
$$e_{21} = e_{22} = e_{23} = e_{26} = 0$$
$$e_{34} = e_{35} = e_{36} = 0$$
$$e_{15} = e_{24}$$
$$e_{14} = -e_{25}$$
$$e_{31} = e_{32}$$

Class $\bar{4}$

(a) permittivity

$$\varepsilon_{12} = \varepsilon_{13} = \varepsilon_{23} = 0$$
$$\varepsilon_{11} = \varepsilon_{22}$$

(b) elasticity

$$C_{14} = C_{15} = C_{24} = C_{25} = 0$$
$$C_{34} = C_{35} = C_{36} = 0$$
$$C_{45} = C_{46} = C_{56} = 0$$
$$C_{11} = C_{12}$$
$$C_{13} = C_{23}$$
$$C_{16} = -C_{26}$$
$$C_{44} = C_{55}$$

(c) piezoelectricity

$$e_{11} = e_{12} = e_{13} = e_{16} = 0$$
$$e_{21} = e_{22} = e_{23} = e_{26} = 0$$
$$e_{33} = e_{34} = e_{35} = 0$$
$$e_{14} = e_{25}$$
$$e_{15} = -e_{24}$$
$$e_{31} = -e_{32}$$

Class 4/m
No piezoelectricity, $e_{ij} = 0$ (all i and j).

Class 422

(a) permittivity

$$\varepsilon_{12} = \varepsilon_{13} = \varepsilon_{23} = 0$$
$$\varepsilon_{11} = \varepsilon_{22}$$

(b) elasticity

$$C_{14} = C_{15} = C_{16} = 0$$
$$C_{24} = C_{25} = C_{26} = 0$$
$$C_{34} = C_{35} = C_{36} = 0$$
$$C_{45} = C_{46} = C_{56} = 0$$
$$C_{11} = C_{22}$$
$$C_{13} = C_{23}$$
$$C_{44} = C_{55}$$

(c) piezoelectricity

$$e_{11} = e_{12} = e_{13} = e_{15} = e_{16} = 0$$
$$e_{21} = e_{22} = e_{23} = e_{24} = e_{26} = 0$$
$$e_{31} = e_{32} = e_{33} = e_{34} = e_{35} = e_{36} = 0$$
$$e_{14} = -e_{25}$$

Class $\bar{4}mm$

(a) permittivity

$$\varepsilon_{12} = \varepsilon_{13} = \varepsilon_{23} = 0$$
$$\varepsilon_{11} = \varepsilon_{22}$$

(b) elasticity

$$C_{14} = C_{15} = C_{16} = 0$$
$$C_{24} = C_{25} = C_{26} = 0$$
$$C_{34} = C_{35} = C_{36} = 0$$
$$C_{45} = C_{46} = C_{56} = 0$$
$$C_{11} = C_{22}$$
$$C_{13} = C_{23}$$
$$C_{44} = C_{55}$$

(c) piezoelectricity

$$e_{11} = e_{12} = e_{13} = e_{14} = e_{16} = 0$$
$$e_{21} = e_{22} = e_{23} = e_{25} = e_{26} = 0$$
$$e_{34} = e_{35} = e_{36} = 0$$
$$e_{15} = e_{24}$$
$$e_{31} = e_{32}$$

Class $\bar{4}2m$

(a) permittivity

$$\varepsilon_{12} = \varepsilon_{13} = \varepsilon_{23} = 0$$
$$\varepsilon_{11} = \varepsilon_{22}$$

(b) elasticity

$$C_{14} = C_{15} = C_{16} = 0$$
$$C_{24} = C_{25} = C_{26} = 0$$
$$C_{34} = C_{35} = C_{36} = 0$$
$$C_{45} = C_{46} = C_{56} = 0$$
$$C_{11} = C_{22}$$
$$C_{13} = C_{23}$$
$$C_{44} = C_{55}$$

(c) piezoelectricity

$$e_{11} = e_{12} = e_{13} = e_{15} = e_{16} = 0$$
$$e_{21} = e_{22} = e_{23} = e_{24} = e_{26} = 0$$
$$e_{31} = e_{32} = e_{33} = e_{34} = e_{35} = 0$$
$$e_{14} = e_{25}$$

Class 4/mmm

No piezoelectricity, $e_{ij} = 0$ (all i and j).

Trigonal system

Class 3

(a) permittivity

$$\varepsilon_{12} = \varepsilon_{13} = \varepsilon_{23} = 0$$
$$\varepsilon_{11} = \varepsilon_{22}$$

(b) elasticity

$$C_{16} = C_{26} = 0$$
$$C_{34} = C_{35} = C_{36} = 0$$
$$C_{45} = 0$$
$$C_{11} = C_{22}$$
$$C_{13} = C_{23}$$
$$C_{14} = -C_{24} = C_{56}$$
$$C_{15} = -C_{25} = -C_{46}$$
$$C_{44} = C_{55}$$
$$C_{66} = (C_{11} - C_{12})/2$$

(c) piezoelectricity

$$e_{13} = e_{23} = e_{34} = e_{35} = e_{36} = 0$$
$$e_{11} = -e_{12} = -e_{26}$$
$$e_{14} = -e_{25}$$
$$e_{24} = e_{15}$$
$$e_{21} = -e_{22} = e_{16}$$
$$e_{31} = e_{32}$$

Class $\bar{3}$

No piezoelectricity, $e_{ij} = 0$ (all i and j).

Class 32

(a) permittivity

$$\varepsilon_{12} = \varepsilon_{13} = \varepsilon_{23} = 0$$
$$\varepsilon_{11} = \varepsilon_{22}$$

(b) elasticity

$$C_{15} = C_{16} = C_{25} = C_{26} = 0$$
$$C_{34} = C_{35} = C_{36} = 0$$
$$C_{45} = C_{46} = 0$$
$$C_{11} = C_{22}$$
$$C_{13} = C_{23}$$
$$C_{14} = -C_{24} = C_{56}$$
$$C_{44} = C_{55}$$
$$C_{66} = (C_{11} - C_{12})/2$$

(c) piezoelectricity

$$e_{13} = e_{15} = e_{16} = 0$$
$$e_{21} = e_{22} = e_{23} = e_{24} = 0$$
$$e_{31} = e_{32} = e_{33} = e_{34} = e_{35} = e_{36} = 0$$
$$e_{11} = -e_{12} = -e_{26}$$
$$e_{14} = -e_{25}$$

Class 3m

(a) permittivity

$$\varepsilon_{12} = \varepsilon_{13} = \varepsilon_{23} = 0$$
$$\varepsilon_{11} = \varepsilon_{22}$$

(b) elasticity

$$C_{15} = C_{16} = C_{25} = C_{26} = 0$$
$$C_{34} = C_{35} = C_{36} = 0$$
$$C_{45} = C_{46} = 0$$
$$C_{11} = C_{22}$$
$$C_{13} = C_{23}$$
$$C_{14} = -C_{24} = C_{56}$$
$$C_{44} = -C_{55}$$
$$C_{66} = (C_{11} - C_{12})/2$$

(c) piezoelectricity

$$e_{11} = e_{12} = e_{13} = e_{14} = 0$$
$$e_{23} = e_{25} = e_{26} = 0$$
$$e_{34} = e_{35} = e_{36} = 0$$
$$e_{16} = -e_{22} = e_{21}$$
$$e_{15} = e_{24}$$
$$e_{31} = e_{32}$$

Class $\bar{3}$m
No piezoelectricity, e_{ij} (all i and j).

Hexagonal system

Class 6
(a) permittivity

$$\varepsilon_{12} = \varepsilon_{13} = \varepsilon_{23} = 0$$
$$\varepsilon_{11} = \varepsilon_{22}$$

(b) elasticity

$$C_{14} = C_{15} = C_{16} = 0$$
$$C_{24} = C_{25} = C_{26} = 0$$
$$C_{34} = C_{35} = C_{36} = 0$$
$$C_{45} = C_{46} = C_{56} = 0$$
$$C_{11} = C_{22}$$
$$C_{13} = C_{23}$$
$$C_{44} = C_{55}$$
$$C_{66} = (C_{11} - C_{12})/2$$

(c) piezoelectricity

$$e_{11} = e_{12} = e_{13} = e_{16} = 0$$
$$e_{21} = e_{22} = e_{23} = e_{26} = 0$$
$$e_{34} = e_{35} = e_{36} = 0$$
$$e_{14} = -e_{25}$$
$$e_{15} = e_{24}$$
$$e_{31} = e_{32}$$

Class $\bar{6}$
(a) permittivity

$$\varepsilon_{12} = \varepsilon_{13} = \varepsilon_{23} = 0$$
$$\varepsilon_{11} = \varepsilon_{22}$$

(b) elasticity

$$C_{14} = C_{15} = C_{16} = 0$$
$$C_{24} = C_{25} = C_{26} = 0$$
$$C_{34} = C_{35} = C_{36} = 0$$
$$C_{45} = C_{46} = C_{56} = 0$$
$$C_{11} = C_{22}$$
$$C_{13} = C_{23}$$
$$C_{44} = C_{55}$$
$$C_{66} = (C_{11} - C_{12})/2$$

(c) piezoelectricity

$$e_{13} = e_{14} = e_{15} = 0$$
$$e_{23} = e_{24} = e_{25} = 0$$
$$e_{31} = e_{32} = e_{33} = e_{34} = e_{35} = e_{36} = 0$$
$$e_{11} = -e_{12} = -e_{26}$$
$$e_{21} = -e_{22} = e_{16}$$

Class 6/m and 6/mmmm

No piezoelectricity, $e_{ij} = 0$ (all i and j).

Class 622

(a) permittivity

$$\varepsilon_{12} = \varepsilon_{13} = \varepsilon_{23} = 0$$
$$\varepsilon_{11} = \varepsilon_{22}$$

(b) elasticity

$$C_{14} = C_{15} = C_{16} = 0$$
$$C_{24} = C_{25} = C_{26} = 0$$
$$C_{34} = C_{35} = C_{36} = 0$$
$$C_{45} = C_{46} = C_{56} = 0$$
$$C_{11} = C_{22}$$
$$C_{13} = C_{23}$$
$$C_{44} = C_{55}$$
$$C_{66} = (C_{11} - C_{12})/2$$

(c) piezoelectricity

$$e_{11} = e_{12} = e_{13} = e_{15} = e_{16} = 0$$
$$e_{21} = e_{22} = e_{23} = e_{24} = e_{26} = 0$$
$$e_{31} = e_{32} = e_{33} = e_{34} = e_{35} = e_{36} = 0$$
$$e_{14} = -e_{25}$$

Class 6mm

(a) permittivity

$$\varepsilon_{12} = \varepsilon_{13} = \varepsilon_{23} = 0$$
$$\varepsilon_{11} = \varepsilon_{22}$$

(b) elasticity

$$C_{14} = C_{15} = C_{16} = 0$$
$$C_{24} = C_{25} = C_{26} = 0$$
$$C_{34} = C_{35} = C_{36} = 0$$
$$C_{45} = C_{46} = C_{56} = 0$$

$$C_{11} = C_{22}$$
$$C_{13} = C_{23}$$
$$C_{44} = C_{55}$$
$$C_{66} = (C_{11} - C_{12})/2$$

(c) piezoelectricity

$$e_{11} = e_{12} = e_{13} = e_{14} = e_{16} = 0$$
$$e_{21} = e_{22} = e_{23} = e_{25} = e_{26} = 0$$
$$e_{34} = e_{35} = e_{36} = 0$$
$$e_{15} = e_{24}$$
$$e_{31} = e_{32}$$

Class 6̄m2

(a) permittivity

$$\varepsilon_{12} = \varepsilon_{13} = \varepsilon_{23} = 0$$
$$\varepsilon_{11} = \varepsilon_{22}$$

(b) elasticity

$$C_{14} = C_{15} = C_{16} = 0$$
$$C_{24} = C_{25} = C_{26} = 0$$
$$C_{34} = C_{35} = C_{36} = 0$$
$$C_{45} = C_{46} = C_{56} = 0$$
$$C_{11} = C_{22}$$
$$C_{13} = C_{23}$$
$$C_{44} = C_{55}$$
$$C_{66} = (C_{11} - C_{12})/2$$

(c) piezoelectricity

$$e_{13} = e_{14} = e_{15} = e_{16} = 0$$
$$e_{21} = e_{22} = e_{23} = e_{24} = e_{25} = 0$$
$$e_{31} = e_{32} = e_{33} = e_{34} = e_{35} = e_{36} = 0$$
$$e_{11} = -e_{12} = -e_{26}$$

Cubic system

Class 23 and 4̄3m

(a) permittivity

$$\varepsilon_{12} = \varepsilon_{13} = \varepsilon_{23} = 0$$
$$\varepsilon_{11} = \varepsilon_{22} = \varepsilon_{33}$$

(b) elasticity

$$C_{14} = C_{15} = C_{16} = 0$$
$$C_{24} = C_{25} = C_{26} = 0$$
$$C_{34} = C_{35} = C_{36} = 0$$
$$C_{45} = C_{46} = C_{56} = 0$$
$$C_{11} = C_{22} = C_{33}$$
$$C_{12} = C_{13} = C_{23}$$
$$C_{44} = C_{55} = C_{66}$$

(c) piezoelectricity

$$e_{11} = e_{12} = e_{13} = e_{15} = e_{16} = 0$$
$$e_{21} = e_{22} = e_{23} = e_{24} = e_{26} = 0$$
$$e_{31} = e_{32} = e_{33} = e_{34} = e_{35} = 0$$
$$e_{14} = e_{25} = e_{36}$$

Classes m3, 432 and m3m

No piezoelectricity, $e_{ij} = 0$ (all i and j).

Isotropic body

No piezoelectricity, $e_{ij} = 0$ (all i and j).

Exercises

1. Quartz has the following constants in a given configuration (MKSA):

$$C_{11} = 0.8674 \times 10^{11}$$
$$\rho = 2.65 \times 10^3$$

Calculate the velocity of sound and the elastic potential energy as functions of strain. Calculate also the displacement of the face of a 1 cm³ cubic crystal when the stored energy is 1 J.

2. For the same conditions as in Exercise 1, you are given that

$$C_{11} = 0.8674 \times 10^{11}$$
$$\rho = 2.65 \times 10^3$$
$$\varepsilon_r = 4.5$$
$$e_{11} = 0.171$$

Evaluate the ratio of the electric energy to the total stored energy when the crystal is compressed (eqn 1.27).

Chapter 2

Plane Waves: Bulk and Surface Piezoelectric Permittivity

Piezoelectric waves are basically acoustic tremors accompanied by a relatively weak electric field (Cady 1946; Auld 1973; Dieulesaint and Royer 1974). Nevertheless, in signal processing, it is the electric field that contains the real information and is used to generate as well as to detect the waves. It is therefore interesting to present piezoelectric data in purely electric form. This elegant formulation is very simple for bulk waves, and will be described first. For surface waves, the same formulation is also a useful tool for classifying the different possible vibration branches.

This simplification is possible only because the velocity of acoustic waves is much smaller than that of electromagnetic waves (the ratio is of the order of 10^{-5}). The corresponding approximation, called *quasistatic*, relies on the assumption that the electromagnetic field propagates instantaneously. The electric field can then be derived from a potential.

2.1 Generalities: bulk waves

From the viewpoint of wave propagation, the piezoelectric problem is closely related to the purely acoustic problem. In fact, it can be shown (Feldmann 1973b) that, in an infinite homogeneous medium, piezoelectric waves propagate in the form of plane waves. For a given direction of the wave vector, there are three acoustic modes that can propagate in each direction: two with transverse polarization (or quasitransverse) and one with longitudinal polarization (or quasilongitudinal). It is convenient to add to these piezoelectric modes the purely electrostatic field which, in our approximation, propagates with infinite velocity.

When the direction of propagation is fixed, and so is the polarization of the mode, the piezoelectric problem leads to a scalar problem. The corresponding general mathematical problem is treated in Section 2.2 in the case of surface waves.

2.1.1   Scalar model of piezoelectricity

In the scalar model, there is only a single component u of mechanical displacement, a single component T of the stress tensor and a single component D of electric displacement. The constitutive equations then reduce to

$$T \; = \; C\frac{\partial u}{\partial x} + e\frac{\partial V}{\partial x} \qquad D \; = \; e\frac{\partial u}{\partial x} - \varepsilon\frac{\partial V}{\partial x} \qquad (2.1)$$

where $\partial u/\partial x$ represents the (unique) component of the strain tensor and V is the electrostatic potential. The electric field E is given by $E = -\partial V/\partial x$. In these expressions, c is the modulus of elasticity in a constant field, e is the piezoelectric coefficient and ε is the permittivity of the medium (at constant strain).

The equations of motion are limited, as far as electrostatics is concerned, to Poisson's equation

$$\frac{\partial D}{\partial x} \; = \; \mu \qquad (2.2)$$

where μ is the volume charge density,[†] equal to zero throughout, except over metallized surfaces that act as electrodes, the medium being an *electric insulator*.

As regards mechanics, the equation of motion (on the assumption of small displacements) is

$$\frac{\partial T}{\partial x} \; = \; \rho\frac{\partial^2 u}{\partial t^2} \qquad (2.3)$$

where ρ is the density of the medium.

2.1.2   Plane-wave solution in the case of an infinite rod

Consider plane waves of the form

$$\exp[j(\omega t - Kx)]$$

Introducing eqns (2.1)–(2.3) and eliminating the mechanical variables u and T, we obtain

$$\frac{\mu(j\omega, K)}{V(j\omega, K)} \; = \; \varepsilon^* \frac{K^2 - K_\infty^{\;2}}{K^2 - K_0^{\;2}} K^2 \qquad (2.4)$$

[†]We denote by μ the volume charge density, by σ the surface density, by q the linear density, and by Q the electric charge.

where $\mu(j\omega, K)$ and $V(j\omega, K)$ are the Fourier transforms of $\mu(t, x)$ and $V(t, x)$, and

$$\varepsilon^* = \varepsilon\left(1 + \frac{e^2}{\varepsilon C}\right) \quad K_0 = \frac{\omega}{v_0} \quad \text{and} \quad K_\infty = \frac{\omega}{v_\infty}$$

Finally, the velocities v_0 and v_∞ are defined by

$$v_0^{\ 2} = \frac{C}{\rho} \quad v_\infty^{\ 2} = \frac{C}{\rho}\left(1 + \frac{e^2}{\varepsilon C}\right) = \frac{C^*}{\rho}$$

The name *coefficient of piezoelectric coupling* is usually given to the quantity

$$\kappa^2 = \frac{e^2}{\varepsilon C} = \frac{v_\infty^{\ 2} - v_0^{\ 2}}{v_0^{\ 2}} \tag{2.5}$$

The *coefficient of effective coupling* is the quantity

$$k^2 = \frac{\kappa^2}{1 + \kappa^2} = \frac{v_\infty^{\ 2} - v_0^{\ 2}}{v_\infty^{\ 2}} \tag{2.6}$$

Note that κ^2 is restricted to positive values, whereas k^2 can be between 0 and 1. When the coupling is weak, we have

$$\kappa^2 \simeq k^2 \simeq 2\frac{v_\infty - v_0}{v_\infty} = \frac{2\Delta v}{v_\infty}$$

where Δv is written for the quantity $v_\infty - v_0$.

2.1.3 Bulk piezoelectric permittivity

2.1.3.1 Definition
Equation (2.4) can be written in the form

$$\frac{V}{\mu} = \frac{1}{\varepsilon_p K^2} \tag{2.7}$$

Using eqns (2.4)–(2.6), we obtain (after rather laborious calculations)

$$\frac{1}{\varepsilon_p(v)} = \frac{1}{\varepsilon}\left(1 - \frac{k^2}{1 - v^2/v_\infty^{\ 2}}\right) \tag{2.8}$$

where $v = \omega/K$ is to be interpreted as the phase velocity and k^2, v_∞ and ε have already been defined. When $k^2 = 0$, eqn (2.7) describes the electrostatic field.

The quantity ε_p may be called the piezoelectric permittivity. Its velocity dispersion is completely analogous to the frequency dispersion of the most

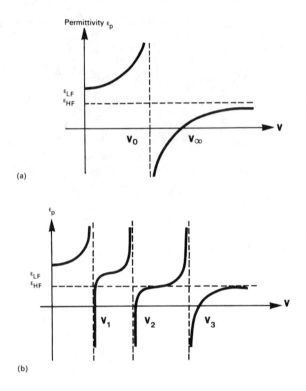

Fig. 2.1 Bulk piezoelectric permittivity as a function of phase velocity: (a) single-branch model; (b) three-branch model.

commonly used media. For a nonpiezoelectric medium ($k^2 = 0$), the permittivity ε_p is constant as a function of phase velocity. The variation of ε_p as a function of the velocity v is shown in Fig. 2.1a. We note that the velocity v_0 has the equivalent of a resonance. In reality, this resonance corresponds to one branch of acoustic vibration (Chapter 1).

More generally, had we considered the three-dimensional problem (Glowinski 1972b), we would have had to examine the three vibration acoustic branches of the crystal, and the variation of the piezoelectric permittivity would have as shown in Fig. 2.1b, where these three vibration branches are obvious. If we denote by ε_{HF} the permittivity at infinite velocity, which occurs at high frequency, the bulk piezoelectric permittivity takes the form

$$\frac{1}{\varepsilon_p(v)} = \frac{1}{\varepsilon_{HF}}\left(1 - \sum_{i=1}^{3}\frac{k_i^2}{1 - v^2/v_i^2}\right) \qquad (2.9)$$

The model with one mode thus corresponds to the case where two of the three modes have zero coupling. The single mode with nonzero coupling is then called *pure*.

2.1.3.2 Slowness curve

We shall see in Appendix 2.1 that v_i are the piezoelectric wave velocities corresponding to the different polarizations (longitudinal or transverse) of mechanical displacement. We can, of course, represent the velocity curve graphically. We prefer, in general, to consider the reciprocal of velocity, i.e. the slowness a_i, which allows us to examine the notions of group velocity and energy transport velocity (Section 2.1.3.3).

By way of example, Fig. 2.2 shows the slowness curve of lithium niobate on the (y, z) plane, and Fig. 2.3 that of gallium arsenide on the $\langle 110 \rangle$ plane.

It can be shown (cf. Appendix 2.1) that the slowness surface is an algebraic surface of the sixth degree (in the general case). In each direction,

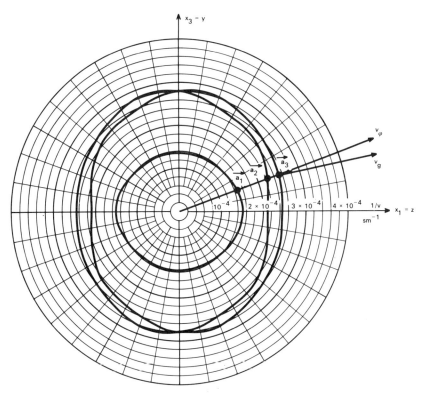

Fig. 2.2   Section of the slowness surface of lithium niobate by the (y, z) plane.

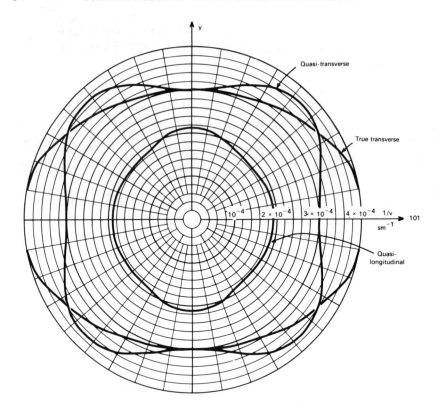

Fig. 2.3 Section of the slowness surface of gallium arsenide by the $\langle 110 \rangle$ plane.

the radius vector cuts the surface at the three points corresponding to $a_1 = 1/v_1$, $a_2 = 1/v_2$ and $a_3 = 1/v_3$.

2.1.3.3 Group velocity

The angular frequency ω, the wave vector $\boldsymbol{K}$ and the slowness $\boldsymbol{a}$ are related by

$$\boldsymbol{K} = \boldsymbol{a}\omega \qquad (2.10)$$

so that plane waves vary in accordance with the relation

$$\exp[j(\omega t - \boldsymbol{K} \cdot \boldsymbol{r})] = \exp(j\phi) \qquad (2.11)$$

where $\boldsymbol{r}$ represents the point in space observed at time t. A group of waves with frequencies in the neighborhood of ω interfere (reinforcing each other) when they have the same phase ϕ. A variation $d\boldsymbol{K}$ of the wave vector must

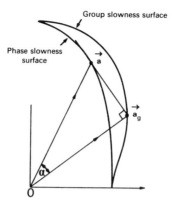

Fig. 2.4 Phase and group slowness surfaces.

correspond to a variation $d\omega$ of the angular frequency in such a way that

$$d\phi = d\omega t - d\boldsymbol{K} \cdot \boldsymbol{r} = 0$$

so that the point of reinforcement therefore moves with velocity $\boldsymbol{v}_G$ defined by $\boldsymbol{r} = \boldsymbol{v}_G t$ where

$$d\omega = \boldsymbol{v}_G \cdot d\boldsymbol{K} \tag{2.12}$$

Taking the differentials of eqn (2.10) on the slowness surface, we obtain

$$d\boldsymbol{K} = d\boldsymbol{a} \cdot \omega + \boldsymbol{a} \cdot d\omega \tag{2.13}$$

By definition, $d\boldsymbol{a}$ is perpendicular to the normal $\boldsymbol{n}$ to the slowness surface (Fig. 2.4). Taking the scalar product of $\boldsymbol{n}$ with both sides of eqn (2.13), and using eqn (2.12) we obtain

$$d\omega = \frac{\boldsymbol{n}}{(\boldsymbol{n} \cdot \boldsymbol{a})} \cdot d\boldsymbol{K} = \boldsymbol{v}_G \cdot d\boldsymbol{K} \tag{2.14}$$

where $\boldsymbol{v}_G = \boldsymbol{n}/(\boldsymbol{n} \cdot \boldsymbol{a})$ is the *group velocity* of the piezoelectric wave, which is seen to be normal to the slowness surface.

2.1.3.4 Piezoelectric energy flux

In a *nondissipative* medium, the group velocity represents the *velocity of energy transport* (cf. Appendix 2.2).

The notion of piezoelectric flux (eqn 1.19) can be extended so as to define the complex flux vector (Glowinski 1972b)

$$P_i = T_{ij}\dot{u}_j^* - V\dot{D}_i^* \tag{2.15}$$

where the asterisk denotes the complex conjugate.

We can readily verify that the real part of P_i is the mean flux, and the modulus of P_i is the fluctuating flux in a plane sinusoidal wave. Similarly, we can define the complex energy density W as follows:

$$\boldsymbol{P} + \boldsymbol{v}_G W = 0$$

where $\boldsymbol{v}_G$ is the group velocity of the plane wave (cf. Appendix 2.2).

2.2   Surface waves

A piezoelectric surface wave is a solution of the acoustic and electro-magnetic equations that satisfies the boundary conditions on the mechanically free surface and is attenuated exponentially in the interior of the material (Farnell 1978). It can be visualized as an ordinary swell wave (a gravity wave) or as a skin effect in conductors (electromagnetic wave). A rigorous solution of the mathematical problem is quite difficult: it involves the constitutive equation, the equations of motion and the boundary conditions. Before going into detail, we note that, in general, a solution can be found in the form of a plane wave propagating without attenuation on the surface of the material, in which the material particles execute elliptic motion and there is an analogous variation of the associated electric field. In certain crystals, and for certain cuts of the material, it is, moreover, possible to distinguish certain simple special cases. In the so-called Rayleigh waves, for example, mechanical displacement occurs in the plane containing the direction of propagation and the normal to the plane of propagation. In Bleustein–Gulyaev waves, the electric field and the mechanical displacement have fixed directions. We shall see, however, that despite the complication due to the large number of parameters, the problem can be reduced to a formulation quite close to that for bulk waves. Let us first examine the case of the *electrostatic wave*.

2.2.1   Electrostatic model

Consider a dielectric bounded by the $x_3 = 0$ plane; we are interested in the surface electrostatic field that can vary only in the x_1-direction. The equations of equilibrium are

$$\boldsymbol{D} = -\varepsilon \,\mathrm{grad}\, V \qquad (2.16)$$

$$\mathrm{div}\, \boldsymbol{D} = 0 \qquad (2.17)$$

where $\boldsymbol{D} = (D_1, D_2, D_3)$ is the electric displacement vector, V the electrostatic potential and ε the permittivity of the medium, assumed isotropic.

Let us look for surface waves whose time-independent variation is of the form

$$\exp[-(K_3 x_3 + jK x_1)]$$

If the medium corresponds to positive values of x_3, the amplitude must diminish with distance in the interior of the dielectric, i.e. for $x_3 > 0$.

Substituting in eqns (2.16) and (2.17), we have

$$K_3^2 = K^2 \qquad D_3 = K_3 \varepsilon V$$

Demanding that the real part of K_3 be positive, and eliminating D_1 and D_2,[†] we obtain

$$\frac{D_3}{V} = |K|\varepsilon \qquad (2.18)$$

It is worth noting that, first, if the surface is insulating and electrically uncharged, D_3 is continuous across the surface; if the surface is conducting, the value D_3 in the piezoelectric medium must be taken. Second, we note that the wave vector (in the Ox_1-direction) appears only in the form of its modulus $|K|$. This reflects the reciprocity of the system and, in particular, the equivalence of the two directions Ox_1 and $-Ox_1$. From the mathematical viewpoint, there is no difficulty in principle, but the calculation is much more complicated: the inverse Fourier transform of $|K|$ is $-2vp(1/x_1^2)$, whereas that of K is $-j\delta'$ (vp is the Cauchy principal value and δ' is the derivative of the Dirac measure; (Lavoine 1963, p. 196).

We shall use eqn (2.18) to define surface piezoelectric permittivity for a piezoelectric medium.

2.2.2 Mathematics of surface-wave propagation

At the cost of laborious calculation, and with the help of a computer in the numerical work, but without any special conceptual difficulties, it is possible to find plane wave solutions of the general piezoelectric system for a given material, given cut of the material, and given direction of propagation.

The problem need not be immediately reduced to the scalar case as for bulk waves, and the piezoelectric equations are written in their general tensor form. The space coordinates x_1, x_2, x_3, will be the components of the vector r; and t will denote the time. We shall define the mechanical state of the medium by two tensor quantities, namely, mechanical *stress* and *strain*, with components T_{jk} and S_{jk} respectively. The strains are related to the relative

[†]If the dielectric corresponds to negative x_3, we must choose $K_3 < 0$ and $D_3 = -|K|\varepsilon V$.

displacement of parts of the medium. They can be described as functions of the components of the mechanical displacement vector $u(r, t)$ by the expression

$$S_{jk} = \frac{1}{2}\left(\frac{\partial u_j}{\partial x_k} + \frac{\partial u_k}{\partial x_j}\right)$$

The tensors T_{jk} and S_{jk} are symmetric.

The electrical state of the medium is defined by two vectors, namely the electric field $E(r, t)$ and the electric displacement vector $D(r, t)$.

In the quasistatic approximation to the electromagnetic field, we can define a scalar electric potential $V(r, t)$, so that the electric field has the components

$$E_k = -\frac{\partial V}{\partial x_k}$$

In the piezoelectric medium, we must express the constitutive relations connecting the stresses, the mechanical strains, and the electric field (for adiabatic changes) in the form (Dieulesaint and Royer 1974)

$$T_{jk} = C_{jklm}S_{lm} - e_{ljk}E_l$$
$$D_l = \varepsilon_{lm}E_m + e_{ljk}S_{jk}$$

The indices take the values 1, 2 and 3 and we are using the summation convention for repeated indices (omitting the symbol Σ, assumed to occur as many times as there are different repeated indices).

The elastic, piezoelectric and dielectric constants C_{jklm}, e_{ljk} and ε_{lm} possess certain symmetries with respect to the indices (cf. Section 1.3):

$$C_{jklm} = C_{kjlm} = C_{jkml} = C_{lmjk}$$
$$e_{ljk} = e_{lkj}$$
$$\varepsilon_{lm} = \varepsilon_{ml}$$

We are assuming throughout that all changes are small, so that $\partial/\partial t$ and d/dt are interchangeable. For example, we shall write, in the case of displacement,

$$\frac{\partial u}{\partial t} = \frac{du}{dt} = \dot{u} \qquad \frac{d^2 u}{dt^2} = \ddot{u}$$

For brevity we shall write ∂_k for $\partial/\partial x_k$.

Since we have a scalar electric potential, and the elastic and piezoelectric coefficients have the above symmetries, the constitutive equations may now be written in the form

$$T_{jk} = C_{jklm}\partial_l u_m + e_{ljk}\partial_l V$$
$$D_l = -\varepsilon_{lm}\partial_m V + e_{ljk}\partial_j u_k$$

$$(2.19)$$

Finally, in the quasistatic approximation, Maxwell's equations reduce to the Poisson equation

$$\text{div } \boldsymbol{D} \equiv \partial_l D_l = 0 \qquad (2.20)$$

in the absence of electric charges, while Newton's second law may be written (in the absence of internal forces) in the form

$$\partial_j T_{jk} = \rho \ddot{u}_k \qquad (2.21)$$

We shall suppose, in what follows, that the equation of the surface to be studied is $x_3 = 0$, and that the piezoelectric medium occupies the half-space $x_3 > 0$. Moreover, we are interested in surface waves propagating in the Ox_1-direction. This will be called the *canonical* frame of reference. Starting with the crystallographic frame of reference, in which the various constitutive tensors are known (cf. Appendix 1.2), we transform to the canonical axes by means of the formulae given in Appendix 1.1. This yields the plane waves

$$\exp[j(\omega t - Kx_1)] \exp(-K_3 x_3) \qquad (2.22)$$

where K_3 is complex.

Differentiating eqn (2.19), and using eqns (2.20) and (2.21), we have

$$\begin{cases} C_{jklm} \partial_j \partial_l u_m + e_{ljk} \partial_j \partial_l V = \rho \ddot{u}_k \\ -\varepsilon_{lm} \partial_l \partial_m V + e_{ljk} \partial_l \partial_j u_k = 0 \end{cases} \qquad (2.23)$$

This set of equations is solved in Appendix 2.1.

By substituting eqn (2.22) in eqn (2.23) we obtain a linear algebraic equation in which the variables are the complex amplitudes (u_1, u_2, u_3) and the velocity V of the plane wave. So that the amplitudes should not all be zero, the determinant of the system must be zero, which gives us the so-called *dispersion* or *secular* equation. By taking $v = \omega/K$ as a parameter, we can see that this equation is of the eighth degree in K_3. For each value of v we than have a priori eight solutions satisfying eqn (2.23) (Figs 2.5 and 2.13).

In fact, these eight possible plane waves split into four waves that propagate or are attenuated in the positive x_3-direction and four that propagate or are attenuated in the negative x_3-direction. We can readily distinguish between them when K_3 has a nonzero real part: the physically possible modes are attenuated in the positive x_3-direction, so that only the modes with positive real part of K_3 are acceptable. More precise analysis shows that this case corresponds to small values of $v = \omega/K$; the corresponding modes are *true* surface modes (to distinguish them from the accompanying modes). As the velocity increases, two of the eight roots become purely imaginary, and actually describe bulk waves. Distinction is then effected through the *group velocity* of the waves (cf. Fig. 2.5): one of the

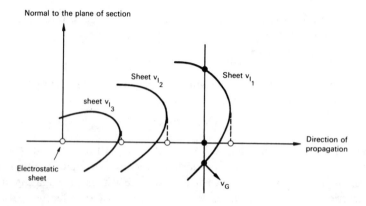

Fig. 2.5 Determination of the velocity of surface waves.

bulk waves moves toward the interior of the solid and the other travels from infinity toward the surface. Only the first has a physical meaning. We proceed in the same way when four, six or eight solutions are purely imaginary. The solution of the secular equation thus gives four physically acceptable values of K_3 for each value of v, and therefore four sets of complex amplitudes (u_1, u_2, u_3, V), as solutions of eqn (2.23). All that remains is to take account of the boundary conditions by linearly superimposing these solutions with four weighting parameters $\alpha_1, \alpha_2, \alpha_3, \alpha_4$ that are the new unknowns for each value of v.

The mechanical boundary conditions almost always refer to the case of a free surface, on which the normal stresses $T_{3i}(i = 1, 2, 3)$ are zero (for $x_3 = 0$):

$$T_{3i} = 0|_{x_3 = 0} \qquad (2.24)$$

We thus have three linear equations in four unknowns $(\alpha_1, \alpha_2, \alpha_3, \alpha_4)$. The last equation is obtained from the electric boundary conditions. It is convenient to introduce these conditions by writing the fourth equation in the form (Ingebrigtsen 1969):

$$\left.\frac{D_3}{V}\right|_{x_3 = 0} = |K|\varepsilon_s(v) \qquad (2.25)$$

where ε_s is a (complex) function to be determined.

Equations (2.24) and (2.25), taken together with eqn (2.19), now give four linear relations between the four unknowns $\alpha_1, \alpha_2, \alpha_3, \alpha_4$. The compatibility condition between these four equations defines unambiguously the function $\varepsilon_s(v)$, which we shall call the *piezoelectric surface permittivity* or, more simply, the *surface permittivity*.

Comparing eqn (2.25) with eqn (2.18), we see that the function $\varepsilon_s(v)$ reduces to a constant ε when the medium is not piezoelectric. When the exterior ($x_3 < 0$) is occupied by a dielectric of permittivity ε_e, the electric boundary conditions can be written (Ingebrigtsen 1969, 1972; Engan *et al.* 1969) in the form

$$\varepsilon_s(v) + \varepsilon_e = 0 \qquad (2.26)$$

For further information on this section, readers may consult Campbell and Jones (1968).

2.2.3   Discussion of surface permittivity

The analysis of Section 2.2.2 has enabled us to define a function $\varepsilon_s(v)$ so as to take account of electric conditions on the surface. The phase velocity $v = \omega/K$ is a solution of eqn (2.26) if the exterior is a dielectric of permittivity ε_e:

$$\varepsilon_s(v) + \varepsilon_e = 0 \qquad (2.27)$$

In particular, there is, in general, a surface-wave solution of velocity v_∞ that corresponds to an *open circuit*, i.e. to a fictitious external medium of permittivity zero. Similarly, the real pole of $\varepsilon_s(v)$ defines the propagation velocity v_0 when the surface is short-circuited by a conducting film. Figures 2.6 and 2.7 show the slowness curves v_∞ for the Y-cut of lithium niobate and the $\langle 101 \rangle$ cut of gallium arsenide respectively. We shall discuss the algebraic form of $\varepsilon_s(v)$, but, as a preliminary, it is useful to return to the above mathematical development from the point of view of possible decoupling.

2.2.3.1   Decoupling

Generalized Rayleigh waves   No simplification was used at any stage in Section 2.2.2, so that the secular equation of degree 8 in K_1 represented the compatibility condition for the system of four equations in the four unknowns u_1, u_2, u_3, V.

Rayleigh waves stricto sensu   When the (x_1, x_3) plane is a plane of symmetry, the component u_2 does not occur and the vibration is confined to the sagittal plane. The secular equation is of degree 6. Such a simplification occurs in the z-direction in Fig. 2.6.

Bleustein–Gulyaev waves   In a certain number of configurations, geometric symmetries lead to a decomposition of eqn (2.23) into the two independent sets,

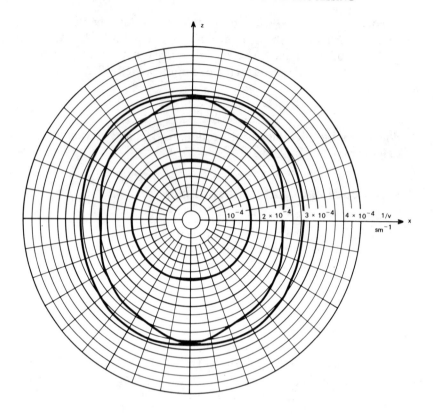

Fig. 2.6 Slowness surface of lithium niobate (Y-section): surface modes and pseudomodes.

one of which involves the components u_1 and u_3 (to the exclusion of V) and is therefore purely acoustic; the other involves the components u_2 and V and is therefore purely piezoelectric. The secular equation of this piezoelectric subset is of degree 4 in K_1. This simplification occurs in the direction $(\bar{1}, 0, 1)$ in Fig. 2.7.

For further information, readers may consult Bleustein (1968), Gulyaev (1969) and Greebe (1971).

Résumé   In general, the set of linear equations obtained from eqn (2.23) involves the four unknowns (u_1, u_2, u_3, V). It splits into $(3 + 1)$ sets in the case of Rayleigh waves and into $(2 + 2)$ in the case of Bleustein waves. We are interested only in the piezoelectric subset containing V and at least one displacement component, i.e. a subset of dimension 4, 3 or 2, containing the electric component V, and 3, 2 or 1 mechanical components respectively.

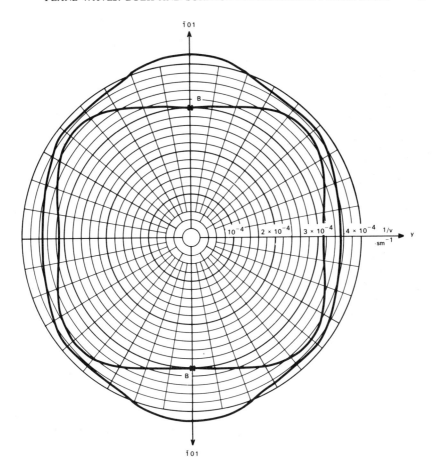

Fig. 2.7 Slowness curve of gallium arsenide, $\langle 110 \rangle$ section: surface modes and pseudomodes.

2.2.3.2 Algebraic approximations for surface permittivity

General case   Since we have chosen waves that must be attenuated or propagate in the interior of the solid, the piezoelectric permittivity is a relatively complicated function, possessing, in particular, branch points. In general, these branch points are situated quite far from the poles and zeros of the function, and it is legitimate to use an algebraic approximation for the function. A surface mode, for example, will involve, as for bulk waves, a pole and a zero (cf. eqn 2.8):

$$\frac{1}{\varepsilon_s(v)} \approx \frac{1}{\varepsilon}\left(1 - \frac{k^2}{1 - v^2/v_\infty^2}\right) \tag{2.28}$$

In fact, there are, in general, four solutions: the first is the true surface mode, the second and the third contain, respectively, one and two bulk waves, and the last contains not more than three bulk waves that combine with the electrostatic mode and correspond therefore to an infinite velocity. The second and third solutions are called pseudobranches of the surface or *leaky surface waves*. They are attenuated exponentially by the leakage of energy into the interior of the medium: the pole and the zero are complex, and we can evaluate the permittivity in the neighborhood of these points from

$$\frac{1}{\varepsilon_s(v)} \approx \frac{1}{\varepsilon}\left[1 - \frac{k_a^2}{(1 - v/v_a)(1 + v/v_a^*)}\right] \tag{2.29}$$

where v_a is complex and v_a^* is the complex conjugate of v_a.[†] By definition, we can evaluate the complete function from

$$\frac{1}{\varepsilon_s(v)} \approx \frac{1}{\varepsilon_{HF}}\left(1 - \frac{k_1^2}{1 - v^2/v_1^2} - \frac{k_2^2}{1 + jvb_2 - v^2/v_2^2}\right.$$
$$\left. - \frac{k_3^2}{1 + jvb_3 - v^2/v_3^2} - k_4^2\right) \tag{2.30}$$

Terms like k_1, k_2, k_3 are determined as residues of $\varepsilon_s(v)$ at the poles v_1, v_2, v_3. The term k_4^2 corresponds to bulk radiation normal to the surface, and the constant ε_{HF} can be identified with the permittivity in the absence of piezoelectricity: $\varepsilon_{HF} = \varepsilon_{11}\varepsilon_{33} - \varepsilon_{13}^2$.

As for bulk waves (see Section 2.1.4), the low-frequency permittivity is

$$\varepsilon_{LF} = \frac{\varepsilon_{HF}}{1 - k_1^2 - k_2^2 - k_3^2 - k_4^2} \tag{2.31}$$

REMARK. Since we are confining ourselves to a single surface mode, we can take the approximate form eqn (2.28) instead of eqn (2.30). Since the velocity of the surface wave is less than that of the pseudomodes, we can determine the contribution of the leaky surface waves by putting $v = 0$ in eqn (2.30):

$$\frac{1}{\varepsilon_s(v)} \approx \frac{1}{\varepsilon_{HF}}\left(1 - \frac{k_1^2}{1 - v^2/v_1^2} - k_2^2 - k_3^2 - k_4^2\right) \tag{2.32}$$

[†]We can see directly that $\varepsilon_s(v)$ is, locally, an even function of v. However, when we change v into $-v$ we change determination, so that the physical result contains terms linear in v.

which can be rewritten, using eqn (2.28), in the form

$$\frac{1}{\varepsilon_s(v)} \approx \frac{1}{\varepsilon}\left(1 - \frac{k^2}{1 - v^2/v_\infty^2}\right)$$
(2.33)

where

$$v_\infty = v_1 \qquad k^2 = \frac{k_1^2}{1 - k_2^2 - k_3^2 - k_4^2}$$

and

$$\varepsilon = \frac{\varepsilon_{HF}}{1 - k_2^2 - k_3^2 - k_4^2}$$
(2.34)

Since, in general, k_1^2 is small in comparison with $k_2^2 + k_3^2 + k_4^2$, the value of ε obtained in this way is close to ε_{LF} given by eqn (2.31).

Rayleigh waves stricto sensu   In this case, the behavior is the same as before, but we must superimpose one true surface mode, one single pseudomode and bulk radiation: the second pseudomode disappears.

Bleustein–Gulyaev waves   We might think of using the same formalism here, but this is not possible because the branch point now coincides with the pole. The calculation can, however, be carried out right to the end in exactly the same way (Van Dalen 1973), and the result is as follows:

$$\frac{1}{\varepsilon_s(v)} = \frac{1}{\varepsilon_{HF}}\left[1 - \left(\frac{k^2}{1 - v^2/v_\infty^2}\right)^{1/2} - k_2^2\right]$$
(2.35)

We shall see that this expression shows the very different behavior of the piezoelectric wave.

For further information, readers may consult Bleustein (1968), Gulyaev (1969) and Greebe (1971).

Special cases: SSBW waves   In certain cases, the rational approximation is not possible because a branch point is situated very close to a pole or a zero of the permittivity. The behavior is then similar to that of a Bleustein–Gulyaev wave, with the additional possibility of bulk radiation. These "pathological" modes are often referred to as surface skimming bulk waves (SSBW) (Lewis 1977), even though there is a certain confusion between Bleustein–Gulyaev modes, pseudomodes and SSBW.

2.2.4   Discussion and other modes

The preceding calculations concern plane waves that, by definition, propagate in an infinite homogeneous medium. Under these conditions, only the true surface modes confine the acoustic energy to the surface of the medium. In practice, the devices have finite dimensions, and we can also use surface pseudomodes, for example, in resonators (cf. Chapters 5 and 6). In addition, in nonhomogeneous media, e.g. in periodic networks, we can trap the acoustic energy at the surface of the material by perturbing the pseudomodes or even bulk modes. In particular, when transverse bulk modes or surface pseudomodes are used in this way, we can benefit from lower temperature coefficients and higher coupling coefficients (surface transverse waves (STW) modes) (Auld *et al.* 1982, Renard *et al.* 1981). Moreover, these modes, with their high propagation velocity, are better adapted to high frequencies.

2.2.5   Geometric and wave acoustics

The anisotropy of the slowness surface implies particular features in the propagation of acoustic rays. An acoustic ray can be characterized by the angle θ_0 between its wave vector and the Ox-axis (Fig. 2.8) and by the intercept y_0. In the gaussian approximation, which we are taking here, all the angles are supposed small. After traversing a distance L in the Ox-direction, a ray in an "acoustic pencil" will arrive not at distance $y_0 + L\theta_0$ from the Ox-axis as in an isotropic medium, but at a distance $y_0 + L\phi$, where ϕ defines the direction of the group velocity of the wave (or the energy transport velocity, cf. Appendix 2.3).

Parabolic anisotropy
We now consider the case where the slowness curve can be approximated by the arc of a parabola (Fig. 2.9). The angle ϕ characterizing the normal to

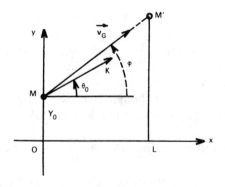

Fig. 2.8   Characterization of an acoustic ray.

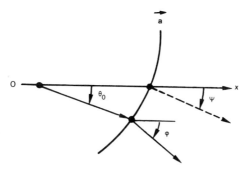

Fig. 2.9 Parabolic approximation to the slowness surface.

the slowness curve is then related linearly to the angle θ_0:

$$\phi = \psi + m\theta_0 + \ldots$$

where ψ is a constant. In a general treatment, the above expansion would have had an infinite number of terms. When we limit ourselves to the first term in θ_0, we say that the anisotropy is *parabolic*. This approximation is valid for most cases of surface waves. Unfortunately, there are notable exceptions, such as the *YZ* configuration of lithium niobate, for which this simplification is valid only for very small angles θ_0 ($< 3°$ in this case). When $\theta_0 = 0$, we have $\phi = \psi$. This angle ψ is called the *beam steering angle* or *power flow angle*. It is also convenient to replace the axis Ox by a new axis Ox' at the angle ψ to Ox, which indicates the mean direction of the bundle of rays, and then measure the deviation of the ray in successive sections of the bundle relative to this new axis (Fig. 2.10).

To the first order in θ_0, distances measured along Ox and Ox' are the same. The propagation can be described in matrix form by the relation

$$\begin{bmatrix} y' \\ \theta \end{bmatrix}_{x'_0 + L} = \begin{bmatrix} 1 & mL \\ 0 & 1 \end{bmatrix} \begin{bmatrix} y'_0 \\ \theta_0 \end{bmatrix}_{x'_0}$$

This equation shows that a ray characterized by x'_0, θ_0, y'_0 within the bundle will, after the transformation, be characterized by $x' = x'_0 + L$, $y' = y'_0 + m\theta_0 L$ and the same angle $\theta = \theta_0$ of the wave vector to the Ox axis.

DEFINITION. The quantity $m = d\phi/d\theta$ is called the scale factor.

RULE. In a parabolic anisotropic medium, propagation takes place strictly as in an isotropic medium, provided that distances along the axis are multiplied by the scale factor m, the axis being rotated through the beam steering angle ψ.

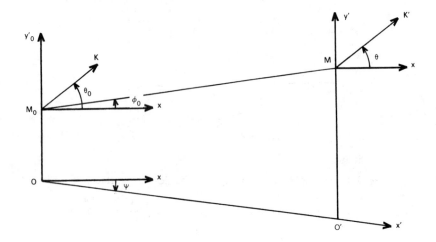

Fig. 2.10   Propagation of an acoustic ray.

REMARK. The scale factor m can be negative or even zero; in this latter case, there is no spatial dispersion (cf. exercise).

Acoustic lens

It is possible to deflect acoustic rays by changing the shape of the surface. More simply, the metallization of a piezoelectric surface (Fig. 2.11) reduces the velocity by a factor $k^2/2$ (cf. Section 2.1.2) and therefore the relative index (in the sense of the optical index) of a metallized medium is $n \simeq 1 + k^2/2$. We can then construct acoustic lenses, and the corresponding

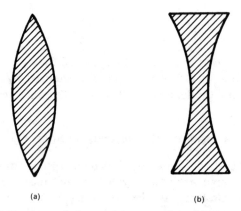

(a)   (b)

Fig. 2.11   Acoustic lenses: (a) converging; (b) diverging.

formulae are identical with those in optics if we assume that the lenses are thin (propagation does not come into play):

$$f^2 = \frac{RR'}{(n-1)^2}$$

where f is the focal length of the lens of index n, and R and R' are the radii of curvature. The effect of a thin lens of this kind on the above vector (y'_0, θ_0) is given by the formula (Feldmann 1971)

$$\begin{bmatrix} y' \\ \theta \end{bmatrix} = \begin{bmatrix} 1 & 0 \\ -1/f & 1 \end{bmatrix} \begin{bmatrix} y'_0 \\ \theta_0 \end{bmatrix}$$

$\Delta v/v$ guide

As in optics, total reflexion occurs as the boundary between a medium and a denser medium. When the denser medium is obtained simply by metallization of the surface of a piezoelectric medium, we call the corresponding waveguide a "$\Delta v/v$ guide" by analogy with the formula $\Delta v/v = k^2/2$ (Fig. 2.12). A description of such systems can be found in Oliner (1978) and Coussot (1973).

Passage to wave acoustics

The matrix relation describing an acoustic system in the parabolic approximation is

$$\begin{bmatrix} y' \\ \theta \end{bmatrix} = \begin{bmatrix} A \end{bmatrix} \begin{bmatrix} y' \\ \theta_0 \end{bmatrix} \tag{2.36}$$

where the matrix

$$\begin{bmatrix} A \end{bmatrix} = \begin{bmatrix} \alpha & \beta \\ \gamma & \delta \end{bmatrix}$$

is obtained by multiplying the propagation and lens matrices. This description is formally identical with that of optical systems, and enables us to pass formally to wave acoustics (Feldmann 1971).

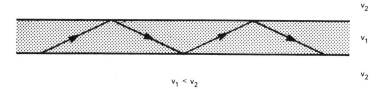

Fig. 2.12 $\Delta v/v$ waveguide.

Substituting $y = y'$ and $K = \theta/\tilde{\lambda}$ (where $\tilde{\lambda}$ is equal to the wavelength λ divided by 2π), we can show that the matrix $[A]$ describes a homogeneous refracting system, equivalent to the original acoustic system whose rays have the set of differential equations

$$
\begin{cases}
\dfrac{dy}{dt} = \dfrac{\partial \omega}{\partial K} \\[2ex]
\dfrac{dK}{dt} = -\dfrac{\partial \omega}{\partial y}
\end{cases}
\tag{2.37}
$$

where

$$
\omega = \omega_0 + \tfrac{1}{2}[uy^2 + vK^2 + w(yK + Ky)]
$$

and ω_0 is the angular frequency of the acoustic wave. Identifying this with the matrix (2.36), we obtain

$$
u = \frac{-\gamma}{s\tau\tilde{\lambda}} \qquad v = \frac{\beta\tilde{\lambda}}{s\tau} \qquad w = \frac{1}{2}\frac{\alpha - \delta}{s\tau}
$$

where τ is the time of axial propagation of the wave across the acoustic system, $s = \sin \xi/\xi$, and the eigenvalues of A are $\exp(\pm j\xi)$. The proof of this assertion consists simply in the verification that eqns (2.37) and (2.36) are indeed identical. The new (differential) formulation (2.37) (no longer integral, like eqn 2.36) takes the form of Hamilton's equation. It is shown in Feldmann (1971) that the angular frequency ω can be quantized according to the rules of quantum mechanics, i.e.

$$
y \to y \qquad K \to \frac{1}{j}\frac{d}{dy}
$$

and the Schrödinger equation for the system is none other than the wave equation

$$
\omega \to \Omega \triangleq \omega_0 + \frac{1}{2}\left[uy^2 - v\frac{d^2}{dy^2} + \frac{w}{j}\left(y\frac{d}{dy} + \frac{d}{dy}y\right)\right]
\tag{2.38}
$$

(where $\triangleq$ stands for "identical with"). Finally, the equation for the field $E \exp(j\omega t)$ is

$$
\Omega E(y) = \omega E(y)
$$

where Ω is the operator in eqn (2.38) and ω is the natural angular frequency (a scalar). When we set up an acoustic path in the form of a closed circuit (Kogelnik 1965), we obtain the equation for the eigenmodes of the corresponding (plane) cavity. Problems of diffraction can be dealt with in a similar way by starting with the eigenmodes of the operator Ω.

2.3   Exercise

Using the parabolic approximation, trace the propagation of an acoustic bundle when the slowness surface has the following forms:

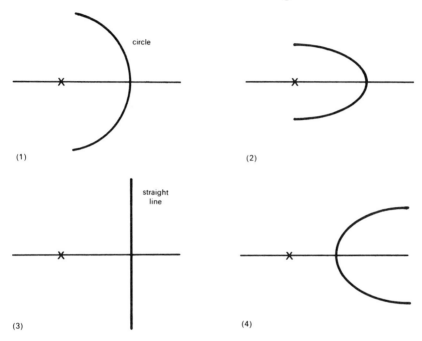

(1)

circle

(2)

(3)

straight line

(4)

Appendix 2.1   Determination of the slowness curve

To solve the system[†] (eqn 2.23):

$$C_{jklm}\partial_j\partial_l u_m + e_{ljk}\partial_j\partial_l V = \rho \ddot{u}_k$$
$$e_{jlm}\partial_j\partial_l u_m - \varepsilon_{jl}\partial_j\partial_l V = 0$$

for plane waves with the propagation law

$$\exp[j(\omega t - \beta_1 x_1 - \beta_2 x_2 - \beta_3 x_3)]$$

By substitution, we obtain a set of four equations in four unknowns:

$$(C_{jklm}\beta_j\beta_l)u_m + (e_{ljk}\beta_j\beta_l)V = \rho\omega^2 u_k \qquad (2.39)$$
$$(e_{jlm}\beta_j\beta_l)u_m + (-\varepsilon_{jl}\beta_j\beta_l)V = 0 \qquad (2.40)$$

[†]We use the Einstein summation convention.

Bulk waves

The wave vector $(\beta_1, \beta_2, \beta_3)$ has the direction $\mathbf{n}$. Let

$$\beta_j = n_j\beta \quad (j = 1, 2, 3)$$

where n_j represents a unit vector and β is the wave number. We can simplify the notation further by displaying:

(a) the acoustic parameters: $\Gamma_{km} = C_{jklm}n_jn_l/\rho$;
(b) the piezoelectric parameters: $\gamma_k = e_{ljk}n_ln_j/\rho^{1/2}$;
(c) the scalar dielectric parameter: $\varepsilon = \varepsilon_{lm}n_ln_m$.

Eliminating V from eqn 2.40 and substituting in eqn 2.39, we obtain

$$\left(\Gamma_{km} + \frac{1}{\varepsilon}\gamma_k\gamma_m\right)u_m = v^2 u_k \tag{2.41}$$

where $v = \omega/\beta$ is the required phase velocity.

Equation (2.41) shows that three bulk modes can propagate. They correspond to the eigenvectors of the operator for the first term; the phase velocities are the corresponding eigenvalues. The secular equation is simply the equation satisfied by the eigenvalues. It is of degree 3 in v^2 (degree 6 in v). Strictly speaking, we should add the electrostatic mode defined by $v = \infty$ and $u_m = 0$ ($m = 1, 2, 3$) but $V \neq 0$. In $1/v$, the secular equation including this mode would be of degree 8, and the slowness curve is therefore an algebraic surface of degree 8.

For further information, readers may consult Glowinski (1972).

Surface waves

Consider a canonical frame of reference such that the free surface is normal to the x_3 axis and propagation occurs in the x_1-direction. Suppose that $\beta_2 = 0$ and put

$$\beta_1 = K \qquad j\beta_3 = K_3$$

First, we hold K constant and let $\omega = 1$; we seek nonzero solutions of the set of equations. The determinant of this set must be zero. In practice, we are led to look for the intersection between the straight line $\beta_1 = K$ and the section of the slowness curve by the $\beta_2 = 0$ plane. This gives $\beta_3 = K_3/j$. This equivalent formulation has the advantage of providing simple geometric support, since we have already calculated the bulk-wave slowness curve in the

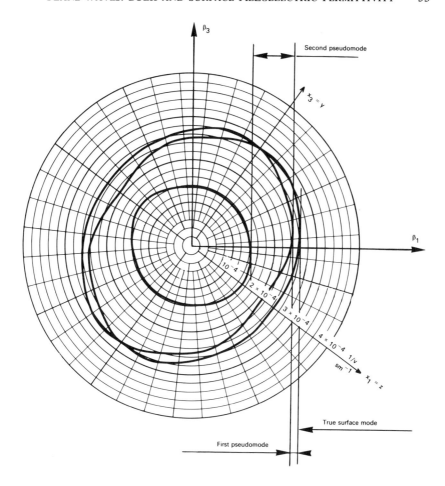

Fig. 2.13 Intersection of $\beta_1 = K$ with the slowness curve.

(x_1, x_3) plane (Fig. 2.13). Thus, K must be taken to be greater than the greatest real value of β_1 on the curve, if we are to obtain a true surface mode (imaginary intersection with the curve). The first pseudomode is obtained by choosing K in such a way that the straight line $\beta_1 = K$ cuts the curve at two (and two only) real points. The two points can be distinguished by means of the group velocity: only the half-sheet resulting in radiation into the volume has physical meaning.

We proceed in the same way for the second and third pseudomodes; the latter correspond to bulk radiation with $\beta_1 = 0$.

Appendix 2.2   Energy transport velocity

Consider a *nondissipative* system in which there is a piezoelectric field. The field is characterized by the piezoelectric flux vector P_i (see eqn 1.19) and the energy density (eqn 1.20)

$$\frac{\partial W}{\partial t} - \partial_i P_i = 0$$

Rewriting this equation as an equation of continuity, we have

$$\frac{\partial W}{\partial t} + \partial_i (v_i W) = 0$$

where we define the energy transport velocity by

$$v_i = -\frac{P_i}{W}$$

Consider *real isomorphic waves* in which all wave amplitudes (stresses, strains, etc.) vary in accordance with

$$\text{Re}[\exp(pt - \boldsymbol{Q} \cdot \boldsymbol{r})] \tag{2.42}$$

Put $p = \sigma + j\omega$ and $\boldsymbol{Q} = \boldsymbol{L} + j\boldsymbol{K}$, $\boldsymbol{r}$ being the radius vector and t the time. We shall be interested in the *mean energy* and the corresponding propagation velocity:

$$v_i = -\frac{\langle P_i \rangle}{\langle W \rangle} \tag{2.43}$$

To ensure that at time $t = -\infty$ the field is finite, we shall suppose that $\sigma \geqslant 0$. The vector P_i, obtained as the product of two real quantities varying in accordance with eqn (2.42), then takes the form

$$P_i = \text{Re}[P'_i \exp(\phi + \phi^*) + P''_i \exp(2\phi)]$$

where

$$\phi = pt - \boldsymbol{Q} \cdot \boldsymbol{r}$$

The *mean power* varies as

$$\exp(\phi + \phi^*) = \exp(2\sigma t - 2\boldsymbol{L} \cdot \boldsymbol{r})$$

and the *fluctuating* part does not interest us here. On the other hand, we have

$$W(t) = \int_{-\infty}^{t} \partial_i P_i \, dt$$

and hence

$$\langle W(t) \rangle \;=\; \mathrm{Re} \int_{-\infty}^{t} -2L_i P'_i \exp(\phi + \phi^*)\,\mathrm{d}t$$

Putting Re $P'_i = \langle P_i \rangle$, and integrating, we have

$$\langle W \rangle \;=\; -\frac{L_i}{\sigma} \langle P_i \rangle \qquad\qquad (2.44)$$

Suppose now that the wave becomes plane- and time-harmonic, i.e. σ and L_i tend to zero. We can then consider σ and L as imaginary increments $\mathrm{d}\omega/j$ and $\mathrm{d}K/j$ on ω and K respectively, so that

$$\langle W \rangle \;=\; -\frac{\mathrm{d}K_i}{\mathrm{d}\omega} \langle P_i \rangle \qquad\qquad (2.45)$$

Comparing eqns (2.45) and (2.43), we get

$$\mathrm{d}\omega \;=\; v_i \mathrm{d}K_i \qquad\qquad (2.46)$$

Comparing this with eqn (2.14), we conclude that the energy transport velocity v_i is identical with the group velocity $\boldsymbol{v}_G$ of the plane wave.

Appendix 2.3   Reciprocal relations in the time-harmonic regime

Piezoelectricity is described by the constitutive eqns (2.19), the Poisson eqn (2.20), and Newton's second law (eqn 2.21). In the time-harmonic regime (Auld 1973), we suppose that all the fields T_{jk}, u_m, V and D_1 have the time dependence $\exp(j\omega t)$, and we omit this exponential factor for the sake of brevity. Only eqn (2.21) then needs to be rewritten: it becomes

$$\partial_j T_{jk} \;=\; -\rho\omega^2 u_k$$

In a reciprocal medium, the Onsager symmetry relations for the coefficients (described in Chapter 1) can be expressed in terms of the fields alone (and no longer the coefficients). This leads to the following theorem.

THEOREM. *Given two time-harmonic solutions (1) and (2) corresponding to the same nonzero frequency ω (but with possibly different boundary conditions), the bilinear form*

$$\partial_k R_k \;=\; \partial R_1/\partial x_1 + \partial R_2/\partial x_2 + \partial R_3/\partial x_3$$

where

$$R_k = (u_i^{(1)} T_{ik}^{(2)} - u_i^{(2)} T_{ik}^{(1)}) + (V^{(1)} D_k^{(2)} - V^{(2)} D_k^{(1)})$$

is zero in the interior of the crystal.

PROOF. All that needs to be done is to replace the stresses and the electric displacement components using eqns (2.19)–(2.21) and the symmetry of the coefficients C_{ikjl} and ε_{lm}.

APPLICATION. Perturbation of the surface of a piezoelectric medium. Consider an unperturbed crystal and a surface wave (1) that propagates in the form of a plane wave in the direction of increasing x_1, independently of the second coordinate x_2 on the plane. All the fields are then of the form:

$$\exp(jK_1 x_1) f(x_3)$$

Consider now the same crystal with its surface perturbed (which has the effect of changing the boundary conditions) and a plane surface wave (2) propagating in the direction of decreasing x_1 (x_2 is still not involved).
The fields are then of the form

$$\exp(-jK_2 x_1) f_2(x_3)$$

and

$$R_k = \exp[j(K_1 - K_2)x_1] r_k(x_3)$$

The reciprocal relation may be written

$$j(K_1 - K_2) r_1(x_3) + \frac{dr^3(x_3)}{dx_3} = 0$$

When we make the perturbation of solution (2) tend to zero, we find the boundary conditions for solution (1), the only difference being the propagation direction. In a lossless medium, it is sufficient to take the complex conjugates of each of the terms to pass from solution (1) to solution (2). We then have [omitting the index 1]

$$r_k = 2j \, \mathrm{Im}(u_i T^*_{ik} - VD^*_{ik})$$

where the asterisk denotes the complex conjugate.
Comparing this with eqns (1.19) and (2.15), we see that

$$-j\omega r_k = 2 \, \mathrm{Re}(P_k)$$

represents the mean energy flux of the unperturbed wave. This vector points in the direction x_1 of the group velocity. For weak perturbations we have

$$r_1 \simeq -2 \, \mathrm{Re}(P)/j\omega$$

and

$$K_1 - K_2 \approx \frac{\omega}{2 \, \mathrm{Re}(P)} \frac{\mathrm{d}r_3(x_3)}{\mathrm{d}x_3}$$

where P is the amplitude of the energy flux vector.

REMARK. When the crystal is not reciprocal, we can define a fictitious medium that is the time reverse or transpose of the original crystal. The same property applies, provided one of the solutions (1) and (2) belongs to the original crystal and the other to the transposed crystal.

This method is useful for calculating the effect of the finite mass of electrodes or gratings (cf. Chapter 5).

Chapter 3

Piezoelectric Depolarization Waves

In Chapter 2, we defined bulk and surface *piezoelectric permittivity* which is an important concept because it summarizes all the piezoelectric properties of the medium. In this chapter, we shall see how this function enables us to determine the distribution of the electric field, and how a piezoelectric medium reacts to an electrical stress by emitting depolarization waves.

We are, of course, primarily concerned with surface waves. We shall, however, discuss at some length the phenomenon of bulk waves, even though the model we shall use will not be very realistic. These calculations are interesting because of their close resemblance to those encountered later in the case of surface waves. They have the advantage of providing a rigorous mathematical description that will enable us to identify general relationships concerning the conservation of energy and the behavior of certain other parameters.

3.1 Bulk waves

Of course, piezoelectric permittivity is merely ordinary permittivity in the case of a nonpiezoelectric medium. We shall begin by examining the use of this formalism in this limiting case before going on to actual piezoelectric cases.

3.1.1 Purely electrostatic model

Consider the one-dimensional model studied in Chapter 2 where the distributions of the volume charge density $\mu^{\dagger}$ and of the potential V depend

---

†We recall that μ denotes the volume density of electric charge, σ the surface density, q the linear density and Q the electric charge.

only on the coordinate $x_1 = x$ and (possibly) on the time t. The plane-wave analysis leading to eqn (2.7) now gives

$$\frac{V(\omega, K)}{\mu(\omega, K)} = \frac{1}{K^2 \varepsilon_p(\omega/K)} \tag{3.1}$$

In the purely electrostatic case, we have $\varepsilon_p = \varepsilon$ (the permittivity of the medium), so that eqn (3.1) can be written in the form

$$\mu(\omega, K) - \varepsilon K^2 V(\omega, K) = 0 \tag{3.2}$$

We note, first, that the angular frequency ω does not occur explicitly in the electrostatic case, and we can therefore abbreviate the notation by specifying only the wave number K, i.e. by replacing $V(\omega, K)$ and $\mu(\omega, K)$ with $V(K)$ and $\mu(K)$ respectively.

We see therefore that eqn (3.2) is simply the spatial Fourier transform of the equation[†]

$$\mu(x) + \varepsilon \frac{d^2 V(x)}{dx^2} = 0 \tag{3.3}$$

Moreover, we can formally deduce eqn (3.3) from eqn (3.2) by replacing K with jd/dx.

If the charge density $\mu(x) = \mu_0(x)$ is known, the response $V_0(x)$ can be deduced by double integration.

3.1.2   The case of a single capacitance

Consider a system consisting of two electrodes immersed in a dielectric of permittivity ε (Fig. 3.1).

The very theoretical model that we shall use consists of a rod, cut so that it has plane faces at $\pm h/2$. The faces are then metallized and the whole system is then reassembled again as shown. The elastic charge then consists of two Dirac functions of magnitude $\pm \sigma_0$.

[†]For brevity, and whenever this does not lead to confusion, we use (abusing the notation to some extent) the same letter (μ and V) to denote a function and its Fourier transform.

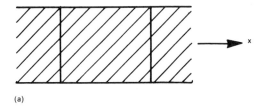

(a)

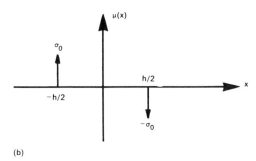

(b)

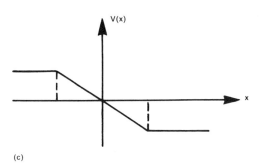

(c)

Fig. 3.1 Electrodes immersed in a dielectric: (a) schematic representation; (b) distribution of charge; (c) distribution of potential.

Integrating twice, we see that the potential varies linearly in the region between the electrodes, but is constant elsewhere. Moreover (Fig. 3.1c),

$$V = V_0\left(-\frac{h}{2}\right) - V_0\left(\frac{h}{2}\right) = \frac{\sigma_0 h}{\varepsilon} \tag{3.4}$$

The charge on an area S is $Q_0 = S\sigma_0$, so that the capacitance C is given by

$$C = \frac{Q_0}{V} = \varepsilon\frac{S}{h} \tag{3.5}$$

and the distribution of potential is (Fig. 3.1c)

$$
V_0(x) = \begin{cases} -\dfrac{\sigma_0 x}{\varepsilon} & |x| \leqslant \dfrac{h}{2} \\[2ex] -\dfrac{\sigma_0 h}{2\varepsilon} \operatorname{sgn} x & |x| \geqslant \dfrac{h}{2} \end{cases} \tag{3.6}
$$

where sgn x means "the sign of x".

3.1.3 Single-mode piezoelectric model

Consider now a piezoelectric medium with piezoelectric permittivity given by eqn (2.8):

$$
\frac{1}{\varepsilon_p(v)} = \frac{1}{\varepsilon}\left(1 - \frac{k^2}{1 - v^2/v_\infty^2}\right) \tag{3.7}
$$

We recall that the phase velocity is $v = \omega/K$. The velocity v_∞, the effective piezoelectric coupling k^2 and the permittivity ε are all constants.

We shall solve eqn (3.1) in three stages, assuming that the charge distribution $\mu(t, x)$ is known.

(i) First, we suppose that $k^2 = 0$ in eqn (3.7); if we know the charge distribution $\mu_0(x)$, we can deduce from it (Section 3.1.1) the electrostatic potential $V_0(x)$.

(ii) Second, we suppose that k^2 is nonzero, and introduce the charge $\mu_0(x)$ at $t = 0$; the charge will remain fixed for $t > 0$ and is thus known at every instant. Equation (3.1) can then be solved with the help of a table of Fourier transforms. The result is given in Appendix 3.1, and is remarkably simple. It may be written (for $t \geqslant 0$)

$$
V(t, x) = (1 - k^2)V_0(x) + \frac{k^2}{2}[V_0(x - v_\infty t) + V_0(x + v_\infty t)] \tag{3.8}
$$

(iii) Third, when the charge varies with time (but is still known at every instant), we superimpose the different solutions obtained from eqn (3.8).

3.1.4 Piezoelectric capacitor

Consider again the two electrodes immersed in a medium. The latter will now be assumed to be a piezoelectric medium (Fig. 3.1).

(i) The electrical potential was calculated in Section 3.1.1 and is given by eqn (3.6).

(ii) If the charge σ_0 is introduced at $t = 0$, the potential is given by eqn (3.8) for $t > 0$. Figure 3.2b shows the electrostatic potential deduced from eqn (3.8). It is perhaps clearer if we differentiate this equation with respect to x to obtain the electric field: $-\partial V/\partial x = E(t, x)$ which applies for $t > 0$ (Fig. 3.2d):

$$E(t, x) = (1 - k^2)E_0(x) + \frac{k^2}{2}[E_0(x - v_\infty t) + E_0(x + v_\infty t)] \quad (3.9)$$

where $E_0(x)$ is the electrostatic field, given by

$$E_0(x) = \begin{cases} \dfrac{\sigma_0}{\varepsilon} & |x| < \dfrac{h}{2} \\[2mm] 0 & |x| > \dfrac{h}{2} \end{cases} \quad (3.10)$$

The field $E_0 = \sigma_0/\varepsilon$ is thus seen to decompose into a fraction $1 - k^2$ that remains fixed between the electrodes, and two fractions $k^2/2$ that "break off" and propagate, one to the right and one to the left, at the constant velocity v_∞ and "disappear" into the medium.

(iii) To calculate the response of the system to an arbitrary time-dependent charge, it is sufficient to notice that charging the capacitance at time $t = 0$ is equivalent to injecting a Dirac pulse. The potential difference between the two plates of the capacitor is, by definition, the *impulse response* of the dipole (Feldmann 1981). It is now very easy to obtain this potential difference $V(t)$ from eqn (3.8) (cf. Fig. 3.2). It is clear that $V(t)$ (equal to zero for $t < 0$) takes the value $\sigma_0 h/\varepsilon$ at $t = 0$, decreases linearly for the time $2\tau = h/v_\infty$, and then assumes the constant value $(1 - k^2)\sigma_0 h/\varepsilon$ for $t > 2\tau$ (Fig. 3.3). For a section of area S, the total charge is $Q_0 = S\sigma_0$, the capacitance is $C = \varepsilon S/h$, and the impulse response is

$$Z(t) = V(t)/Q_0$$

By definition, the impedance is the Laplace transform of $Z(t)$ (Feldmann 1973), and we can easily obtain it from a table of transforms (Angot 1961, p. 547). The result is

$$Z(s) = \frac{1}{Cs}\left\{1 - \frac{k^2}{2s\tau}[1 - \exp(-2s\tau)]\right\} \quad (3.11)$$

If we prefer the time-harmonic response, we obtain for $s = j\omega$

$$Z(j\omega) = R(\omega) + jX(\omega) = \frac{k^2\tau}{C}\left(\frac{\sin \omega\tau}{\omega\tau}\right)^2 + \frac{1}{jC\omega}\left(1 - k^2\frac{\sin 2\omega\tau}{2\omega\tau}\right)$$

$$(3.12)$$

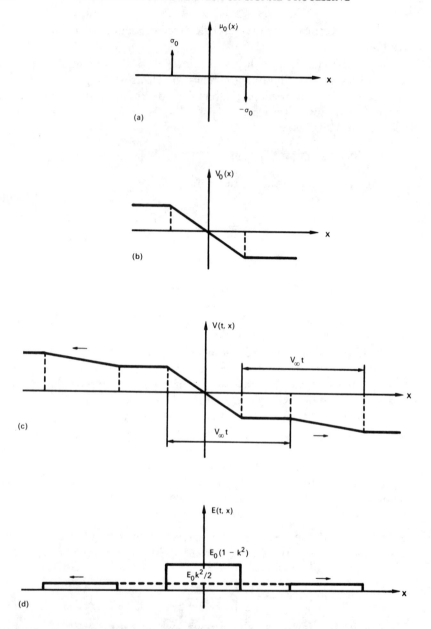

Fig. 3.2 Piezoelectric depolarization bulk wave: (a) distribution of charge for $t \geqslant 0$; (b) distribution of potential for $t = 0$; (c) distribution of potential for $t > 0$; (d) electric field for $t > 0$.

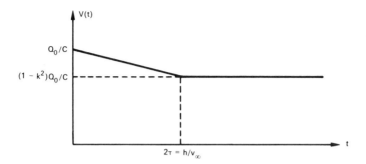

Fig. 3.3 Potential difference between the terminals of the capacitor of Fig. 3.1 after the application of a point charge Q_0 at $t = 0$. The Laplace transform of $V(t)$ for $Q_0 = 1$ is the input impedance of the dipole.

3.1.5 Physical interpretation: depolarization waves

Equation (3.8) and Fig. 3.2c can be interpreted as follows. At time $t = 0$, the potential is equal to the electrostatic potential of a piezoelectric medium of permittivity ε. Two depolarization waves appear for $t > 0$ and propagate (one in each direction) at constant velocity v_∞, tending to reduce the potential. A new equilibrium is established for large t, and corresponds to the electrostatic response of a system identical to the original system, but with permittivity given by

$$\varepsilon_{LF} = \frac{\varepsilon}{1 - k^2} \tag{3.13}$$

From the macroscopic viewpoint, a piezoelectric medium is thus seen to behave as a medium that reacts to an electric field by reducing the potential difference between the electrodes. Whereas in a conductor this occurs as a result of the displacement of the electric charges, a similar result is produced in a piezoelectric insulator by slow depolarization waves. If the medium were infinitely piezoelectric ($k^2 = 1$), the electric field would be permanently zero in equilibrium in the interior of the material.

At the microscopic level, it is the crystalline chain that is deformed, with the result that the dipolar field acts in the opposite direction to the electric field. Indeed, this explains the slowness of the phenomenon.

3.1.6 Energy balance: radiation resistance

The electrostatic energy stored in a capacitor at time $t = 0$ is equal to $Q_0^2/2C$. The energy remaining after depolarization is $(1 - k^2)Q_0^2/2C$, and the remainder propagates through the medium in the form of a piezoelectric wave. From the viewpoint of circuit theory, the dipole has a high-frequency capacitance $C_{HF} = C$ that is different from the low-frequency capacitance

$$C_{LF} = \frac{C}{1 - k^2} \qquad (3.14)$$

It is shown in circuit theory (Feldmann 1981, p. 195) that this dependence of capacitance on frequency implies the existence of a resistance $R(\omega)$ satisfying the integral relation

$$\int_0^\infty R(\omega) \, d\omega = \frac{\pi}{2}\left(\frac{1}{C_{HF}} - \frac{1}{C_{LF}}\right) = \frac{k^2 \pi}{2C} \qquad (3.15)$$

This relation is, of course, satisfied by the impedance (eqn 3.12).[†] The resistance $R(\omega)$ is called the *radiation resistance*.

By eqn (3.12), the ratio of resistance to reactance is (with $\theta = 2\omega\tau$)

$$y = \frac{R}{X} = \frac{2k^2 \sin^2(\theta/2)}{\theta - k^2 \sin \theta} \qquad (3.16)$$

and when $\theta \to 0$,

$$y \underset{\theta \to 0}{\approx} \frac{\theta}{2}\frac{k^2}{1 - k^2} \qquad (3.16a)$$

We shall see an application of this relation in Chapter 4.

3.1.7 Propagation of depolarization waves

Consider a depolarization wave generated by a capacitance consisting of two electrodes immersed in a piezoelectric medium. We are interested in its propagation outside the region between the electrodes. When the capacitance is suddenly charged at the instant $t = 0$, we observe, according to eqns (3.9) and (3.10), a rectangular electric field pulse that is displaced with velocity v_∞ and therefore reaches the point x with the delay $|x|/v_\infty$. In the frequency domain, the *field* observed at the point x is therefore (Fig. 3.2d)

$$E(\omega, x) = \frac{k^2}{2}\left(\frac{2 \sin \omega\tau}{\omega}\right) \exp(-j\omega|x|/v_\infty) \frac{\sigma_0}{\varepsilon} \qquad (3.17)$$

The exponential in this expression is the Fourier transform of the delay and $2(\sin \omega\tau)/\omega$ is the transform of the rectangle.

[†]We are using the result $\int_{-\infty}^{+\infty} (\sin x/x) \, dx = \pi$ and integration by parts.

We can rewrite this formula in terms of the depolarization potential $e(\omega, x)$ (after integration):

$$e(\omega, x) = \frac{k^2}{2C} \operatorname{sgn} x \left(\frac{\sin \omega\tau}{\omega\tau} \right) \exp(-j\omega|x|/v_\infty)Q(\omega) \qquad (3.18)$$

where $C = \varepsilon S/h$ is the capacitance, S is the cross-sectional area, $Q(\omega)$ is the charge on the capacitance (we can also use the current $I(\omega) = j\omega Q(\omega)$), and sgn x signifies the sign of x.

3.1.8 Characteristic impedance

A piezoelectric medium behaves, finally, like a lossless line in which the velocity is v_∞. If we consider a capacitor as a transmitter located in this line, the total power emitted in both directions at frequency ω is by eqn (3.12)

$$P = RI^2 = \frac{k^2\tau}{C} \left(\frac{\sin \omega\tau}{\omega\tau} \right)^2 I^2 \qquad (3.19)$$

where I is the effective current entering the capacitor. The effective potential propagating along the line is by eqn (3.18)

$$|e(\omega)| = \frac{k^2}{2C\omega} \left| \frac{\sin \omega\tau}{\omega\tau} \right| I \qquad (3.20)$$

We can therefore regard the medium as a line with the real characteristic impedance

$$R_c = \frac{|e^2|}{P/2} = \frac{k^2 v_\infty}{\varepsilon S\omega^2} \qquad (3.21)$$

We take $P/2$ to allow for the splitting of the input power between the two directions of propagation.

3.1.9 Reception of depolarization waves

Consider, first, a capacitance C_1 localized at the point $x = 0$. It transmits (in the positive x-direction) a depolarization wave given by eqn (3.18):

$$e_1(\omega, x) = \frac{k^2}{2jC_1\omega} \operatorname{sgn} x \left(\frac{\sin \omega\tau_1}{\omega\tau_1} \right) \exp(-j\omega|x|/v_\infty)I_1(\omega) \qquad (3.22)$$

Suppose now that a second capacitance C_2 (on open circuit) is placed in the path of the wave (with the same cross-section S). If the electrodes of the second capacitance are respectively at $x_{12} - h/2$ and $x_{12} + h/2$, the voltage between the electrodes will be

$$e_{21}(\omega) = e_1\left(\omega, x_{12} - \frac{h_2}{2}\right) - e_1\left(\omega, x_{12} + \frac{h_2}{2}\right)$$

or

$$e_{21} = Z_{21}I_1 \tag{3.23}$$

where

$$Z_{21} = \frac{2k^2 v_\infty}{\varepsilon S}\left(\frac{\sin \omega\tau_1}{\omega}\right)\left(\frac{\sin \omega\tau_2}{\omega}\right)\exp(-j\omega|x_{12}|/v_\infty) \tag{3.24}$$

If now the terminals of C_2 are no longer on open circuit, but a current $I_2(\omega)$ is allowed to flow, the voltages V_1 and V_2 at the terminals of the two capacitances will be described by

$$\begin{cases} V_1 = Z_{11}I_1 + Z_{12}I_2 \\ V_2 = Z_{21}I_1 + Z_{22}I_2 \end{cases} \tag{3.25}$$

Supposing, first, that $I_2 = 0$, we see that Z_{11} is given by eqn (3.11), applied to capacitance C_1. Similarly Z_{22} is given by eqn (3.11), applied to capacitance C_2. The transfer impedance Z_{12} is given by eqn (3.24) and Z_{12} is equal to Z_{21} (by the symmetry of eqn 3.24). In general, piezoelectricity is a reciprocal phenomenon (cf. Feldmann 1981, p. 78), so that

$$Z_{12} = Z_{21} \tag{3.26}$$

3.1.10   Radiation resistance and self-depolarization

When capacitances 1 and 2 coincide, eqn (3.23) gives the depolarization voltage induced by a piezoelectric capacitance in itself:

$$e_{11} = R_1 I_1 \tag{3.27}$$

where

$$R_1 = \frac{k^2\tau_1}{C_1}\left(\frac{\sin \omega\tau_1}{\omega\tau_1}\right)^2$$

We find again that the radiation resistance is given by eqn (3.12). The radiation reactance

$$X_1 = \frac{k^2}{C_1\omega}\left(\frac{\sin 2\omega\tau_1}{2\omega\tau_1}\right)$$

can be easily obtained by applying the Bayard–Bode causality relations (Feldmann 1981, p. 200).

3.1.11 Multimode problems

When several vibration branches are possible, we must start with the more general piezoelectric permittivity (eqn 2.9). We can verify that the calculation is the same: we must simply add the contribution of each vibration branch. The depolarization potential corresponding to a single capacitance is then given simply by

$$e(\omega, x) = \sum_i e_i(\omega, x) \tag{3.28}$$

where e_i represents the contribution of mode i.

3.2   Surface waves

We shall now examine what happens to the formalism of piezoelectric depolarization waves in the case of surface modes. It will be useful to start again with the purely electrostatic problem before discussing different algebraic approximations to surface permittivity.

3.2.1   Purely electrostatic model

We showed in Chapter 2 that the surface permittivity of a dielectric occupying the half-space $x_3 > 0$ was (eqn 2.18)

$$\frac{D_3(K)}{V_0(K)} = |K|\varepsilon \tag{3.29}$$

When the dielectric occupies the other half-space, we have to take $-|K|$ instead of $|K|$.

The wave number K occurs in the nonalgebraic form $|K|$. This mathematical difficulty leads to the following complication: if the surface is alternatively conducting and insulating (for example, if we use two finite electrodes), there is no solution consisting of a finite number of plane waves alone. It can be shown that only an infinite superposition of plane waves has any physical meaning (we shall nevertheless be led to the evaluation of piezoelectric depolarization, using only two plane waves; the result will prove to be only approximate).

Suppose now that the other half-space is occupied by a dielectric (usually air or vacuum) of permittivity ε_e. If the surface is partially metallized, we take account of this by adding to the electrodes a charge density $\sigma_0(x)$, which makes them equipotential.

Let D_{3_e} and V_{0_e} be the values of the normal component of electric displacement vector and the potential at the interface, respectively. We have in wave-number space:

$$\frac{D_{3_e}(K)}{V_{0_e}(K)} = -|K|\varepsilon_e \tag{3.30}$$

The boundary conditions are

$$V_{0_e}(K) = V_0(K) \tag{3.31}$$

$$D_3(K) - D_{3_e}(K) = \sigma_0(K) \tag{3.32}$$

Hence the final relation is

$$\frac{V_0(K)}{\sigma_0(K)} = \frac{1}{|K|\varepsilon^*} \tag{3.33}$$

where

$$\varepsilon^* = \varepsilon + \varepsilon_e \tag{3.34}$$

Equation (3.33) is the surface-wave equivalent of the bulk-wave relation given by eqn (3.1). Note that we often have $\varepsilon_e \ll \varepsilon$ and $\varepsilon^* \simeq \varepsilon$. However that may be, and for brevity, we shall almost always omit the asterisk in eqn (3.33).

3.2.2 Electrostatic capacitance

Consider a system consisting of two identical electrodes, placed on the interface between two dielectrics whose permittivities have the sum ε (Fig. 3.4a). The Schwartz–Christoffel conformal transformation (Durand 1953) can be used to map the upper half-plane (or similarly the lower half-plane) onto the interior of a rectangle (Fig. 3.4b). Conversely, starting with a uniform charge distribution over the two sides of the rectangle, it is possible to return to the charge distribution on the original two electrodes (cf. Appendix 3.2).

In practice, we are seldom concerned with two isolated electrodes; on the contrary, we usually have a periodic system of electrodes as indicated in Fig. 3.5.

Mathematically, the problem (dealt with in Appendix 3.2) is hardly more complex; there is simply a small difference in the shape of the lines of force

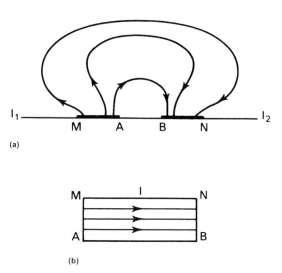

Fig. 3.4 Conformal transformation of a half-plane onto the interior of a rectangle.

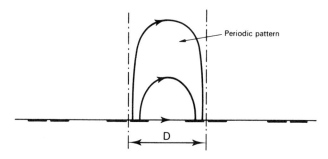

Fig. 3.5 Periodic pattern of an array of electrodes capable of transformation onto the interior of a rectangle according to Fig. 3.4b (each electrode is notionally divided into two parts).

in the field. It will be convenient in what follows to study a single electrostatic capacitance, extracted from a periodic array of capacitances. For this, we imagine each electrode to be cut into two equal parts, and consider the elementary "pattern" consisting of two half-electrodes and the free interval between the electrodes. The lines of force and the distributions of charge, potential and electric field are sketched in Fig. 3.6. Starting with a finite network with $(N + 1)$ electrodes, we obtain in this way N elementary

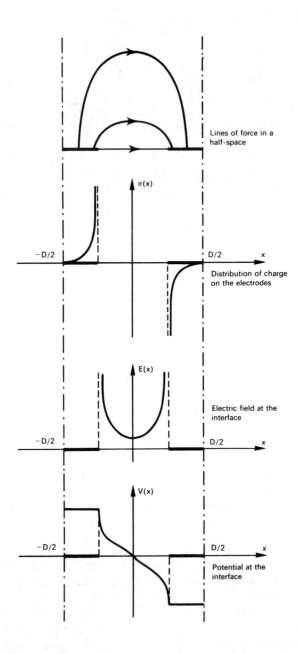

Fig. 3.6 Electrostatic parameters corresponding to the pattern of Fig. 3.5.

capacitances[†]. If we consider an elementary capacitance centered on the origin, its value for a metallization ratio of 50% is (see Appendix 3.2)

$$C = \tfrac{1}{2}\varepsilon W \tag{3.35}$$

where W is the length of the electrode at right angles to the x_1-axis.

Note that this capacitance is *independent of the spacing of the array*.

3.2.3 Piezoelectric mode model

Consider now an actual piezoelectric medium with surface permittivity given by eqn (2.28):

$$\frac{1}{\varepsilon_s(v)} = \frac{1}{\varepsilon}\left(1 - \frac{k^2}{1 - v^2/v_\infty^2}\right) \tag{3.36}$$

Exactly as for bulk waves (Section 3.1.3), the phase velocity is $v = \omega/K$, and v_∞, the coupling coefficient k^2 and the permittivity ε are constants. Again as in Section 3.1.3, we shall first try to solve the electrostatic problem. However, to begin with, we must transform eqn (2.28), which relates the electric displacement to the potential, into a relation between the charge density and the potential. Proceeding as in Section 3.2.2, we can readily see that

$$\frac{V(\omega, K)}{\sigma(\omega, K)} = \frac{1}{|K|(\varepsilon_s(v) + \varepsilon_e)}$$

where ε_e is the permittivity of the external medium. This equation can be rewritten in the form

$$\frac{V(\omega, K)}{\sigma(\omega, K)} = \frac{1}{|K|\varepsilon^*_s(v)} \tag{3.37}$$

where

$$\frac{1}{\varepsilon^*_s(v)} = \frac{1}{\varepsilon^*}\left[1 - \frac{(k^*)^2}{1 - v^2/(v^*_\infty)^2}\right] \tag{3.38}$$

and

$$(v^*_\infty)^2 = v_\infty^2\left(1 - k^2\frac{\varepsilon_e}{\varepsilon_e + \varepsilon}\right)$$

$$\varepsilon^* = \varepsilon_e + \varepsilon \tag{3.39}$$

$$(k^*)^2 = k^2/[1 + (\varepsilon_e/\varepsilon)(1 - k^2)]$$

[†]We are neglecting end effects.

Equation (3.18) is formally identical with eqn (3.36). Moreover, ε_e is often small in comparison with ε, so that the parameters ε^*, v^*_∞ and k^* are almost equal to ε, v_∞ and k. For brevity, we shall omit the asterisk. We can now proceed.

(i) First, we suppose that $k^2 = 0$ in eqn (3.36), or more precisely $k^{*2} = 0$ in eqn (3.38). If we knew the charge distribution $\sigma_0(x)$, we could use eqn (3.37) to deduce from it the static potential $V_0(x)$. We note at once an important difference from the bulk-wave model: we do not know the distribution $\sigma_0(x)$ at the outset and we must, in general, obtain it by other methods, such as conformal transformation. Be that as it may, this purely electrostatic problem admits of a unique solution $\sigma_0(x)$, $V_0(x)$.

(ii) Second, suppose that k^2 is nonzero and apply the electrostatic charge $\sigma_0(x)$ at time $t = 0$. If we suppose that this charge remains fixed for $t > 0$, it is possible to solve eqn (3.37) with the help of a table of Fourier transforms. The result for the permittivity eqn (3.36) is, of course, identical with that obtained for bulk waves (eqn 3.8):

$$V(t, x) \; = \; (1 - k^2)V_0(x) + \frac{k^2}{2} [V_0(x - v_\infty t) + V_0(x + v_\infty t)]$$

(3.40)

Compared with the bulk-wave model, the essential difference is that the distribution $\sigma_0(x)$ will not retain its static form. Equation (3.40) thus amounts to the *fixed charge approximation*: this approximation improves with decreasing current between the electrodes, which can be achieved, at least notionally, by splitting each electrode into isolated subelectrodes. We can calculate the actual charge distribution by reconnecting the subelectrodes by means of an external circuit, thus transforming the currents in the electrodes into currents between the electrodes which we can calculate from circuit theory.

We shall suppose later on that this partition of each electrode into isolated parts has been carried out, so as to make the fixed-charge approximation valid.

(iii) We can then immediately extend this solution to cases with variable charge distribution by superimposing responses such as eqn (3.40).

3.2.4 Piezoelectric capacitance

We return to the model with two half-electrodes separated by an insulating gap and constituting the elementary pattern of a regular array (Fig. 3.5). We note that, in this model, each electrode of the original array has been (notionally) divided into two, which has the effect of limiting the current between the electrodes. We shall see later that such a half-electrode has the dimension of the order of $\frac{1}{8}$ of a wavelength, i.e. $\frac{1}{16}$ in the case of "double-electrode" devices, so that the fixed-charge approximation will be valid in transducer calculations.

(i) The electrostatic potential is determined by the conformal transformation. The form of this potential is given in Fig. 3.6. The mathematical formulation is described in Appendix 3.2.

(ii) If the electrostatic charge distribution (Fig. 3.7a) is applied at the time $t = 0$, and remains fixed for $t > 0$, the electric potential at the surface is given by eqn (3.40). Figure 3.7(b) and (c) show this potential for $t = 0$ and $t > 0$. As for bulk waves, it is more informative to examine the electric field E_0 shown in Fig. 3.7(d): it may be decomposed into a fraction $1 - k^2$ that remains "attached" to the interelectrode gap, and two fractions $k^2/2$ that propagate to the right and to the left, respectively, with the constant velocity v_∞.

The depolarizing potential at the point x is calculated from eqn (3.40) in the form (cf. Appendix 3.3)

$$e(\omega, x) \;=\; \frac{k^2}{2} E_0(\omega, K_\infty) \exp(-\mathrm{j}|K_\infty x|) \tag{3.41}$$

where $K_\infty = \omega/v_\infty$ (for $x > 0$) is the wave number corresponding to the velocity v_∞ and angular frequency ω. To make eqn (3.41) easier to read when the field $E_0(x)$ is applied at $t = 0$, we put

$$E_0(t, x) \;=\; \Upsilon(t)E_0(x) \tag{3.42}$$

where $\Upsilon(t)$ is the Heaviside unit step function, so that

$$E_0(\omega, K) \;=\; E_0(K)/\mathrm{j}\omega \tag{3.43}$$

It is also convenient to make explicit the spatial variation of the field as a function of the charge. If we suppose that the capacitor width in the x_2-direction is W, the total electrostatic charge is Q_0, and

$$\alpha(K) \;=\; \frac{W}{2\mathrm{j}Q_0} \int_{-\infty}^{+\infty} \sigma(x) \exp(\mathrm{j}kx)\,\mathrm{d}x \tag{3.44}$$

we obtain instead of eqn (3.41),

$$e(\omega, x) \;=\; k^2\alpha(K_\infty) \frac{Q_0(\omega)}{\varepsilon W} \exp(-\mathrm{j}\omega K_\infty x) \tag{3.45}$$

where

$$K_\infty \;=\; \omega/v_\infty \; \mathrm{sgn}\, x$$

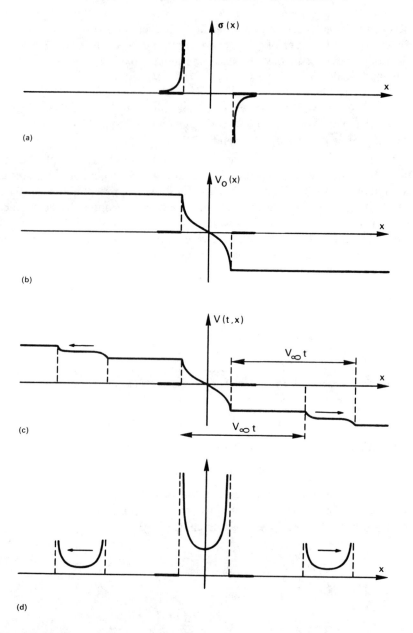

Fig. 3.7 Surface-wave piezoelectric depolarization of an isolated capacitance: (a) charge distribution for $t = 0$—the charge is supposed fixed for $t > 0$; (b) distribution of the interface potential at $t = 0$; (c) distribution of the interface potential for $t > 0$; (d) electric field for $t > 0$.

(where sgn x represents the sign of x) and

$$Q_0(\omega) \;=\; Q_0/j\omega \qquad\qquad (3.46)$$

Note that eqn (3.44) and Fig. 3.7a show that $\alpha(-K) = -\alpha(K)$. The pure number $|\alpha(K_\infty)|$ is usually of the order of 0.8.

(iii) If the charge Q_0 is no longer applied at time $t = 0$ and instead a variable charge $Q(t)$ is stored in the capacitor, we can ignore eqns (3.43) and (3.46) and take $Q(\omega)$ equal to the Fourier transform of $Q(t)$. Moreover, it will be convenient to replace the current

$$I(\omega) \;=\; j\omega Q(\omega) \qquad\qquad (3.47)$$

with the final formula

$$e(\omega, x) \;=\; k^2 \alpha(\omega/v_\infty)\,\frac{I(\omega)}{j\varepsilon W\omega}\,\text{sgn } x\,\exp(-j\omega|x|/v_\infty) \qquad (3.48)$$

where $\alpha(K)$, given by eqn (3.44), is taken for $K = \omega/v_\infty$, and sgn x represents the sign of x.

In contrast to bulk waves, it is difficult to determine the voltage measured at the terminals of the capacitor for a given charge, since this requires the analytic form of the interelectrode potential. Moreover, the approximate character of the assumption of fixed charges makes such a procedure illusory. We shall therefore evaluate the input impedance by a more indirect method in Section 3.2.7.

3.2.5   Depolarization waves and radiation resistance

The results of Sections 3.1.5 and 3.1.6 on bulk waves remain perfectly valid for surface waves. The essential consequence is the asymptotic behavior of the capacitance: the high-frequency value $C_{HF} = C$ increases at low frequencies to $C_{LF} = C/(1 - k^2)$. The counterpart of this variation of reactance is the radiation resistance that satisfies the integral resistance theorem (eqn 3.15). Similarly, at low frequencies, the formula given by eqn (3.16a) remains valid with

$$\theta \;=\; \omega D/v_\infty \qquad\qquad (3.49)$$

where D is the period of the array from which the capacitance has been extracted (cf. Fig. 3.5).

3.2.6   Reception of depolarization waves

Consider a capacitance C_1 localized at $x = 0$ and transmitting a depolarization wave described by eqn (3.48), with eqn (3.45) taken into account:

$$e_1(\omega, x) = \frac{k^2}{2jC_1\omega} \alpha_1(K_\infty) \operatorname{sgn} x \exp(-j\omega|x|/v_\infty)I_1(\omega) \qquad (3.50)$$

Suppose now that a second capacitance C_2 (on open circuit) is placed in the path of the wave (with the same width W). The voltage between the terminals of C_2 is

$$e_{21} = Z_{21}I_1 \qquad (3.51)$$

Because the system is reciprocal, we must have

$$Z_{21} = Z_{12} \qquad (3.52)$$

From the analogy between eqns (3.50) and (3.22), associated respectively with surface and bulk waves, we can deduce the equivalent of eqn (3.24) for surface waves, namely,

$$Z_{21} = \frac{2k^2}{\varepsilon W\omega} \alpha_1(K_\infty)\alpha_2(K_\infty) \exp(-j\omega|x_{12}|/v_\infty) \qquad (3.53)$$

where x_{12} is the distance between the centers of the two capacitors. The reception term $\alpha_2(K_\infty)$ is calculated for C_2 from eqn (3.44), i.e. by regarding it as a transmitter. Reciprocity implies, in fact, that the gain factors for emission and reception are equal. In any case, this formulation, which is made under the assumption of fixed charges, is only an approximation.

3.2.7   Radiation resistance and self-depolarization

When the capacitances 1 and 2 are coincident, eqn (3.53) enables us to calculate the surface-wave radiation resistance as in Section 3.1.10:

$$R_0 = \frac{2k^2}{\varepsilon W\omega} \alpha^2(K_\infty) \qquad (3.54)$$

The radiation reactance can be obtained from eqn (3.54) by applying the Bayard–Bode relations to the function $\alpha^2(\omega/v_\infty)$. In practice, the charges are not fixed, and the approximation used in the calculation of α makes this precision illusory. More simply, we take $\alpha(K_\infty) = \alpha(\omega_0/v_\infty)$, where ω_0 is the central working frequency, so that α^2 is taken to be independent of frequency, the associated reactance being zero.

3.2.8 Piezoelectric two-port network

Consider a set of two piezoelectric capacitances C_1 and C_2 that are no longer restricted to being of the same size W but, on the contrary, may have different widths W_1 and W_2 respectively. If diffraction can be ignored, we may consider that the larger capacitance consists of two connected capacitances, one having the smaller width and the other being its complement (Fig. 3.8).

For example, let $W_1 \geqslant W_2$. When C_1 transmits towards C_2, we observe at the terminals of C_2 the voltage given by eqns (3.51) and (3.53) with $W = W_1$. The voltage at the terminals of C_2 is not in fact affected by the "overflowing" piezoelectric wave. We see, similarly, that if C_1 and C_2 overlap partially, we must replace eqn (3.53) with the more general formula

$$Z_{21} = \frac{2k^2}{\varepsilon\omega} \frac{W_{12}}{W_1 W_2} \alpha_1 \alpha_2 \exp(-j\omega\tau_{12}) \qquad (3.55)$$

where W_{12} is the width of the overlap between C_1 and C_2, each of width W_1 and W_2 respectively, and $\tau_{12} = (x_{12}/v_\infty)$ is the transfer time at velocity v_∞ between the centers of the two capacitances.

The coefficients α_1 and α_2 characterize the geometry of the capacitances and, particularly, the metallization ratio. For a ratio of 50% in a periodic array, we have $\alpha_1 = \alpha_2 \simeq 0.8$.

It is reasonable, finally, as in Section 3.1.9, to consider a complete two-port array without demanding that the receiving capacitance remains on open circuit. We then have from eqn (3.54)

$$Z_{11} \approx \frac{2k^2}{\varepsilon W_1 \omega} \alpha_1^2 + \frac{1}{jC_1\omega} \qquad (3.56)$$

$$Z_{22} \approx \frac{2k^2}{\varepsilon W_2 \omega} \alpha_2^2 + \frac{1}{jC_2\omega} \qquad (3.57)$$

where $Z_{12} = Z_{21}$ is given by eqn (3.55).

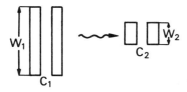

Fig. 3.8 Two capacitors of unequal width.

3.2.9 Characteristic impedance

Repeating the arguments of Section 3.1.8, with eqns (3.54) and (3.48) respectively in place of eqns (3.12) and (3.18), we see that we can consider the *surface-wave delay line* as a lossless line with the real characteristic impedance

$$R_{\mathrm{c}} = \frac{k^2}{\varepsilon W \omega} \tag{3.58}$$

3.3 Surface pseudowaves

We can extend the above results, particularly eqns (3.55)–(3.57), to the case of surface pseudowaves. All we need to do is to include an attenuation term in the propagation factor $\exp(-\mathrm{j}\omega\tau_{12})$. We shall not reproduce the proof, which follows quite closely the case of true surface modes, but with additional difficulties due to the nonconservation of energy. Remembering the approximate nature of the depolarization parameters, we can evaluate α from eqn (3.44), neglecting attenuation.

3.4 Model for a Bleustein–Gulyaev type branch

3.4.1 Depolarization waves

Suppose now that the surface permittivity is given by eqn (2.35). Actually, we shall suppose that the modified permittivity can be written in the form (analogous to eqn 3.37)

$$\frac{V(\omega, K)}{\sigma(\omega, K)} = \frac{1}{\varepsilon|K|}\left[1 - \left(\frac{k^2}{1 - v^2/v_\infty^2}\right)^{1/2}\right] \tag{3.59}$$

The constant ε takes into account the possible presence of an external dielectric.

Suppose first that the electrostatic problem is being solved:

$$\frac{V_0(K)}{\sigma_0(K)} = \frac{1}{\varepsilon|K|} \tag{3.60}$$

Next, suppose that we apply the electrostatic charge (and potential) at time $t = 0$, and that the charge remains fixed at subsequent time. Then, taking the space–time transform, we obtain for $t > 0$ the piezoelectric potential in a form equivalent to eqn (3.40), which is now more complicated (cf. Appendix 3.4), but its explicit form is not of direct interest to us here. The asymptotic form can be obtained directly: when t is close to zero, the piezoelectric potential is equal to the electrostatic potential, and when t tends to infinity, the result can be obtained by taking $\omega = 0$ in eqn (3.44). This gives

$$V_{LF}(K) = \frac{\sigma_0(K)}{\varepsilon|K|}(1 - k) \qquad (3.61)$$

The equilibrium state is similar to the electrostatic case with permittivity increased by the factor $1/(1 - k)$ (and no longer $1/(1 - k^2)$ as for Rayleigh-type waves).

3.4.2 Depolarization of a capacitance

We now consider the potential outside the region between the electrodes of a capacitance (cf. Fig. 3.5). The mathematical problem (solved in Appendix 3.4) leads to the following rigorous result:

$$e(\omega, x) = \frac{k}{2\varepsilon} H_0(K_\infty|x|) * \sigma_0(\omega, x) \qquad (3.62)$$

where the asterisk denotes spatial convolution, $K_\infty = \omega/v_\infty$, and H_0 is the Hankel function, defined in terms of Bessel functions of the first kind (J_0 and Y_0) by the relation

$$H_0(z) = J_0(z) - jY_0(z) \qquad (3.63)$$

At large distances,

$$H_0(z) \approx (2/\pi z)^{1/2} \exp(-jz) \exp(j\pi/4) \quad (z \gg 1)$$

It is then convenient to evaluate the convolution in the form (for $x > 0$)

$$e(\omega, x) \approx \frac{k}{2\varepsilon} \exp(j\pi/4) \left(\frac{2}{\pi K_\infty|x|}\right)^{1/2} \exp(-jK_\infty x) \int \sigma_0(\omega, h) \exp(jK_\infty h)\, dh \qquad (3.64)$$

$$\approx \frac{k}{2\varepsilon} \exp(j\pi/4) \left(\frac{2}{\pi K_\infty|x|}\right)^{1/2} \exp(-jK_\infty x) 2j\alpha(K_\infty)q_0(\omega) \qquad (3.65)$$

where $2j\alpha(K_\infty)$ is the Fourier transform of the charge distribution for a unit charge q_0 and wave number $K_\infty = \omega/v_\infty$.

By analogy with eqn (3.53), the depolarization potential of a capacitance 2 by a capacitance 1 can be described by

$$e_{21}(\omega) = \frac{2jk\alpha_1\alpha_2 \exp(j\pi/4)}{\varepsilon W\omega} \left(\frac{2}{\pi K_\infty(x)}\right)^{1/2} \exp(-jK_\infty|x|)I_1(\omega) \quad (3.66)$$

where I_1 is the input current of capacitance 1 and α_1 and α_2 are the charge distribution factors defined above. The formula is not valid for the self-depolarization of the capacitance, but we can take the following formula as the analog formula of eqn (3.54):

$$R_0 \approx \frac{k\alpha^2}{\varepsilon W\omega} \quad (3.67)$$

3.4.3 Piezoelectric two-port network

By analogy with Section 3.2.8, we can define the following impedance matrix between two capacitances C_1 and C_2 of width W_1 and W_2 respectively, and with an overlap of width W_{12},

$$Z_{11} \approx \frac{1}{jC_1\omega} + \frac{k}{\varepsilon W_1\omega}\alpha_1{}^2 \quad (3.68)$$

$$Z_{22} = \frac{1}{jC_2\omega} + \frac{k}{\varepsilon W_2\omega}\alpha_2{}^2 \quad (3.69)$$

$$Z_{12} = Z_{21} = \frac{2jk}{\varepsilon\omega}\frac{W_{12}}{W_1 W_2}\alpha_1\alpha_2 \exp(j\pi/4)\left(\frac{2}{\pi\tau_{12}\omega}\right)^{1/2}\exp(-j\omega\tau_{12}) \quad (3.70)$$

where τ_{12} is the transfer time at velocity v_∞ between the two capacitances.

3.5 SSBW waves

An explicit expression for depolarization waves in the case of a complex branching point of surface permittivity could be obtained in the form of an integral. However, in practice, we shall treat this type of wave as if we were concerned with a Bleustein–Gulyaev wave (Section 3.4).

In fact, since the algebraic formulation of the surface permittivity is unsuitable, only numerical integration is possible. We saw in Section 2.3.4.2 that this mode was characterized by the existence of a branching point in the immediate vicinity of the characteristic velocities. We can deduce from this that the behavior of the Fourier transform is like that of the Bleustein–Gulyaev, namely, a diminution in the coupling coefficient as the square root of the propagation time. Finally, we shall use eqns (3.68)–(3.70) in which the notation is the same as in Section 3.4 and the coupling coefficient is evaluated, in accordance with eqn (2.6), by the difference between the squares of the velocities on short circuit and on open circuit.

3.6   Multimode problem

The multimode surface-wave problem can be handled, as with bulk waves, by simply combining the contributions of all branches, as in eqn (3.28). The depolarization potential corresponding to a single capacitance will be obtained from eqn (3.28). According to Section 2.2.3.2, we have to add the contributions of the true surface mode and of two surface pseudomodes to eqn (3.28) in this case. There can be degeneracies of type Rayleigh, Bleustein–Gulyaev or SSBW. In practice, it is exceptional to have to take account of all these modes, but we can integrate these parameters to calculate the level of "deviant behavior" with respect to the ideal solution.

Appendix 3.1   Inversion of eqn (3.7)

Let

$$\Phi(j\omega, K) = \left(1 - k^2 \frac{K^2}{K^2 - K_\infty^2}\right) \Phi_0(j\omega, K)$$

It is convenient to use the Laplace transform, Φ_0 being a unit step function (of time):

$$\Phi_0(s, K) = \frac{1}{s} \Phi_0(K)$$

where s is the Laplace variable. We then have

$$\Phi(s, K) = \frac{1}{s}\left(1 - k^2 \frac{K^2}{K^2 + s^2/v_\infty^2}\right) \Phi_0(K)$$

Hence we deduce (Lavoine 1963) that

$$\Phi(t, K) = [1 - k^2(1 - \cos K v_\infty t)]\Phi_0(K)$$

The spatial Fourier transform then gives

$$\Phi(t, x) = (1 - k^2)\Phi_0(x) + \frac{k^2}{2}[\delta(x - v_\infty t) + \delta(x + v_\infty t)] * \Phi_0(x)$$

where δ is the Dirac function and the asterisk represents convolution. The final result (eqn 3.8) may be deduced from this.

Appendix 3.2   Evaluation of electrostatic capacitances

Consider a set of segments on the surface of a piezoelectric material, with arbitrary widths and separations. The form of the lines of force (Fig. 3.9) suggests that only neighboring electrodes have a perceptible influence on one another. More precisely, we may suppose that each electrode $A_k B_k$ has two zones of influence: $A_k M_k$ with the electrode on the left (number $k - 1$) and $M_k B_k$ with the electrode on the right (number $k + 1$). When the distances from the neighboring electrodes are equal, M_k is the midpoint of $A_k B_k$. When this is not the case, we can make it so by a bilinear transformation. We then have

$$\frac{\overline{M_k A_k}}{\overline{M_k B_k}} = \frac{\overline{M_k B_{k-1}}}{\overline{M_k A_{k+1}}}$$

Denoting by $a_k, b_k, a_{k+1}, b_{k-1}$ and m_k the positions of $A_k, B_k, A_{k+1}, B_{k-1}$ and M_k respectively, we deduce from this that

$$m_k = \frac{b_{k-1} - b_k - a_k + a_{k+1}}{b_{k-1} + b_k - a_k - a_{k+1}}$$

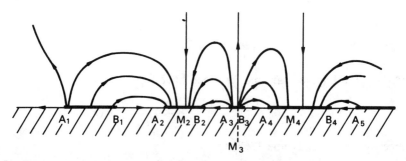

Fig. 3.9   A set of segments and the approximate form of lines of force. Each segment is bounded by the points $A_k B_k$ and is divided into two zones of influence by the point M_k. The lines of force of the segment $A_k M_k$ end on electrode $k - 1$ and those of the segment $M_k B_k$ on the electrode $k + 1$. We assume that the line of force issuing from M_k is a straight line, normal to the plane of the intermediate electrode and parallel to the plane for the terminal electrodes.

For the first and the last electrodes of number N we obviously have

$$m_1 = a_1 \quad \text{and} \quad m_N = b_N$$

When the point M_k is the midpoint of $A_k B_k$, the line of force $M_k I$ (which extends to infinity) can be taken to be a straight line normal to $A_k B_k$. We may also suppose that, as the point M_k is displaced the straight line $M_k I$ is also displaced, parallel to itself. This will clearly be a poor approximation when M_k tends to A_k or B_k. In the limit, for $M_1 = A_1$, the line of force coincides with the surface of the piezoelectric medium.

We shall evaluate the capacitances, assuming that we have one of these two limiting cases: either $M_k I$ is a straight line perpendicular to $A_k B_k$, or $M_k I$ is the line $A_k B_k$ (terminal electrodes). For the sake of simplicity, we shall omit the index k, and write for the section $M_k M_{k+1}$.

$$M_k = M \qquad B_k = B \qquad A_{k+1} = A \qquad M_{k+1} = N$$

Consider the section $I_1 MNI_2$ (Fig. 3.10), consisting of the zone of influence of two neighboring electrodes. By a homothetic transformation we convert the segment MN to length π, and by a translation we take the point N to the origin of the complex plane.

Let $-\theta_a$ and $-\pi + \theta_b$ be the positions of the points A and B. The conformal transformation $z_1 = \cos z$ transforms the strip into a half-plane. We now carry out a second conformal transformation to take the points M, B, A, N to $-1/l$, -1, $+1$, $+1/l$; a bilinear transformation suffices.

Substituting

$$\beta = \frac{\frac{1}{2}(\cos \theta_a - \cos \theta_b) + \cos \theta_a \cos \theta_b + 1}{\cos \theta_a + \cos \theta_b}$$

we find that

$$l = \beta - (\beta^2 - 1)^{1/2} \quad \text{for } 0 < l < 1$$

If

$$\theta_a = \theta_b = \frac{\Delta}{2} \quad \text{we have} \quad h = \cos \frac{\Delta}{2}$$

When AN is the last electrode, the section $I_1 MNI_2$ forms a quarter-plane, and we must carry out the conformal transformation $z_1 = z^2$ before making the bilinear transformation. We then have

$$\beta = \frac{[(m - b)^2 + (m - c)^2](m - n)^2 - 2(m - b)^2(m - c)^2}{(m - n)^2[(m - c)^2 - (m - b)^2]}$$

where a, b, m, n are the coordinates of A, B, M and N and, as always,

$$l = \beta - (\beta^2 - 1)^{1/2}$$

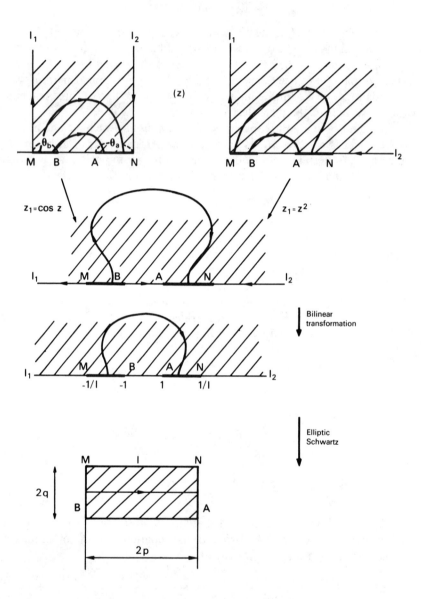

Fig. 3.10 Sequence of conformal transformations mapping a section bounded by two portions of electrodes onto the interior of a rectangle.

The half-plane is next transformed into a rectangle by the Schwartz transformation

$$Z = Z_0 \int_0^{z_2} \left(z + \frac{1}{l}\right)^{-1/2} (z + 1)^{-1/2}(z - 1)^{-1/2} \left(z - \frac{1}{l}\right)^{-1/2} dz$$

This can be recognized as the elliptic integral of the second kind. Let $2p$ and $2q$ be the sides of the rectangle. The capacitance C of the portions of MC and AN is (per unit length normal to the sagittal plane)

$$C_k = \varepsilon \frac{q}{p}$$

The numerical calculation can be carried out very conveniently by means of the algorithm described in Amstutz (1959). It turns out that

$$\frac{q}{p} = \frac{1}{2} \frac{\gamma(1, (1 - l^2)^{1/2})}{\gamma(1, l)}$$

where $\gamma(a, b)$ is the common limit of the very rapidly converging sequence defined by

$$a_0 = a \qquad b_0 = b \qquad a_{n+1} = \tfrac{1}{2}(a_n + b_n) \qquad b_{n+1} = (a_n b_n)^{1/2}$$

We must now calculate the capacitance matrix (Durand 1953) of the complete set of electrodes.

Let V_k and q_k be the potential and the charge of the electrode E_k, confined to the segment $A_k B_k$ and having the point M_k as its limiting point of influence. Let q'_k be the charge on the segment $A_k M_k$ and q''_k the charge on the segment $M_k B_k$. We have

$$q'_k = C_{k-1}(V_k - V_{k-1})$$
$$q''_k = C_k(V_k - V_{k+1})$$

where C_k and C_{k-1} are, respectively, the capacitances of the portions of electrodes having influence on E_k, namely E_{k+1}, E_{k-1}.

Hence we deduce that:

$$q_k = -C_{k-1} V_{k-1} + (C_{k-1} + C_k)V_k - C_k V_{k+1}$$

which can be written

$$q_k = \sum C_{ki} V_i \qquad \begin{cases} C_{kk} = C_k + C_{k-1} \\ C_{k,k+1} = -C_{k+1,k} = -C_k \\ C_{ki} = 0 \text{ otherwise} \end{cases}$$

The set of electrodes is thus seen to be closed in terms of electrical influence. We have therefore completely solved the electrostatic problem.

Appendix 3.3   Calculation of the depolarization potential as a function of the electrostatic charge (the case of Rayleigh modes)

Let

$$e(s, K) = -\frac{k^2}{\varepsilon} \frac{|K|}{K^2 + s^2/v_\infty^2} \sigma(s, K)$$

be the depolarization potential where s and K are the Laplace and Fourier variables respectively. The charge is applied at the instant $t = 0$, so that

$$\sigma(s, K) = \frac{\sigma(K)}{s}$$

Let

$$\psi(K) = |K| \sigma(K)$$

and similarly let

$$\psi(x) = \frac{1}{2\pi} \int \psi(K) \exp(-jKx)\, dK$$

(its inverse Fourier transform). We can show that $\psi(x)$ tends to infinity as $1/x^2$. Moreover, the relation

$$\psi(K) \sim K^2 \Phi_0(K)$$

where Φ_0 is the electrostatic potential, shows that

$$\psi(x) \sim -\frac{d^2}{dx^2} \Phi_0(x)$$

The function $\psi(x)$ thus vanishes on the electrodes. Let $\sigma_a(x)$ be the electric charge density of a given electrode a, and let

$$\psi_a(K) = |K| \sigma_a(K)$$

Suppose that the electrode a interacts electrostatically with only a single adjacent electrode: then $\psi(x)$ takes nonzero values only in the interval separating the two electrodes. The depolarization potential induced by electrode a may be written:

$$e_a(s, K) = -\frac{k^2}{\varepsilon s} \frac{\psi(K)}{K^2 + s^2/v_\infty^2}$$

The inverse Fourier transform can be calculated on the assumption that s has a positive real part, to ensure causality. We thus get

$$e_a(s, x) = -\frac{k^2}{s}\frac{v_\infty}{2s}\exp\left(-s\left|\frac{x}{v_\infty}\right|\right) * \psi_a(x)$$

Suppose now that the geometric center of the electrode is situated at $x = 0$. On the right of the interval where ψ_a is nonzero, we have

$$e_a(s, x) = \frac{k^2}{\varepsilon s}\frac{v_\infty}{2s}\int \psi_a(x')\exp(-jK_\infty|x - x'|)\,dx'$$

Since $\psi_a(K) = |K|\sigma_a(K)$, we deduce from this that, for $x > 0$ and $K_\infty = \omega/v_\infty > 0$, that:

$$e_a(s, x) = \frac{jk^2}{2\varepsilon}\frac{\sigma_a(K_\infty)}{s}\exp(-jK_\infty|x|)$$

Substituting

$$\sigma_a(K_\infty) = q_a\alpha_a\exp(jK_\infty x_a)$$

with $q_a = \sigma_a(K)_{K=0}$, we obtain, finally,

$$e_a(s, x) = -\frac{k^2}{2j\varepsilon}\frac{q_a}{s}\exp(-jK_\infty|x - x_a|)$$

This expression is exact for $x > x_a$ since $\psi_a(x) = 0$. We get an identical formulation for $x < 0$, but the proof does not hold in the interval where $\psi_a(x)$ takes nonzero values.

Note that for $\omega = 0$, we have $\alpha_a = 1$. We can also verify that

$$x_a(0) = \frac{1}{q_a}\int x\sigma_a(x)\,dx$$

In other words, the electrical center of the electrode coincides with the center of gravity of the charge at zero frequency.

Appendix 3.4   Calculation of the depolarization potential as a function of the electrostatic potential

Rayleigh branches

If $V_0(x)$ is the electrostatic potential corresponding to a charge distribution $q_0(x)$, the piezoelectric potential is the solution of the equation (in Fourier space)

$$V(\omega, K) = \frac{\varepsilon_0}{\varepsilon_p(\omega/K)} V_0(\omega, K)$$

$V_0(t, x)$ corresponds to a sudden application of $V_0(x)$ at $t = 0$, where ε_p is the piezoelectric permittivity (surface or volume) and ε_0 is the permittivity obtained by removing the piezoelectric coupling in ε_p. For volume waves or "ordinary" surface waves (of Rayleigh type), the permittivity is given by eqn (2.8) or eqn (3.28). We therefore have

$$V(\omega, K) = \left(1 - \frac{k^2}{1 - v^2/v_\infty^2}\right) \frac{V_0(K)}{j\omega}$$

where $1/j\omega$ is the Fourier transform of the unit step function

$$V(\omega, K) = \frac{1}{j\omega}\left(1 - k^2 \frac{K^2}{K^2 - \omega^2/v_\infty^2}\right) V_0(K)$$

Then, using the inverse (temporal) Fourier transform (for $t > 0$) (Hadik 1969, p. 179) with $s = j\omega$ (cf. Angot 1961, p. 542), we have

$$V(t, K) = \{1 - k^2[1 - \cos(Kv_\infty t)]\} V_0(K)$$

The spatial transform gives finally (for $t > 0$)

$$V(t, x) = (1 - k^2)V_0(x) + \frac{k^2}{2}[V_0(x - v_\infty t) + V_0(x + v_\infty t)]$$

The depolarizing potential on its own can thus be written in the form

$$e(\omega, K) = -k^2 \frac{K^2}{K^2 - K_\infty^2} V_0(\omega, K)$$

where we have put $K_\infty = \omega/v_\infty$. Moreover, we note that $-jKV_0(\omega, K) = E_0(\omega, k)$ is the static electric field $E_0(K)/j\omega$, that is zero outside the inter-electrode space. In addition, $jK/(K^2 - K_\infty^2)$ is to be taken on the assumption that $\pm jK_\infty = j\omega/(\pm v_\infty)$ has a positive real part (evanescent) to ensure causality. Under these conditions, the inverse Fourier transform is (Lavoine 1963, p. 102)

$$e(\omega, x) = \frac{k^2}{2} \operatorname{sgn} x \exp(-jK_\infty|x|) * E_0(\omega, x)$$

which always corresponds to a delay (and not to a noncausal advance) (cf. Fig. 3.11).

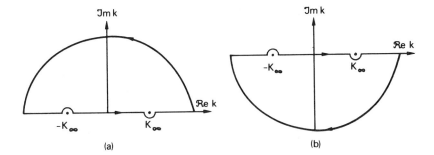

Fig. 3.11 Paths of integration for the inverse Fourier transform: (a) $x > 0$; (b) $x < 0$.

To complete the calculation, we consider the zone outside the electrodes where the static field E_0 is zero. For example, for positive values of x, we have

$$e(\omega, x) = \frac{k^2}{2} \int_{-\infty}^{x} \exp[-jK_\infty(x - X)]E_0(\omega, X)\,dx$$

$$- \frac{k^2}{2} \int_{x}^{\infty} \exp[jK_\infty(X - x)]E_0(\omega, X)\,dx$$

The upper limit of the first integral can be extended to infinity and the second integral is zero because $E_0(\omega, X)$ is zero for $X > x$. Consequently,

$$e(\omega, x) = \frac{k^2}{2} E_0(\omega, K_\infty) \exp(-jK_\infty x)$$

The general formula is, finally,

$$e(\omega, x) = \frac{k^2}{2} \operatorname{sgn} x E_0(\omega, \operatorname{sgn} x K_\infty) \exp(-jK_\infty|x|)$$

with

$$K_\infty = \omega/v_\infty \qquad v_\infty > 0$$

Case with singular branches

We can proceed in a similar way in the case where the surface permittivity is of the form

$$\frac{1}{\varepsilon(v)} = \frac{1}{\varepsilon}\left[1 - \left(\frac{k^2}{1 - v^2/v_\infty^2}\right)^{1/v}\right]$$

We can then write

$$e(\omega, K) = -\left(\frac{k^2 K^2}{K^2 - K_\infty^2}\right)^{1/\nu} V_0(\omega, K)$$

It is convenient to return to the charge $q_0(\omega, k)$ given by the relation $\sigma_0(\omega, k) = |K| \varepsilon V_0$. We confine ourselves to the cases where $\nu = 2$. We thus get

$$e(\omega, K) = \frac{k/\varepsilon}{\pm (K^2 - K_\infty^2)^{1/2}} \sigma_0(\omega, K)$$

The inverse spatial Fourier transform must be taken with judicious choice of the value of the square root and with due regard to causality. We thus take

$$(K^2 - K_\infty^2)^{-1/2} = \begin{cases} \dfrac{1}{(K_\infty^2 - K^2)^{1/2}} & |K| < K_\infty \\[4mm] \dfrac{j}{(K^2 - K_\infty^2)^{1/2}} & |K| > K_\infty \end{cases}$$

From this we obtain (Lavoine 1963, pp. 132 and 141)

$$e(\omega, x) = \frac{k}{2\varepsilon} H_0(K_\infty |x|) * \sigma_0(\omega, x)$$

This relation involves the Hankel function H_0 which can be expressed in terms of the Bessel functions J_0 and Y_0:

$$H_0(z) = J_0(z) - j Y_0(z)$$

To make use of this expression, it is convenient to take an asymptotic expansion of $H_0(\beta)$ for large values of the variable (Angot 1961, p. 375):

$$H_0(z) \cong \left(\frac{2}{\pi z}\right)^{1/2} \exp(-jz)[\exp(j\pi/4)]$$

If we suppose, in addition, that the charge consists of two Dirac impulses a distance h apart,

$$\sigma_0(\omega, x) \cong q_0(\omega)\left[\delta\left(x - \frac{k}{2}\right) - \delta\left(x + \frac{k}{2}\right)\right]$$

we obtain at large distances

$$e(\omega, x) \cong \frac{k}{2\varepsilon} q_0(\omega)\left[H_0\left(K_\infty \left|x - \frac{h}{2}\right|\right) - H_0\left(K_\infty \left|x + \frac{h}{2}\right|\right)\right]$$

Using the relations

$$\frac{dH_0}{dz} = -H_1(z) \quad \text{and} \quad H_1(z) \cong \left(\frac{2}{z\pi}\right)^{1/2} \exp(-jz)\exp(3\pi j/4)$$

we obtain, finally,

$$e(\omega, x) \cong -\frac{kK_\infty h}{2\varepsilon}\left(\frac{2}{\pi z}\right)^{1/2} \exp(-jz)\left(\frac{j-1}{2}\right) q_0(\omega) \operatorname{sgn} x$$

where $z = K_\infty|x|$.

Exercise

Consider the purely reactive two-port network whose impedance matrix is

$$[Z] = \frac{1}{jC\omega}\begin{bmatrix} 1 - k^2\sin 2x/2x & \dfrac{k^2}{2}\dfrac{\sin x}{x} \\ \dfrac{k^2}{2}\dfrac{\sin x}{x} & 0 \end{bmatrix}$$

(where $x = \omega\tau$), loaded by the frequency-dependent "resistance"

$$R = \frac{k^2}{4C\omega^2\tau}$$

Calculate the input impedance

Interpret this in terms of eqns (3.12) and (3.21).

Show that the two-port array violates causality but that by adding a series delay line of delay 2τ and characteristic impedance R we obtain a causal two-port network. What is the driving point impedance of the first port when the second port is loaded by a resistance R?

Chapter 4

Piezoelectric Transducers

This chapter deals with surface-wave piezoelectric transducers. It uses only the elements of circuit theory and the models discussed in earlier chapters, summarized in Sections 4.1 and 4.2.

4.1 Piezoelectric capacitance models

4.1.1 Single capacitance

A capacitance deposited on a piezoelectric substrate actually constitutes a complex dipole with impedance given by

$$Z(j\omega) = \frac{1}{jC\omega} + R_0(\omega) \tag{4.1}$$

4.1.1.1 Electrostatic capacitance
The capacitance C is the electrostatic capacitance. Let us take a system of $N + 1$ electrodes in the form of a regular interdigital comb. We can decompose this system into N equal (neglecting end effects) capacitances whose values depend on the metallization ratio. When this ratio is 50%, we have

$$C = \tfrac{1}{2}\varepsilon W \tag{4.2}$$

where W is the useful length of the electrodes (see Fig. 4.1) and ε is the permittivity. Convenient formulae corresponding to different metallization ratios are given in Appendix 4.1. Which permittivity is actually involved depends on the mode of operation, the piezoelectric coupling and the external medium.

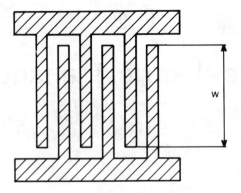

Fig. 4.1 Interdigital comb.

"Ordinary" Rayleigh-type surface modes   Tables of constants give the "high-frequency" and "low-frequency" permittivities ε_{HF} and ε_{LF} respectively. For the coupling constant k^2 we must take the permittivity

$$\varepsilon \approx \varepsilon_{LF}(1 - k^2) + \varepsilon_e \qquad (4.3)$$

where ε_e is the permittivity of the external medium (in general, vacuum or air). In practice, we often take simply ε_{LF}.

Rayleigh-type surface pseudomode   If there exists a surface mode with coupling k_1^2, and if the pseudomode is the first one with coupling k_2^2, the formula given by eqn (4.3) applies if we take $k^2 = k_1^2 + k_2^2$. In the same way, if we have a second pseudomode with coupling k_3^2, we can use eqn (4.3) with $k^2 = k_1^2 + k_2^2 + k_3^2$.

Bleustein–Gulyaev and SSBW modes   This time the formula is

$$\varepsilon = \varepsilon_{LF}(1 - k) \qquad (4.4)$$

where $k^2 = \Delta v/v$ is the piezoelectric coupling constant. We have, more generally,

$$\varepsilon = \varepsilon_{LF}(1 - k_1^{2/v_1} - k_2^{2/v_2}) \qquad (4.5)$$

if we consider a mode 2 whose velocity is greater than that for the first mode 1, where v_1 and v_2 are equal to 1 for the Rayleigh and to 2 for the Bleustein modes respectively.

4.1.1.2 Radiation resistance
The radiation resistance varies very slowly with frequency. It is convenient to consider the surface distribution $\sigma(x)$ of electrostatic charge over the

electrodes. We then put

$$\alpha(K) = \frac{W}{2jQ_0} \int_{-\infty}^{+\infty} \sigma(x) \exp(jkx)\,dx \qquad (4.6)$$

where Q_0 is the charge on the capacitance (of length W). For an ordinary Rayleigh-type mode, we have

$$R_0 \approx \frac{2k^2\alpha^2(K_\infty)}{\varepsilon W\omega} \approx \frac{1.4k^2}{\varepsilon W\omega} \qquad (4.7)$$

where $K_\infty = \omega/v_\infty$ and v_∞ is the velocity of the piezoelectric mode on open circuit. In practice, $\alpha^2 \simeq 0.7$ for an interdigital comb with a metallization ratio of 50% and in the neighborhood of resonance.

Moreover, the product $y = CR_0\omega$ is a maximum for this metallization ratio (see Appendix 4.1). For an attenuated mode, K_∞ is complex and we must take $-\alpha(K_\infty)\alpha(-K^*_\infty)$ in place of α^2.

For a *Bleustein-type* mode, the radiation resistance can be evaluated from the formula

$$R_0 \approx \frac{k\alpha^2}{\varepsilon W\omega} \approx \frac{0.7k}{\varepsilon W\omega} \qquad (4.8)$$

where α^2 is written for $\alpha^2(K_\infty)$. Moreover, causality implies a reactive counterpart to R_0, but we shall neglect it in comparison with the static capacitance.

4.1.2 Two-capacitance system

A two-capacitance system constitutes a two-port array, whose impedance matrix gives the relation between the voltages and input currents:

$$\begin{aligned} V_1 &= (1/jC_1\omega + R_1)I_1 + Z_{12}I_2 \\ V_2 &= Z_{21}I_1 + (1/jC_2\omega + R_2)I_2 \end{aligned} \qquad (4.9)$$

Since piezoelectricity is a reciprocal phenomenon, we have $Z_{12} = Z_{21}$, where Z_{11} and Z_{22} are given by eqn (4.1). The value of Z_{12} used here is considered in the following section.

4.1.2.1 Rayleigh-type mode

Let W_1 and W_2 be the lengths of the electrodes of the two capacitances. We must also define an effective length W_{12} to account for the overlap of the

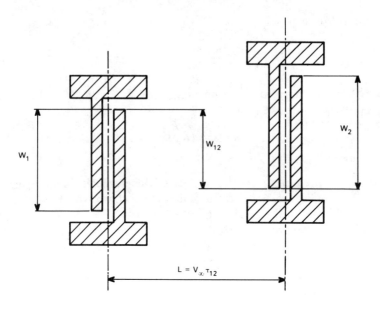

Fig. 4.2   Two-capacitance system.

two capacitances (Fig. 4.2). We can use the velocity v_∞ to define the time

$$\tau_{12} = \frac{L}{v_\infty} \qquad (4.10)$$

where L is the distance between the centers.

The transfer impedance Z_{21} is then given by

$$Z_{21} = \frac{2k^2 \alpha_1 \alpha_2 W_{12}}{\varepsilon W_1 W_2 \omega} \exp(-j\omega\tau_{12}) \qquad (4.11)$$

In the (usual) case in which $W_1 = W_2 = W_{12}$ and $\alpha_1 = \alpha_2$, we have

$$R_1 = R_2 = R_0 \qquad C_1 = C_2 = C \qquad Z_{21} = Z_{12} = R_0 \exp(-j\omega\tau_{12}) \quad (4.12)$$

For the Rayleigh-type (leaky) pseudomode, the same formula applies but with complex τ_{12}. The open-circuit velocity v_a is itself complex, and we put

$$\frac{1}{v_a} = \frac{1}{v_\infty}(1 - jb) \qquad \tau_{12} = \frac{L}{v_\infty} - \frac{jbL}{v_\infty} \qquad (4.13)$$

In practice, tables of constants give the attenuation a in decibels as a function of wavelength. We therefore have

$$b \approx \frac{2.3a}{2\pi \times 20} = 0.0183a \qquad (4.14)$$

4.1.2.2 Bleustein–Gulyaev and SSBW-type modes

For a strict Bleustein-type mode, we have an "exact" but complicated formula involving Hankel functions. In practice, it is convenient to take the asymptotic form of these functions. For the different SSBW-type modes, the "exact" formulation would itself be very complicated, and the asymptotic approximation to the Hankel functions could reasonably be employed. We shall therefore use the following approximate formula in all these cases:

$$Z_{12} = Z_{21} \approx \frac{1.2k}{\varepsilon W \omega} \left(\frac{1}{\omega \tau_{12}} \right)^{1/2} \exp[-j(\omega \tau_{12} + \pi/4)] \qquad (4.15)$$

We note the presence of a *phase shift* and, most important, the attenuation factor $(1/\tau_{12})^{1/2}$.

When the lengths W_1 and W_2 are different, we replace $(1/W)$ with $W_{12}/W_1 W_2$, as in eqn (4.11). When, in addition, the mode is a leaky pseudo-mode, we can take the attenuation into account (as in eqn 4.13) by taking τ_{12} to be complex in the exponential.

4.2 Rayleigh-type depolarization waves

A piezoelectric capacitance emits a surface wave that propagates on both sides away from the source. Let us now summarize its characteristics, confining ourselves at first to ordinary Rayleigh-type surface waves.

4.2.1 Effective amplitude

A capacitance carrying a current I_0 has across its terminals a voltage $e_0 = R_0 I_0$ in phase with I_0 where

$$e_0 = R_0 I_0 \qquad R_0 = \frac{2k^2}{\varepsilon W \omega} \alpha_0^{\,2} \quad (\alpha_0^{\,2} \approx 0.7)$$

In addition, it emits two piezoelectric waves with amplitudes

$$e^* = \pm \frac{2k^2}{\varepsilon W \omega} |\alpha_0| I_0 > e_0$$

CONVENTION. It is convenient to define an effective amplitude $\alpha_0 e^*$ of the piezoelectric wave, equal to the amplitude e_0. The effective depolarization wave is then given by

$$e(\omega, x) = R_0 I_0 \exp(-j\omega\tau) \qquad (4.16)$$

where $\tau = |x|/v_\infty$ is the delay time, due to propagation between the source and detector with velocity v_∞. Note that sgn x of eqn (3.48) is absorbed by this method of "normalization". In what follows, we shall confine our attention to effective amplitudes. A surface-wave line is then a delay line with propagation velocity v_∞, that is nondispersive and has a real characteristic impedance equal to $2R_0$. The mean power of such a wave (in terms of the root-mean-square (r.m.s.) *effective* voltage[†]) is (in W)

$$P = \frac{|e^2|}{2R_0} \tag{4.17}$$

The mean energy density is (in $\mathrm{J\,m^{-1}}$)

$$w = P/v_\infty \tag{4.18}$$

It is often convenient to use the wave parameter A with reference to the radiation resistance R_0, rather than the effective potential. This is defined by

$$A = \frac{e}{(2R_0)^{1/2}} \tag{4.19}$$

so that eqn (4.17) may be written

$$P = |A|^2 \tag{4.20}$$

4.2.2 Interaction between a piezoelectric wave and a capacitance

Consider a piezoelectric capacitance receiving an incident wave A_1 and hence having an effective potential $e_1 = (2R_0)^{1/2}A_1$ (Fig. 4.3). The capacitance

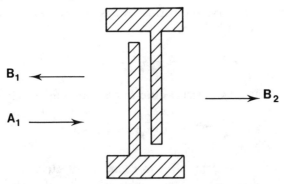

Fig. 4.3 Incident and emerging waves.

[†]The r.m.s. voltage is the peak voltage divided by $\sqrt{2}$.

re-emits two depolarization waves, and we shall consider the resultant waves. The voltage V across the terminals of the capacitance is given by

$$V = \left(\frac{1}{jC\omega} + R_0 \right) I + e_1 \qquad (4.21)$$

If the current I flowing through the capacitance is not zero, the emerging waves are

$$B_1 = \frac{R_0 I}{(2R_0)^{1/2}} \qquad (4.22)$$

$$B_2 = A_1 + \frac{R_0 I}{(2R_0)^{1/2}} \qquad (4.23)$$

When the capacitance is short-circuited, we have $V = 0$ and, using eqn (4.21), we obtain

$$I = - \frac{e_1}{1/jC\omega + R_0} = - \frac{j(2R_0)^{1/2} A_1 C\omega}{(1 + jR_0 C\omega)} \qquad (4.24)$$

Substituting

$$y = R_0 C\omega \approx k^2 \alpha^2 \qquad (4.25)$$

and using eqns (4.22) and (4.23), we have

$$B_1 = - \frac{jy}{1 + jy} A_1 \qquad (4.26)$$

$$B_2 = \frac{1}{1 + jy} A_1 \qquad (4.27)$$

It is readily verified that

$$|B_1|^2 + |B_2|^2 = |A_1|^2$$

Similarly, if there is a second incident wave A_2, we finally obtain (after some simple algebra) the following transfer matrix:

$$\begin{bmatrix} A_1 \\ B_1 \end{bmatrix} = \begin{bmatrix} 1 + jy & jy \\ -jy & 1 - jy \end{bmatrix} \begin{bmatrix} B_2 \\ A_2 \end{bmatrix} \qquad (4.28)$$

4.2.3 Interaction between a piezoelectric wave and a short-circuited array

A short-circuited array constitutes a bank of capacitances (themselves short-circuited). Let D be the period of the array and let $\tau = D/v_\infty$ be the elementary delay corresponding to velocity v_∞. The transfer matrix similar to eqn (4.28) but corresponding to a simple delay τ is, of course,

$$\begin{bmatrix} \exp(j\omega\tau) & 0 \\ 0 & \exp(-j\omega\tau) \end{bmatrix} \tag{4.29}$$

Since a network is composed of a series of capacitances each followed by a delay τ, the global transfer matrix for an array of N capacitances (and N delays) is obtained simply by raising the following matrix to the power N:

$$[T] = \begin{bmatrix} 1+jy & jy \\ -jy & 1-jy \end{bmatrix} \begin{bmatrix} \exp(j\theta) & 0 \\ 0 & \exp(-j\theta) \end{bmatrix} \tag{4.30}$$

$$\theta = \omega\tau = \omega D/v_\infty \tag{4.31}$$

It is clear that $[T]$ is unitary and then $\det[T] = 1$ and $\operatorname{trace}[T] = 2(\cos\theta - y\sin\theta)$. Let

$$\tfrac{1}{2}\operatorname{trace}[T] = \cos\phi = \cos\theta - y\sin\theta \tag{4.32}$$

We can readily verify that the eigenmodes of $[T]$ are $\exp(j\phi)$ and $\exp(-j\phi)$. These modes therefore propagate with velocity

$$v_0 = \frac{\omega D}{\phi} = v_\infty \left(\frac{\theta}{\phi}\right)$$

To complete the calculation, we must evaluate y as the period of the array tends to zero. It is shown in Appendix 4.1 that

$$\lim_{D \to 0} y \approx \frac{\theta}{2} \frac{k^2}{1-k^2} \tag{4.33}$$

Hence we deduce from eqns (4.31) and (4.32) that

$$\phi^2 \approx \theta^2/(1-k^2) \tag{4.34}$$

so that

$$v_0^2 = v_\infty^2(1-k^2)$$

To the first order in θ, eqn (4.30) may be written in the form

$$[T] = [1] + j\theta[T] \tag{4.35}$$

where [1] represents the unit 2×2 matrix and

$$[T] = \frac{1}{1-k^2} \begin{bmatrix} 1-k^2/2 & k^2/2 \\ -k^2/2 & -(1-k^2/2) \end{bmatrix} \tag{4.36}$$

By passing to the limit as D tends to zero, we obtain the characteristics of an infinitely long conducting line. The coefficient of reflection of the boundary between the insulating surface and the short-circuited surface is therefore (cf. Exercise 4)

$$\frac{B_1}{A_1} = \frac{k^2/2}{(1 - k^2)^{1/2} + (1 - k^2/2)} \approx -\frac{k^2}{4} \tag{4.37}$$

which can also be obtained from the formula

$$\frac{B_1}{A_1} = \frac{v_0 - v_\infty}{v_0 + v_\infty} = -\frac{1 - (1 - k^2)^{1/2}}{1 + (1 - k^2)^{1/2}} \tag{4.38}$$

Thus reflection can be interpreted as the re-emission backwards of depolarization waves induced by the current. Reflection by a single short-circuited capacitance, given by eqn (4.5) (where $y = 0.7k^2$), is in quadrature with the incidence wave, whereas reflection by a metallized region is exactly out of phase (in the effective amplitudes).

The following basic results should be remembered:

(1) the wave velocity is always v_∞ when there are no currents, i.e. when the charges are fixed;

(2) when the potential is held constant, there is redistribution of charge, and the velocity is reduced to $v_0 = (1 - k^2)^{1/2} v_\infty$.

Note that these results were obtained directly, without recourse to further assumptions.

A metallized region is characterized by a current of electric charges that short-circuit the field. These charges can be determined from eqn (3.26):

$$\sigma(x) = \left(\frac{\varepsilon \omega}{v_0}\right) \exp(-j\omega x/v_0) e_1 \tag{4.39}$$

4.3   The two-phase piezoelectric transducer

The classic piezoelectric transducer consists of two interdigital combs: it is shown in Fig. 4.1 (White and Voltmer 1965).

Such a transducer is called "two-phase" because the two combs are each connected to one phase. We shall see in Sections 4.5.3 and 5.6 that there are other transducers (called multiphase) which can be constructed, at the price of complication of the technological process, by interleaving three or four combs, connected to three or four different phases.

4.3.1   Regular transducer

4.3.1.1   Description of the model

Consider an interdigital transducer consisting of $N + 1$ identical electrodes with constant spacing D and constant aperture W. The impedance matrix between the N capacitances can then be obtained as follows:

$$V_l = Z_{li}I_i \quad (i, l = 1, 2, \ldots, N) \tag{4.40}$$

where

$$Z_{ll} \approx 1/jC\omega + R_0 \tag{4.41}$$

$$Z_{li} \approx R_0 \exp(-j\omega|l - i|\tau) \tag{4.42}$$

and

$$\tau = D/v_\infty$$

We have written R_0 in Z_{kk} and Z_{lk}, neglecting the reactive part of the radiation impedance of the individual capacitances.

The values of R_0 and C are given in Appendix 4.1. We recall that, in general, for a metallization ratio of 50%, and in the neighborhood of the resonance frequency, we have

$$C \approx \tfrac{1}{2}\varepsilon W \tag{4.43}$$

$$R_0 \approx \frac{1.4k^2}{\varepsilon W\omega} \tag{4.44}$$

Let V be the voltage applied to the transducer and I the total current. It is clear that

$$V_l = (-1)^l V/2 \tag{4.45}$$

$$I = \sum_{l=1}^{N} I_l \tag{4.46}$$

4.3.1.2   "Exact" solution

Rigorous solution of eqn (4.40), with eqns (4.45) and (4.46) taken into account, is quite difficult (cf. Appendix 4.2). See also Feldmann (1973b). We find that (when N is even)

$$Z(\omega) = \frac{V}{I} = \frac{1}{jC\omega}\left\{\frac{\eta G(\xi) + rF(\xi)}{[N - (N - 2)r]G(\xi) + 2(1 - r)^2 H(\xi)}\right\} \tag{4.47}$$

where

$$r = -\exp(-j\omega D/v_\infty) = \exp(-j\theta) \tag{4.48}$$

$$\eta = (1 - r) + \gamma(1 + r) \tag{4.49}$$

$$F(\xi) = (\xi^{N-1} + 1)/(\xi + 1) \tag{4.50}$$

$$G(\xi) = (\xi^N - 1)/(\xi^2 - 1) \tag{4.51}$$

$$H(\xi) = [(1/2)NF(\xi) - G(\xi)]\xi/(\xi - 1)^2 \tag{4.52}$$

$$= \sum_{n=1}^{(N/2)-1} n[(N/2) - n]\xi^{2n-2} + n[(N/2) - n - 1]\xi^{2n-1}$$

The complex number ξ is one of the roots (either may be chosen) of the equation

$$\xi + \frac{1}{\xi} = r(1 - \gamma) + \frac{1}{r}(1 + \gamma) \tag{4.53}$$

where γ is defined by

$$\gamma = jy \tag{4.54}$$

$$y = R_0 C\omega \approx 0.7k^2 \tag{4.55}$$

This formula is implemented by program GROK. (See Appendix A, page 295.)

We can obtain approximate expressions for the impedance that are simpler than eqn (4.47), but still not very tractable. All the same, it is interesting to note that, in principle, eqn (4.47) is valid for large values of the product Nk^2.

The radiation resistance calculated from eqn (4.47) is plotted in Fig. 4.4 for different values of the product Nk^2 (Hénaff and Feldmann 1979a). We

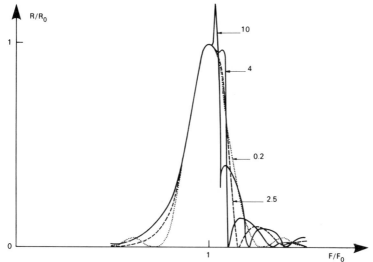

Fig. 4.4 Radiation resistance of a regular transducer for different values of the product Nk^2.

note that, for small values of Nk^2, this function tends to an asymptotic form $[(\sin x)/x]^2$, where $x = N\omega/\omega_0$ and $\omega_0 = v_e\pi/D$, and no longer depends directly on k^2. The velocity v_e involved here is not actually v_∞, but is a slightly lower effective velocity. This behavior is described by eqn (4.53), where we note that $r = \exp(-j\theta)$ is replaced with $\xi = \exp(-j\phi)$ in formulae (4.50)–(4.52). From eqn (4.53) we have

$$\cos \phi = \cos \theta - y \sin \theta \qquad (4.56)$$

where

$$\theta = \omega D/v_\infty - \pi$$

When θ tends to zero, ϕ tends to zero. To the first order in θ, we have

$$\phi^2 = \theta^2 + 2y\theta \qquad (4.57)$$

where

$$y \approx 0.7k^2 \qquad (4.58)$$

The corresponding dispersion curve is shown in Fig. 4.5 and reveals the gap $-2y \leqslant \theta \leqslant 0$.

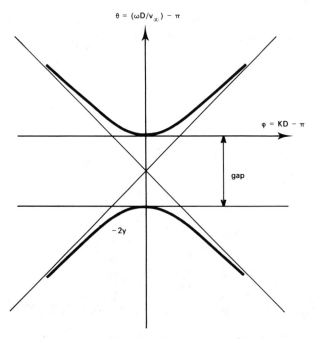

Fig. 4.5 (ω, K) or (θ, ϕ) dispersion diagram for a periodic electrode array.

The existence of the dispersion curve indicates that the concepts of nominal frequency and central frequency are different, the latter being defined by

$$\frac{\omega D}{v_\infty} = \pi - y = \pi\left(1 - \frac{y}{\pi}\right) \tag{4.59}$$

RULE. Piezoelectricity *reduces* the central frequency by the factor $y/\pi \simeq 0.2k^2$.

In the global response of the comb, shown in Fig. 4.4, we always have the same radiation resistance at the nominal frequency, defined by $\omega D/v_\infty = \pi$. On the other hand, in the gap we observe singularities whose amplitude increases with Nk^2. In particular, the radiation resistance can have an appreciable peak when the surface wave is confined to the interior of the comb because of electrical reflections inside the transducer.

4.3.1.3 Approximate formula

We can readily obtain the asymptotic impedance of the transducer for small values of k^2 by solving eqn (4.40) to the first order in k^2. Thus

$$[Z] = \frac{1}{jC\omega} + R_0[M] = \frac{1}{jC\omega}(1 + jy[M]) \tag{4.60}$$

where higher powers of $y \approx 0.7k^2$ are negligible and the components M_{ik} of the matrix $[M]$ are

$$M_{ik} = (-r)^{|i-k|} \quad (i, k = 1, 2, \ldots, N) \tag{4.61}$$

We thus obtain

$$[Z]^{-1} \approx jC\omega(1 - jy[M]) \tag{4.62}$$

Using eqns (4.45) and (4.46), we can show that

$$Z(\omega) = \frac{1}{jNC\omega} + R_0 f(r) \tag{4.63}$$

where

$$f(r) = \frac{1}{N^2}\left[N + 2\frac{(N-1)r - Nr^2 + r^{N+1}}{(1-r)^2}\right] \tag{4.64}$$

This formula can be simplified further in the neighborhood of resonance by substituting

$$x = \frac{N\theta}{2} = \frac{N\tau}{2}(\omega - \omega_0) \tag{4.65}$$

where $\tau = D/v_\infty$ and $\omega_0 = \pi/\tau$.

For $x \ll 1$, we obtain, finally,

$$Z(\omega) = \frac{1}{jNC\omega} + R_0 \left[\left(\frac{\sin x}{x} \right)^2 + j \frac{\sin 2x - 2x}{2x^2} \right] \qquad (4.66)$$

The formula given by eqn (4.66) is the one most often used because of its simplicity (Smith *et al.* 1969a). It shows that there is a static capacitance NC in series with the radiation impedance Z_a which we can rewrite as

$$Z_a = 2R_0 \frac{\exp(-z) + z - 1}{z^2} \qquad (4.67)$$

where

$$z = 2jx = jN\tau(\omega - \omega_0) \qquad (4.68)$$

We sometimes use a parallel representation, obtained to the first order in k^2 from eqn (4.66) (cf. Fig. 4.6):

$$Y(\omega) = \frac{1}{Z(\omega)} = jNC\omega + Y_a \qquad (4.69)$$

where

$$Y_a \approx N^2 C^2 \omega^2 Z_a \qquad (4.70)$$

4.3.1.4   Resonance of a pseudomode

We have seen that a surface pseudobranch is characterized by a complex wave number $K_\infty = \omega/v_\infty$. The pseudoresonance will thus be characterized by

$$DK'_\infty = \pi \qquad (4.71)$$

where K'_∞ is the real part of K_∞. Let

$$a = NDK''_\infty \qquad (4.72)$$

where K''_∞ is the imaginary part of K_∞. The impedance at resonance can then be found from eqn (4.63):

$$r = \exp(-aN) \qquad (4.73)$$

When $y/2N \ll 1$, we obtain

$$R = 2R_0 \frac{\exp(-a) + a - 1}{a^2} \qquad (4.74)$$

where R_0 is the radiation resistance obtained by canceling the attenuation of the pseudobranch (Feldmann 1973b).

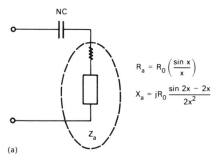

$$R_a = R_0 \left(\frac{\sin x}{x} \right)$$

$$X_a = jR_0 \frac{\sin 2x - 2x}{2x^2}$$

(a)

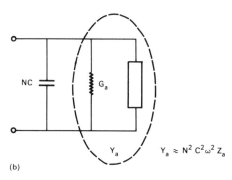

$$Y_a \approx N^2 c^2 \omega^2 Z_a$$

(b)

Fig. 4.6 (a) Series and (b) parallel equivalent circuits of the transducer.

We note that a is simply the total attenuation (in nepers) of the attenuated mode across the $N + 1$ fingers of the comb. By eqn (4.74), the radiation resistance is reduced by a factor that depends only on this total attenuation (Fig. 4.7).

Near the resonance frequency, the impedance of the comb can be found by substituting

$$z = a + 2jx \qquad (4.75)$$

so that

$$Z(\omega) = \frac{1}{jNC\omega} + 2R_0 \frac{\exp(-z) + z -- 1}{z^2} \qquad (4.76)$$

where $2x$ is the change in the total phase shift of the piezoelectric wave and a is the total attenuation across the comb at the frequency ω.

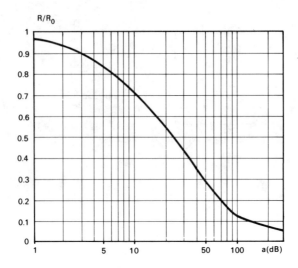

Fig. 4.7 Surface pseudowave: radiation resistance at resonance as a function of wave attenuation across the transducer (from Feldmann 1973b).

4.3.1.5 Multimode problem

In the case of a set of surface branches, the impedance can be obtained directly from eqn (2.18) at the cost of inversion of a complex matrix of dimension N, if we take

$$[A] = \sum_m [A_m] \tag{4.77}$$

the depolarization matrices $[A_m]$ being calculated for each branch.

To the first order, the result is given by eqns (4.63) and (4.76) if we simply add the radiation impedances.

4.3.2 Grating array transducer

When the capacitances constituting a transducer are no longer in parallel, as in interdigital combs, but in series (Fig. 4.8), we get a transducer capable of operating at very high frequencies. Once again, we have (for N capacitances)

$$V_l = Z_{li} I_i \quad (i, l = 1, 2, \ldots, N) \tag{4.78}$$

except that now

$$V = \sum_{l=1}^{N} V_l \qquad I_i = I$$

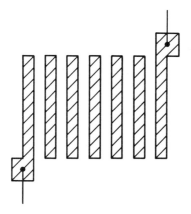

Fig. 4.8 Array transducer with capacitances in series.

Consequently,

$$Z(\omega) = \frac{V}{I} = \sum_l \sum_i Z_{li} \qquad (4.79)$$

For a regular array, we write

$$r = \exp(-j\omega D/v_\infty) \qquad (4.80)$$

Hence, we conclude, that the impedance Z is given by

$$Z(\omega) = \frac{N}{jC\omega} + N^2 R_0 f(r) \qquad (4.81)$$

where $f(r)$ has already been calculated (see eqn 4.64). Near resonance, we have, for example, the formula derived from eqn (4.67):

$$Z(\omega) = \frac{N}{jC\omega} + 2N^2 R_0 \frac{\exp(-z) + z - 1}{z^2} \qquad (4.82)$$

In comparison with the interdigital comb, we note that (i) the impedance level is higher by the factor N^2, and (ii) the resonance frequency is higher by a factor of 2:

$$\frac{\omega_0 D}{v_\infty} = 2\pi \qquad (4.83)$$

The higher impedance of the static capacitance is hardly tolerable except at high frequency. Moreover, the doubling of the resonance frequency is interesting at high frequency, since this can be exploited to double the capability of a given technological process. This procedure was used at 2 GHz in (Hartemann *et al.* 1972).

4.3.3   Unidirectional transducer

4.3.3.1   Reflection at a tuned transducer

Consider a wave incident on a single capacitance C (Fig. 4.9) in parallel with an inductance L, such that $LC\omega_0^2 = 1$.

Equations (4.21)–(4.23) are still valid for the effective amplitudes:

$$V = \left(\frac{1}{jC\omega} + R_0\right) I + A_1 (2R_0)^{1/2} \tag{4.84}$$

$$B_1 = I\left(\frac{R_0}{2}\right)^{1/2} \tag{4.85}$$

$$B_2 = A_1 + I\left(\frac{R_0}{2}\right)^{1/2} \tag{4.86}$$

where V and I are the voltage and current at the terminals of the capacitances, A_1 is the amplitude of the incident wave and B_1 and B_2 are the amplitudes of the emerging waves (the reference impedance being taken as equal to $2R_0$). We have, moreover,

$$V = -jL\omega I \tag{4.87}$$

so that, at the angular frequency ω_0,

$$I = -A_1 \left(\frac{2}{R_0}\right)^{1/2} \tag{4.88}$$

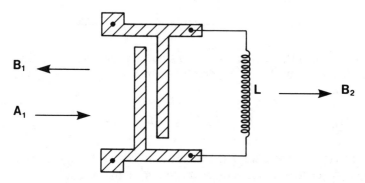

Fig. 4.9   Inductive reflector.

and therefore

$$\begin{cases} B_1 = -A_1^\dagger & (4.89) \\ B_2 = 0 & (4.90) \end{cases}$$

The tuned capacitance is thus a perfect reflector at the frequency ω_0.

At different frequencies, and if we consider an inductance with a quality factor Q, we can readily verify that

$$\frac{B_1}{A_1} = \frac{-y}{y + (2j\delta + 1/Q)} \qquad (4.91)$$

where

$$y = R_0 C\omega \approx 0.7k^2 \qquad (4.92)$$

$$\delta \approx (\omega - \omega_0)/\omega_0 \qquad (4.93)$$

When the single capacitance is replaced by two interdigital combs with N capacitances, the formula remains approximately valid for $\delta \ll 1/N$, provided we take C to be the total capacitance, and therefore $y = 0.7Nk^2$. The relative bandwidth of such a reflector is therefore bounded on the one hand by $0.7Nk^2 + 1/Q$ and, on the other hand, by $1/N$ due to the natural bandwidth of the comb.

4.3.3.2 Unidirectional transducer

Consider two capacitances separated by a distance D, given by

$$D = \frac{3\lambda}{4} \qquad (4.94)$$

where λ is the wavelength.

With the left-hand capacitance 1 tuned to the resonance frequency by the inductance L, we use the right-hand capacitance 2 as a transmitter. It is intuitively clear that the system will act as a unidirectional transducer transmitting to the right (Fig. 4.10). It is readily seen that

$$V_1 = \left(\frac{1}{jC\omega} + R_0\right) I_1 + R_0 \exp(-j\theta)I_2 \qquad (4.95)$$

$$V_2 = \left(\frac{1}{jC\omega} + R_0\right) I_2 + R_0 \exp(-j\theta)I_1 \qquad (4.96)$$

$$A = \left(\frac{R_0}{2}\right)^{1/2} (I_1 \exp(-j\theta) + I_2) \qquad (4.97)$$

$$V_1 = -jL\omega I_1 \qquad (4.98)$$

†The change of sign follows from the convention adopted for the effective amplitudes (Section 4.2.1).

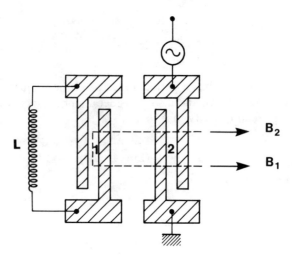

Fig. 4.10 Unidirectional transducer.

where $\theta = \omega D/v_\infty$ and the phase of the emerging wave A is referred to the center (or middle) of the right-hand capacitance (Fig. 4.10). At resonance, $\theta = 3\pi/2$ and $LC\omega^2 = 1$. We thus obtain

$$\frac{V_2}{I_2} = \frac{1}{jC\omega} + R_0[1 - \exp(-2j\theta)] = \frac{1}{jC\omega} + 2R_0 \qquad (4.99)$$

$$A = \left(\frac{R_0}{2}\right)^{1/2} I_2[1 - \exp(-2j\theta)] = I_2(2R_0)^{1/2} \qquad (4.100)$$

Hence, transducer 2 radiates all its energy to the right, and therefore its radiation resistance is doubled. The phase of the merging wave is a function of the frequency:

$$A = I_2(2R_0)^{1/2}j \exp(-j\theta) \sin\theta \qquad (4.101)$$

which shows that the wave appears to come from the center of the left-hand capacitance (i.e. from the center of the reflector).

These results can be extended to the case where the transducers contain several capacitances (Fig. 4.11).

4.4 Multistrip couplers

4.4.1 Description

Multistrip couplers are open-circuit electrode arrays overlapping simultaneously two or more tracks. An incident wave arriving on the first

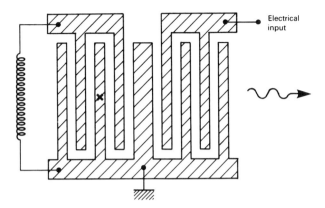

Fig. 4.11 Practical configuration of a unidirectional transducer. The cross represents the origin of phases for the emerging waves propagating to the right.

track (A) meets the capacitance array corresponding to that track. Since the capacitances of the other tracks are connected in parallel, the incident wave induces currents in the circuit, which in turn generates depolarization waves in both directions of each track. In general, the effect will be cumulative only at certain frequencies and on certain tracks.

4.4.2 Mathematical analysis of two-track couplers

4.4.2.1 Diffusion by a capacitance

Let D_A and D_B be the spatial periods of the arrays on tracks A and B, respectively (Fig. 4.12).

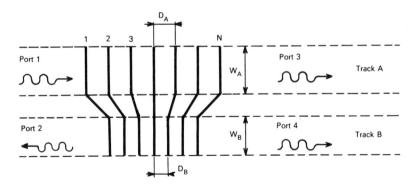

Fig. 4.12 Two-track multistrip coupler.

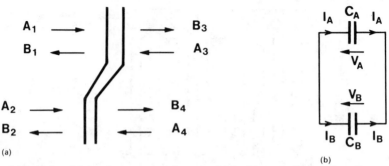

Fig. 4.13 Pair of homologous capacitances: (a) incident and emerging waves; (b) circuit diagram.

On track A, we thus have an array of N capacitances C_A, the radiation resistance of this track being R_A. Each capacitance is capable of receiving waves of amplitudes A_1 and A_3 from the left and the right respectively, and of re-emitting waves of amplitudes B_1 and B_3 respectively (Fig. 4.13a). Each capacitance of track A is, in addition, connected to a corresponding capacitance C_B on track B. We shall denote by R_B the radiation resistance on track B, and by A_2 and A_4 the incident waves and by B_2 and B_4 the emerging waves respectively, as in Fig. 4.13a. Consider a pair of homologous capacitances and let V_A, V_B and I_A, I_B be, respectively, the voltages and currents across the two capacitances (Fig. 4.13b). The piezoelectric equations may be written as

$$V_A = \left(\frac{1}{jC_A\omega} + R_A\right) I_A + \frac{A_1 + A_3}{(2R_A)^{1/2}} \tag{4.102}$$

$$V_B = \left(\frac{1}{jC_B\omega} + R_B\right) I_B + \frac{A_2 + A_4}{(2R_B)^{1/2}} \tag{4.103}$$

Moreover, since the capacitances are connected, we have

$$I_A = -I_B$$
$$V_A = V_B \tag{4.104}$$

The emerging waves are finally given by the following equations:

$$
\begin{aligned}
B_1 &= A_3 + I_A(R_A/2)^{1/2} \\
B_2 &= A_4 + I_B(R_B/2)^{1/2} \\
B_3 &= A_1 + I_A(R_A/2)^{1/2} \\
B_4 &= A_2 + I_B(R_B/2)^{1/2}
\end{aligned} \tag{4.105}
$$

Eliminating V_A, V_B, I_A and I_B between eqns (4.102) to (4.105), we obtain the following transfer equation:

$$
\begin{bmatrix} A_1 \\ B_1 \\ A_2 \\ B_2 \end{bmatrix} = \begin{bmatrix} 1 + jx_1 & jx_1 & -j(x_1x_2)^{1/2} & -j(x_1x_2)^{1/2} \\ -jx_1 & 1 - jx_1 & j(x_1x_2)^{1/2} & j(x_1x_2)^{1/2} \\ -j(x_1x_2)^{1/2} & -j(x_1x_2)^{1/2} & 1 + jx_2 & jx_2 \\ j(x_1x_2)^{1/2} & j(x_1x_2)^{1/2} & -jx_2 & 1 - jx_2 \end{bmatrix} \begin{bmatrix} B_3 \\ A_3 \\ B_4 \\ A_4 \end{bmatrix}
$$

$$(4.106)$$

where we have substituted

$$x_1 = R_A C \tag{4.107}$$

$$x_2 = R_B C \tag{4.108}$$

and

$$\frac{1}{C} = \frac{1}{C_A} + \frac{1}{C_B} \tag{4.109}$$

We shall denote this transfer matrix by $[T_1]$. We can see that $([T_1] - 1)^4 = 0$ (we say that $[T_1] - 1$ is a "nilpotent" matrix). When the two tracks differ only by the values of W_A and W_B, we can verify that

$$
x_1 \approx 0.7k^2 \frac{W_B}{W_A + W_B}
$$
$$
x_2 \approx 0.7k^2 \frac{W_A}{W_A + W_B}
$$
$$(4.110)$$

In particular, when $W_A = W_B$ we have approximately

$$x_1 = x_2 = \frac{y}{2} \approx 0.3k^2 \tag{4.111}$$

4.4.2.2 Complete array

By successively using transfer matrices as in eqn (4.106), we can calculate the cumulative effect of successive reflections on the array. We must insert between successive capacitances a delay corresponding to the period of the array on the corresponding tracks. Let

$$
\theta_A = \omega D_A / v_\infty \qquad \theta_B = \omega D_B / v_\infty
$$
$$
a = \exp(j\theta_A) \qquad b = \exp(j\theta_B)
$$
$$(4.112)$$

The transfer matrix corresponding to a delay of one period may be written in the form

$$[T_2] = \begin{bmatrix} a & 0 & 0 & 0 \\ 0 & 1/a & 0 & 0 \\ 0 & 0 & b & 0 \\ 0 & 0 & 0 & 1/b \end{bmatrix} \tag{4.113}$$

Finally, the elementary transfer is described by the matrix

$$[T] = [T_1][T_2]$$

and the product of N transfers is described by

$$[R] = [T]^N \tag{4.114}$$

We shall be interested mainly in transfers between access ports 1 and 2, on the one hand, and 1 and 4, on the other (Fig. 4.12). We can use the components R_{ij} of the matrix R to show that

$$s = S_{21} = \frac{B_2}{A_1} = \frac{R_{41} R_{33} - R_{43} R_{31}}{R_{11} R_{33} - R_{13} R_{31}} \tag{4.115}$$

$$t = S_{41} = \frac{B_4}{A_1} = -\frac{R_{31}}{R_{11} R_{33} - R_{13} R_{31}} \tag{4.116}$$

4.4.2.3 Eigenmodes of the transfer matrix

It is convenient to write the eigenvalues of the transfer matrix as u, $1/u$, v and $1/v$, where

$$u = \exp(jU) \qquad v = \exp(jV) \tag{4.117}$$

In fact, we can show that the characteristic equation of the matrix $[T]$ can be written in the form

$$\cos U + \cos V = \cos \theta_A + \cos \theta_B - (x_1 \sin \theta_A + x_2 \sin \theta_B)$$

$$\cos U \cos V = \cos \theta_A \cos \theta_B - (x_1 \sin \theta_A \cos \theta_B + x_2 \sin \theta_B \cos \theta_A)$$

$$\tag{4.118}$$

where U and V appear as the values of θ_A and θ_B perturbed by the coupler.

4.4.3 Operation as a transmitter (MSC, MTA)

4.4.3.1 Description

Consider transfer between access ports 1 and 4. The wave emitted at 1 is diffused by the first capacitance to access port 4. The paths transversed along tracks A and B in adjacent elements are D_A and D_B respectively. The two waves are in phase when, approximately,

$$D_A - D_B \approx K\lambda \qquad (4.119)$$

where $\lambda = 2\pi v_\infty/\omega$ is the acoustic wavelength and K is an integer. In particular, when $K = 0$, so that $D_A \approx D_B$, the waves will be in phase at all frequencies, and we have a wide-band coupler. Such a coupler will be denoted by the acronym MSC (multistrip coupler). On the other hand, when the $K \neq 0$, the coupler is selective and will be denoted by the acronym MTA (multistrip transmission array). In terms of the angles θ_A and θ_B (see eqn 4.112), eqn (4.119) may be written in the form

$$\theta_A - \theta_B \approx 2K\pi$$

It will be convenient to substitute

$$\theta_A - \theta_B = 2K\pi + \varepsilon \qquad (4.120)$$

4.4.3.2 Simplified formulation

Let us now consider the case where we can neglect the backward transmission toward access ports 1 and 2. Equation (4.114) can then be simplified by neglecting rows and columns 2 and 4 in the transfer matrix. We shall suppose, in addition, that x_1, x_2 and ε are infinitesimals of the same order. To the first order, we then have:

$$[T] \approx \begin{bmatrix} 1 + jx_1 & -j(x_1x_2)^{1/2} \\ -j(x_1, x_2)^{1/2} & 1 + jx_2 \end{bmatrix} \begin{bmatrix} 1 & 0 \\ 0 & 1 + j\varepsilon \end{bmatrix} \qquad (4.121)$$

The reduced transfer matrix $[T]$ now connects the vectors (A_1, A_2) and (B_3, B_4) for one period of the array.

The matrix $[T]$ can then be written (still to the first order in ε)

$$[T] \approx a \exp(j\delta)(1 + j[M]) \approx a \exp(j\delta) \exp(j[M]) \qquad (4.122)$$

where $\delta = \frac{1}{2}(x_1 + x_2 - \varepsilon)$ and the 2×2 unit matrix is represented by the scalar 1; the $[M]$ matrix has zero trace:

$$[M] = \begin{bmatrix} \dfrac{x_1 - x_2 + \varepsilon}{2} & -(x_1x_2)^{1/2} \\ -(x_1x_2)^{1/2} & \dfrac{x_2 - \varepsilon - x_1}{2} \end{bmatrix} \qquad (4.123)$$

If ϕ and $-\phi$ are the eigenvalues of $[M]$, we have

$$\phi^2 = \frac{1}{4}(x_1 - x_2 + \varepsilon)^2 + x_1x_2 \qquad (4.124)$$

To complete the calculation, we must diagonalize $[T]$. From eqn (4.114) we have

$$\begin{bmatrix} B_3 \\ B_4 \end{bmatrix} = [T]^{-N} \begin{bmatrix} A_1 \\ 0 \end{bmatrix} = \frac{\exp(-jN\delta)}{a^N} [P]$$

$$\times \begin{bmatrix} \exp(-jN\phi) & 0 \\ 0 & \exp(jN\phi) \end{bmatrix} [P]^{-1} \begin{bmatrix} A_1 \\ 0 \end{bmatrix} \quad (4.125)$$

where the diagonalizing matrix $[P]$ is

$$[P] = \begin{bmatrix} (x_1 x_2)^{1/2} & (x_1 x_2)^{1/2} \\ \dfrac{x_1 - x_2 + \varepsilon}{2} - \phi & \dfrac{x_1 - x_2 + \varepsilon}{2} + \phi \end{bmatrix} \quad (4.126)$$

The final result is

$$t = S_{41} = \frac{B_4}{A_1} \approx \frac{j(x_1 x_2)^{1/2}}{\phi} \sin N\phi \exp[-jN(\theta_A + \delta)] \quad (4.127)$$

It is clear from eqn (4.124) that transfer is complete only if $\phi = (x_1 x_2)^{1/2}$ or (by eqns 4.112 and 4.120)

$$D_A - D_B = \frac{v_\infty}{\omega} (2K\pi - x_1 + x_2) \quad (4.128)$$

The number of periods necessary for transfer is then

$$N_{opt} = \frac{\pi}{2\phi} \approx \frac{\pi}{2(x_1 x_2)^{1/2}} \quad (4.129)$$

4.4.3.3 Wide-band coupler (MSC)

The MSC is characterized by $D_A = D_B = D$ or $\varepsilon = 0$ and $W_A = W_B$ or $x_1 = x_2 \simeq 0.3k^2$ and $K = 0$ in eqn (4.120). It is therefore a wide-band coupler, since eqn (4.127) may be written as

$$t = j \sin N\phi \exp[-jN(\theta_A + \delta)] \quad (4.130)$$

where

$$\phi \approx 0.3k^2 \qquad \theta_A = \frac{\omega D}{v_\infty} \qquad \delta = 0.3k^2 \quad (4.131)$$

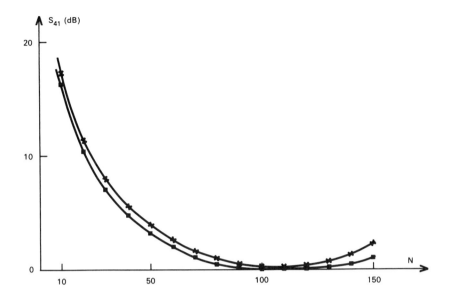

Fig. 4.14 Transmission of the MSC as a function of the number of strips ($F/F_c = 0.8$): (■) $k^2 = 4.5\%$, $N_{opt} = 115$; (X) $k^2 = 5\%$, $N_{opt} = 103$.

Complete transfer is obtained for

$$N_{opt} \approx \frac{5.2}{k^2} \tag{4.132}$$

EXAMPLE. In the case of lithium niobate, with $k^2 = 4.5\%$, we find that $N_{opt} \approx 115$.

Figure 4.14 shows the transmission function of this coupler plotted against the number of strips. In fact, there are rejection frequencies for which backward transmission toward ports 1 and 2 cannot be neglected, which arise in the vicinity of frequencies such as

$$\frac{\omega D}{v_\infty} = K\pi \quad (K \text{ integer})$$

This is obvious from Fig. 4.15, which refers to a multistrip MSC coupler with 115 strips on lithium niobate (the frequency response to the four access ports was calculated from eqn 4.115).

Figure 4.16 gives the transmission S_{41} of the MSC coupler for a track changer A and a power splitter B (a 3 dB coupler) as a function of frequency. It shows the dependence on the number of strips, the coefficient of electromechanical coupling and the behavior near the rejection frequency $F/F_c = 1$.

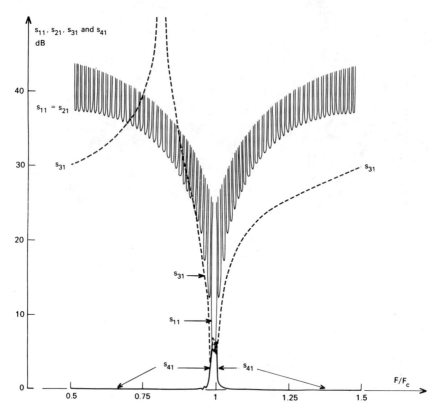

Fig. 4.15 Frequency response of an MSC, calculated from eqn (4.115) with $d_A = d_B = 0.5$, $W_A = W_B$, $N = 115$ and $k^2 = 4.5\%$.

4.4.3.4 Beam compressor

The MSC can act as a beam compressor when W_B is smaller than W_A (it can, of course, also serve as a beam expander). Let

$$W_B = \frac{W_A}{n}$$

From eqn (4.128) with $K = 0$ and eqn (4.110), we see that the complete transfer is obtained for

$$D_B = D_A - \lambda_0 \frac{0.7k^2}{2\pi} \frac{n-1}{n+1}$$

where λ_0 is the wavelength at the tuned frequency ω_0.

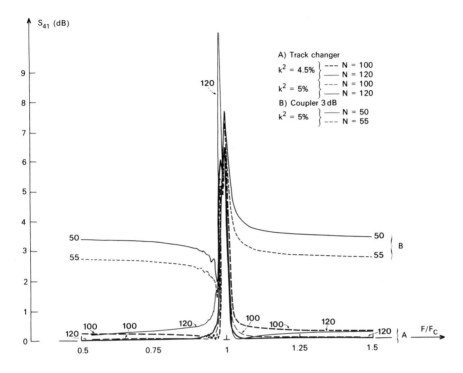

Fig. 4.16 Transmission by an MSC for different values of k^2 and N.

The response is still given by eqn (4.127) but this time

$$\phi \approx \frac{0.7k^2}{n+1}\left[n + \frac{1}{4}(n-1)^2\left(1 - \frac{\omega}{\omega_0}\right)^2\right]^{1/2}$$

$$\theta_A = \frac{\omega D_A}{v_\infty} \qquad \delta \approx \delta_0 = x_1 \quad (\text{at } \omega = \omega_0)$$

Note that ϕ depends explicitly on the frequency. In fact, it depends on it also implicitly via x_1 and x_2, so that the additional dispersion is added to the original dispersion. For large values of n, the bandwidth is reduced. Total transmission takes place at frequency ω_0 for

$$N_{\text{opt}} = \frac{\pi}{2\phi_0} \approx \frac{\pi}{1.4k^2}\frac{n+1}{n^{1/2}} \approx \frac{\pi n^{1/2}}{1.4k^2}$$

EXAMPLE. For YZ lithium niobate with $k^2 \simeq 4.5\%$, we have $N_{\text{opt}} \simeq 150$ for $n = 9$.

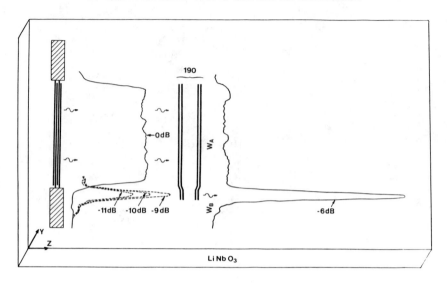

Fig. 4.17   Beam compressor on lithium niobate: $W_A = W_B$, $D_A = 1.01D_B$, $N = 190$.

The compression efficiency obtained is well illustrated by Fig. 4.17, which shows the incident and emerging waves recorded by a laser probe (Maerfeld and Farnell 1973).

4.4.3.5   Selective coupler (MTA)
The MTA is a selective coupler, that can be used as a frequency filter. We shall evaluate the bandwidth of the device with two tracks and two regular $(N + 1)$-strip arrays. We take equation (4.120) with $K \neq 0$ and suppose that $x_1 = x_2 = 0.3k^2$ in eqn (4.121). Suppose further that phase matching can be achieved exactly at the angular frequency ω_0:

$$\theta_{A_0} - \theta_{B_0} = (\omega_0/v_\infty)(D_A - D_B) = 2K\pi$$

For $\omega \neq \omega_0$, the phase difference is

$$\theta_A - \theta_B - 2K\pi = \varepsilon = \frac{\omega - \omega_0}{v_\infty}(D_A - D_B) = 2\pi K \frac{\omega - \omega_0}{\omega_0}$$

If the total transfer is realized for $\omega = \omega_0$, we have from eqn (4.124)

$$\phi^2 \approx (0.3k^2)^2 + 4\pi^2 K^2 \left(\frac{\omega - \omega_0}{\omega_0}\right)^2$$

The frequency response is then given by eqn (4.127)

$$S_{41} \approx \frac{0.3jk^2}{\phi} \sin N\phi \, \exp[-jN(\theta_A + \delta)]$$

where

$$\theta_A \;=\; \frac{\omega D_A}{v_\infty} \quad \text{and} \quad \delta \;=\; 0.3k^2 + K\pi\,\frac{\omega - \omega_0}{\omega_0}$$

$$\theta_A + \delta \;\approx\; 0.3k^2 + \frac{\omega}{2v_\infty}$$

The MTA enables us to construct reasonably wideband devices. By putting several identical MTAs in series, we can operate on the frequency response—as we do with coupled circuits—to obtain, for example, a Butterworth-type behavior. This is illustrated in Fig. 4.18 for different numbers of sections (each of 16 strips) and different values of the electromechanical coupling coefficient. Figure 4.19 shows the classical arrangement of an MTA (filter mask with 7% of the relative bandwidth).

4.4.4   Operation as a reflector (MRA)

4.4.4.1   Description

Consider now transmission between access ports 1 and 2. The wave from access port 1 is reflected by the first capacitance and the first wave is re-emitted. The wave reflected by the next capacitance travels a further distance D_A and the re-emitted wave is additionally delayed on track B by a distance D_B. The two waves are in phase if

$$D_A + D_B \approx K\lambda$$

where $\lambda = 2\pi v_\infty/\omega$ is the acoustic wavelength and K is an integer. Since K is necessarily positive, the coupler is necessarily selective.

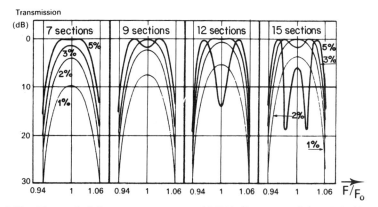

Fig. 4.18   Theoretical frequency response of MTA filters containing 7, 9, 12 and 15 identical 16-strip sections. The parameter is the electromechanical coupling constant k^2 (1, 2, 3 and 5% respectively).

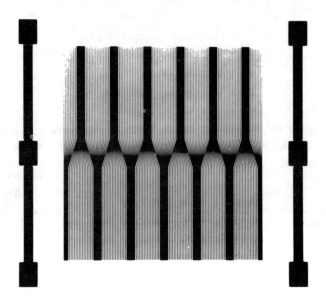

Fig. 4.19 MTA filter mask with 192 strips.

In terms of the angles θ_A and θ_B in eqn (4.112), we have

$$\theta_A + \theta_B \approx 2K\pi$$

and it is convenient to substitute

$$\theta_A + \theta_B = 2K\pi + \varepsilon$$

4.4.4.2 Simplified formulation

Consider the case where backward transmission toward access ports 1 and 4 is negligible. Equation (4.114) can then be simplified. In addition, suppose that $x_1 = x_2 = x$, and consider the case where ε and x are infinitesimals of the same order. We then have

$$[T] \approx \begin{bmatrix} 1 + jx & -jx \\ +jx & 1 - jx \end{bmatrix} \begin{bmatrix} a & 0 \\ 0 & 1/b \end{bmatrix}$$

and the matrix $[T]$ relates (A_1, B_2) to (B_3, A_4). To the first order in ε, we have

$$1/b = a(1 - j\varepsilon)$$

At "synchronism", $\varepsilon = 0$. We can then show that

$$[T] = a^N \begin{bmatrix} 1 + jNx & -jNx \\ jNx & 1 - jNx \end{bmatrix}$$

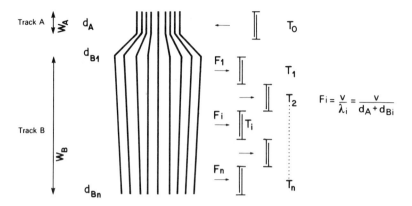

Fig. 4.20 Diagram of a fan-shaped MTA.

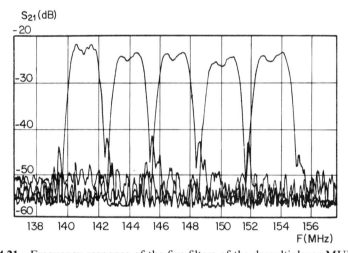

Fig. 4.21 Frequency response of the five filters of the demultiplexer MULT 33.

so that

$$s = \frac{B_2}{A_1} = \frac{jNx}{1 + jNx}$$

$$|s|^2 = \frac{y^2}{1 + y^2}$$

where

$$y = Nx \approx 0.3Nk^2$$

We note that reflections from access port 1 to access port 2 are cumulative. In lithium niobate, for example, 90% of the energy is reflected by $N = 100$ strips.

Similarly, we can obtain a formula in the absence of synchronism, but this proves to be too complicated.

Figure 4.20 illustrates a rather special MRA in which the electrodes in one of the tracks form a fan (Feldmann *et al.* 1976), so that we can construct a bank of filters in a single device.

Figure 4.21 shows the frequency response of a demultiplexer that separates 5 channels, each of which corresponds to 30 telephone channels or 1 video channel (2 Mbit s^{-1}, modulation by 4-state phase shift keying, intermediate frequency in the 150 MHz band).

4.5   Low-loss transducers

Interdigital transducers placed in a delay line produce 15–30 dB insertion loss unless special precautions are taken. When low losses are required (filters at the front end of a device, or a series of filters), special techniques have to be used and can complicate the circuit quite seriously.

4.5.1   Analysis of the different losses

4.5.1.1   Bidirectionality

In an ordinary line, *in the absence of multiple echoes*, each of the transducers is bidirectional and therefore involves an "unavoidable" loss of 3 dB or 6 dB per line. In reality, the total absence of echoes is only an idealization (cf. Section 5.3.1.4 and Fig. 5.11), and the so-called "triple transit echo" modulates this 6 dB loss to the extent that, under certain conditions, the bidirectionality loss is canceled at certain frequencies. It nevertheless remains true that unidirectional transducers have to be used to limit the losses, at least in lines with sufficiently large bandwidth.

4.5.1.2   Ohmic losses

The second important factor is the ohmic loss due to the finite resistance of the electrodes. This can be evaluated at the central frequency by considering the equivalent diagram of the transducer loaded by the radiation resistance $2R_0$ of the line (Fig. 4.22).

An analysis of the losses using a slightly more sophisticated model (and incorporating the following section) is given in (Malocha 1981).

Appendix H gives an interactive program "S_{21}" that computes these effects (they are weaker for $r \ll R_0$). Matching inductances (with finite Q) and connecting resistances must be taken into account.

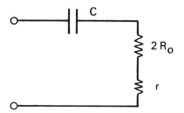

Fig. 4.22 Evaluation of losses due to the resistance of the electrodes, using a simple equivalent diagram of the transducer: R_0 = radiation resistance; C = static capacitance; r = resistance of the electrodes.

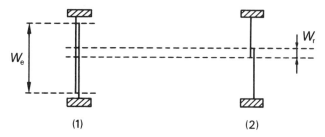

Fig. 4.23 Principle of modulation loss.

4.5.1.3 Modulation losses

Transducer modulation is a particular source of loss (Fig. 4.23). When an emitter of width W_e radiates toward a receiver of width $W_r < W_e$, it is clear that a fraction $1 - W_r/W_e$ of the wave is lost. This loss is a minimum when W_r/W_e approaches unity (or in general $\Sigma_{k=1}^{N} W_{r_k}/NW \approx 1$, where N is the number of weights). It is canceled when a reflector sends back the lost fraction toward the original transducers (e.g. unidirectional transducers).

4.5.1.4 Conversion loss

As it propagates along a transducer or array, a surface wave is converted into bulk waves or surface pseudowaves. This conversion is, on the one hand, a parasitic response but, on the other, it gives rise to a loss of useful signal. It is minimized by a judicious choice of electrodes, crystal configuration and geometry (phase mismatch with parasitic modes, light electrodes to minimize the mass-loading effect and so on).

4.5.1.5 Diffraction loss

The finite width of transducers, especially that resulting from the inevitable modulation of the comb, gives rise to diffraction, which manifests itself to a greater or lesser extent in a distortion of the response out of band

and a conversion loss in the pass band. Diffraction is minimized by limiting modulation and by using poorly diffracting materials (in the parabolic approximation, the ideal configuration corresponding to a slowness curve that is rectilinear in the useful part).

4.5.1.6 Principle of low-loss transducers

The problem of low-loss transducers is hardly significant except for large bandwidths. For narrow bands, ohmic losses are low (large number of electrodes in parallel) and we can use the triple transit echo to cancel losses of bidirectionality. Low-loss transducers are therefore unidirectional and have smooth response (to limit modulation, diffraction and conversion losses).

4.5.2   Unidirectional inductive transducers

For moderate bandwidths and at frequencies at which the inductances have acceptable Q (some hundreds of MHz), unidirectional transducers are conveniently realized without being too complicated by using inductances (Smith *et al.* 1969a, b). We shall not return to this technique (it was described in detail in Section 4.3.3.2). Note that the use of two unidirectional transducers requires strict tuning, which can be critical.

4.5.3   Multiphase air-gap transducers

The multiphase transducer has resulted in a technology that has completely changed surface-wave filters: the construction is distinctly more complex and the controlling circuits are more elaborate. The first realizations described by Texas Instruments (Hartmann *et al.* 1972) used three-phase control with bridging over the electrodes to supply the third phase (Fig. 4.24). Phase 2 is supplied by a raised bus in the form of a periodic bridge that prevents the short-circuiting of phase 3.

It is readily verified that such a transducer, with three electrodes per wavelength and supplied by a three-phase current, is unidirectional. The phase difference is counterbalanced by the delay in the direction in which propagation is cumulative. In the other direction, the three waves, proportional respectively to the three cube roots of unit, cancel identically.

The response modulation of these filters is effected with great precision by the technique of nonrecursive filters (described above). There is, however, an important constraint: the weights must be positive, to avoid further complication of technology. The best results reported are of the order of 2 dB of insertion loss overall at a central frequency of 35 MHz and for a relative bandwidth of 30% (Rosenfeld *et al.* 1974).

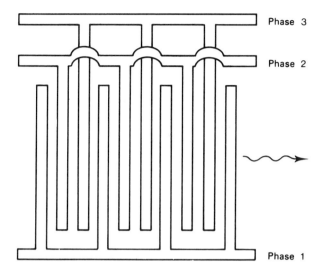

Fig. 4.24 Three-phase air-gap transducer.

We can replace three-phase transducers by four-phase transducers, which simplify the control circuit and makes the device more symmetric. Note that the technological process requires more precision as the number of phases increases.

4.5.4 Unidirectional group transducers

Group transducers consist of "unidirectional sources" or "groups". For example, a group can consist of electrodes supplied by currents in quadrature, as in Fig. 4.25 (Yamanouchi *et al.* 1975).

The wave emerging to the right is proportional to $\exp(j\omega\tau) + j$ where τ is the transit time between the two sources, and to $\exp(j\omega\tau) - j$ for the wave emerging to the left. The group will be unidirectional if the distance between the two sources is a quarter of a wavelength ($\omega\tau = \pi/2$) modulo one wavelength.

Another way of approximately constructing such groups (Fig. 4.26) is to insert internal reflectors (following the principle of charge transfer devices in microelectronics) (Wright and Wilkus 1983).

Global filter synthesis may be effected quite simply by putting together a sufficient number of groups considered as unidirectional sources. Figure 4.27 shows such a filter, obtained by phase shifting in quadrature.

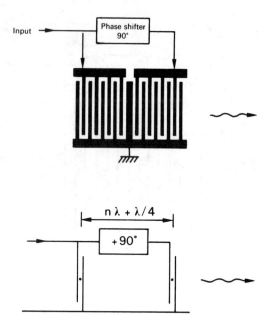

Fig. 4.25 Unidirectional transducer with phase shifter (or "group").

4.5.5 Filter with overlapping access ports

It is possible to use the reflections between the input and output transducers to compensate for the 6 dB bidirectionality loss (Section 4.5.1), but only within a band $\Delta\omega$ that is small in comparison with the transit time τ between the two transducers. This compensation can be obtained over a finite band when τ is zero, i.e. when the two transducers are overlapping, as in Fig. 4.28 (Feldmann 1973b; Lewis 1983).

The disadvantage of this type of device is the large resistance of the central mass connection, which gives rise to direct coupling between input and output.

4.6 Bleustein–Gulyaev and SSBW waves

We can use eqns (4.8) and (4.12)–(4.15) to calculate numerically the impedances and transfer functions of a set of transducers deposited on a piezoelectric crystal operating in SSBW modes.

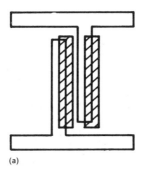

(a)

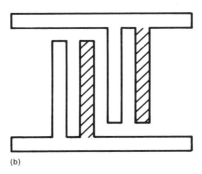

(b)

Fig. 4.26 "Group" consisting of a two-phase transducer rendered unidirectional (approximately) (a) by a discontinuity (produced by insulation, implantation or machining), (b) by additional thickness.

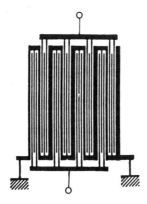

Fig. 4.27 Group filter with a 90° phase shift.

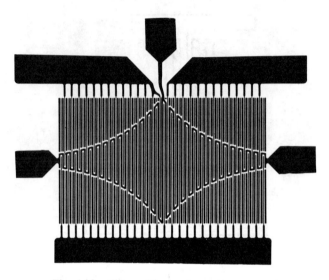

Fig. 4.28   Filter with overlapped access ports.

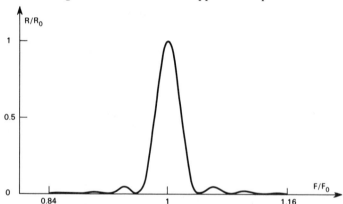

Fig. 4.29   Impedance of a regular comb containing 50 strips on a substrate of lithium tantalate ($k^2 \simeq 1\%$; Rayleigh wave).

The impedance matrix of a system of N capacitances is

$$V_l = Z_{li}I_i \quad (i, l = 1, 2, \ldots, N)$$

where

$$Z_{ll} \approx R_l + 1/jC_l\omega$$

$$R_l \approx 0.7k/\varepsilon W_l\omega$$

$$Z_{li} \approx \frac{1.2k}{\varepsilon\omega} \frac{W_{li}}{W_l W_i} \left(\frac{1}{\omega|\tau_{li}|}\right)^{1/2} \exp\left[-j\left(\omega\tau_{li} + \frac{\pi}{4}\right)\right]$$

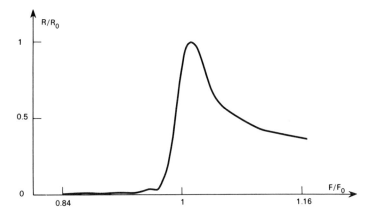

Fig. 4.30 Impedance of a regular comb containing 50 strips ($k^2 = 1\%$; Bleustein–Gulyaev wave).

By way of example, Fig. 4.29 shows the calculated impedance of a regular comb on a substrate of $LiTaO_3$, and Fig. 4.30 shows the transfer function of a Bleustein–Gulyaev line.

It is possible to extend the theory to multistrip couplers, but the advantages of these couplers are relatively limited because of their weak interaction with waves of this type as they propagate far from the surface.

Appendix 4.1   Interdigital transducer with regular geometry

Electrostatic capacitance

The distribution of electric charge in a periodic structure (Fig. 4.31) is a classical problem whose solution can be found in Durand (1953).

Let D be the separation between the centers of two consecutive electrodes, and let $2a$ be the width and W the length of each electrode. The electrostatic

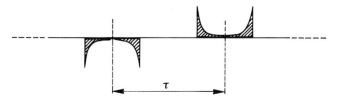

Fig. 4.31 Distribution of electric charge on the fingers of an interdigital transducer.

problem can be conveniently solved by a sequence of conformal transformations. The elementary capacitances can be expressed in terms of elliptic integrals, and we can show (Feldmann 1973b) that

$$C = \frac{1}{2} \frac{\gamma(1, \sin \Delta/2)}{\gamma(1, \cos \Delta/2)} \frac{\varepsilon W}{1 - k^2}$$

where Δ is the angle $2\pi(a/D)$ characterizing the metallization ratio of the comb and $\gamma (a, b)$ is the limit of the very rapidly convergent series defined by

$$a_0 = a \qquad b_0 = b \qquad a_{n+1} = (a_n + b_n)/2 \qquad b_{n+1} = (a_n + b_n)^{1/2}$$

The same conformal transformations show that the charge density $\sigma(x)$ is given by

$$\sigma(x) \approx [\cos(\pi x/2D) - \cos(\Delta/2)]^{1/2}$$

The Fourier transform of $\sigma(x)$ for a complete electrode is (Lavoine 1963)

$$\sigma(K) \approx P_v(\cos \Delta)$$

where $v = KD - \frac{1}{2}$ and $P_v(z)$ is the Legendre function of order v. Note also the following useful property:

$$P_{-1/2}(\cos \Delta) = 1/\gamma(1, \cos \Delta/2)$$

Radiation resistance R

Before we can calculate the radiation resistance, we must have the Fourier transform of $\sigma(K)$. For a half-electrode, this Fourier transform is difficult to find. However, at the resonance frequency ($KD = \frac{1}{2}$), the useful parameter $R\omega$ involves only the symmetric charge distribution:

$$R\omega = \frac{2k^2}{\varepsilon W} \left[\gamma \left(1, \cos \frac{\Delta}{2} \right) \right]^2$$

so that

$$y_0 = RC\omega_0 = \frac{k^2}{1 - k^2} \gamma \left(1, \sin \frac{\Delta}{2} \right) \gamma \left(1, \cos \frac{\Delta}{2} \right)$$

The quantity y_0 differs slightly (by 10%) from the value found by Smith *et al.* (1969a and b), but is identical with the value proposed by Auld and Kino (1971). The maximum value of $RC\omega$ is attained for $\Delta = \pi/2$ and is $0.718k^2/(1 - k^2)$.

At frequencies other than the resonance frequency it is convenient to replace the actual distribution of electric charge

$$\sigma(x) \approx [\cos(\pi x/D) - \cos \Delta]^{-1/2}$$

with the approximate expression

$$\hat{\sigma}(x) \approx (a - x)^{-1/2}$$

The corresponding approximate values of α and θ may be calculated using the Kummer hypergeometric function $_1F_1$. More precisely, substituting

$$z = -j\omega\tau\frac{\Delta}{2\pi}$$

we obtain (Lavoine 1963; Whittaker and Watson 1952):

$$\sigma(K) \sim \exp(-z) \sum_{n=0}^{\infty} \frac{z^n}{(2n + 1)n!}$$

The precision of y is better than 1.5% so long as Δ is less than 135°. Conversely, measurement of y as a function of frequency enables us to reconstruct the actual distribution of charge over the electrodes. Such measurements can be made with a multistrip coupler, but show significant disagreement with the hypothesis that the distribution of electric charge on each half-electrode is identical with the electrostatic distribution. On the other hand, the approximation becomes very good toward the low frequencies. Substituting $y = CR\omega$ and $\theta = \omega\tau$, we obtain, to the first order in θ

$$y = \frac{\theta}{2}\frac{k^2}{1 - k^2}$$

Appendix 4.2 Impedance of the regular comb

Let $[M(r)]$ be the $m \times m$ matrix defined by

$$M_{ij} = r^{|i-j|} \quad i, j = 1, 2, \ldots, m$$

where r is a complex number of modulus $\leqslant 1$ and m is a positive integer.

The mathematical problem of the interdigital transducer amounts to the evaluation of $(1 + \beta[M])^{-1}$ (β is a complex number, in general small).

We show first that, for $r = \pm 1$,

$$(1 + \beta[M])^{-1} = 1 - \frac{\beta}{1 + \beta m}[M]$$

We shall therefore suppose that $r \neq \pm 1$ and $r \neq 0$. Moreover, we shall denote by X the vector with components $X_i = 1$ ($i = 1, 2, \ldots, m$).

Decomposition of the matrix [M]

It can be shown that

$$[M(r)] = \frac{a}{[N] - b}$$

where

$$a = r - 1/r$$
$$b = r + 1/r$$

and $[N(r)]$ is a matrix of dimension m, which commutes with $[M]$ and is defined by

$$N_{i,i+1} = N_{i+1,i} = 1 \quad (i = 1, 2, \ldots, m - 1)$$

all the other components of $[N]$ being zero, except $N_{11} = N_{mm} = r$.

Calculation of $Z = X(1 + \beta[M])^{-1} X$ for $m = 2n$

It is convenient to transform the coordinates by

$$X \rightarrow x = [P]X$$

where

$$P_{ii} = 1/\sqrt{2} \quad (i = 1, 2, \ldots, n)$$
$$P_{ii} = -1/\sqrt{2} \quad (i = n + 1, n + 2, \ldots, m)$$
$$P_{i,m-i+1} = 1/\sqrt{2} \quad (i = 1, 2, \ldots, m)$$

all the other components of $[P]$ being zero.

The matrix $[P]$ is orthogonal and symmetric. Moreover, in this transformation of coordinates, $[M]$ and $[N]$ are put into the form of the direct sum of two submatrices of order n, operating in a fixed manner in two orthogonal subspaces:

$$[N'] = \begin{bmatrix} [N_1] & 0 \\ 0 & [N_2] \end{bmatrix} \quad x = \begin{bmatrix} X_1 \\ 0 \end{bmatrix}$$

It is then sufficient to determine y in a subspace of dimension $n = m/2$:

$$y = X_1'(1 + \beta[M_1])^{-1}X_1'$$

For simplicity, we shall omit the index 1 in what follows. With this convention, we then have

$$X_i = \sqrt{2} \quad (i = 1, 2, \ldots, n)$$

$$N_{i,i+1} = N_{i+1,i} = 1 \quad (i = 1, 2, \ldots, n - 1)$$

$$N_{11} = r$$

$$N_{nn} = 1$$

We denote by $[V]$ the projector with components

$$V_{11} = 1$$

$$V_{ij} = 0 \quad (i \text{ or } j \neq 1)$$

and by $[H]$ the matrix equal to the matrix $[N]$ except for its component H_{11}, which is equal to unity. We then have

$$[N] = [H] + (r - 1)[V]$$

Hence

$$\frac{1}{1 + \beta[M]} = \frac{1}{1 + \beta a/([N] - b)} = 1 - \frac{\beta a}{[N] - b + \beta a}$$

and, finally,

$$Z = X^t X + \beta a X^t (z - [N])^{-1} X$$

where

$$z = b - \beta a = r(1 - \beta) + \frac{1}{r}(1 + \beta)$$

The resolvent $[G(z)] = (z - [N])^{-1}$ can be calculated by the perturbation method due to Kato (1949) and Messiah (1964, pp. 609–611).

Substituting $\lambda = r - 1$ and $[N] = [H] + \lambda[V]$, we have

$$[G_\lambda(z)] = [z - ([H] + \lambda[V])]^{-1} = \sum_{k=0}^{\infty} \lambda^k [G_0]([V][G_0])^k$$

Since $[V]$ is a projector, we have, finally,

$$[G_\lambda(z)] = [G_0(z)] + \frac{\lambda}{1 - \lambda g}[G_0][V][G_0]$$

where

$$[G_0] = (z - [H])^{-1}$$

and $g = \text{Tr}([V][G_0][V]) = (G_0)_{11}$.

Note that X is the eigenvector of $[G_0]$, corresponding to the eigenvalue 2; thus, evaluation of y requires knowledge of g alone. The evaluation of $([G_0])_{11}$ is effected, for example, by recurrence on n.

Substituting $z = \xi + 1/\xi$, we can show that the determinant Δ_n of $z - [H]$ has the value

$$\Delta_n = \left(\xi^n - \frac{1}{\xi^n} \right) \frac{\xi - 1}{\xi + 1}$$

The cofactor D_{n-1} of $z - H_{11}$ can also be evaluated (by recurrence):

$$D_n = \left(\xi^{n+1} + \frac{1}{\xi^n} \right) \frac{1}{1 + \xi}$$

whence we deduce that $g = D_{n-1}/\Delta_n$.

Finally,

$$Z = 2n + \frac{2\beta a}{z - 2} \left[n + \frac{\lambda}{(1 - \lambda g)(z - 2)} \right]$$

The impedance of the interdigital comb can be deduced from this.

Exercises

Exercise 1

Consider the transfer matrix

$$\begin{bmatrix} A_1 \\ B_1 \end{bmatrix} = \begin{bmatrix} F_{11} & F_{12} \\ F_{21} & F_{22} \end{bmatrix} \begin{bmatrix} B_2 \\ A_2 \end{bmatrix}$$

with $F_{11}F_{22} - F_{12}F_{21} = 1$ (reciprocity).

Calculate the reflection coefficient B_1/A_1 and the transmission coefficient B_2/A_1 (for $A_2 = 0$).

Exercise 2

Determine the distribution matrix $[S_1]$ for a pair of capacitances occupying two tracks simultaneously, as in eqns (4.102)–(4.105). Verify the conservation of energy. Hence deduce eqn (4.106).

Verify that the matrix $[T_1] - [1]$ is nilpotent.

Exercise 3

Evaluate the distribution matrix for two piezoelectric capacitances separated by the distance $v_\infty T$. Calculate the multiple echoes as functions of the product $R_0 C$.

Exercise 4

Calculate the eigenvalues of the matrix eqn (4.36). Hence deduce eqn (4.37).

Exercise 5

Consider a broad-band multistrip coupler. Show that the number of strips necessary for complete transfer at low frequencies is given by

$$N_{\text{opt}} = \left(\frac{1 - k^2}{k^2}\right) \frac{\lambda}{D}$$

where $D_A = D_B = D$; $\lambda = 2\pi v_\infty/\omega$, and $D \ll \lambda$ (use eqns 3.16a and 3.49).

Exercise 6

Show that

$$(1 + jy[M])^{-1} = 1 - \frac{jy[M]}{1 + jyN}$$

where $[M]$ is a $N \times N$ matrix with components

$$M_{ik} = 1 \quad (i, k = 1, 2, \ldots, N)$$

Hence deduce the exact impedance of the interdigital transducer at resonance. Compare with eqns (4.47) and (4.66).

Exercise 7

Consider the 2×2 matrix

$$[T] = \lim_{x \to \infty} \exp(j\theta[T])$$

where $[T]$ is given by eqn (4.36) with $\theta = \omega x/v_\infty$.

Show that the eigenvalues of

$$[M] = j\theta[T]$$

are, respectively, $j\phi$ and $-j\phi$, where ϕ is given by eqn (4.34). Consider an incident wave A_1, a reflected wave B_1, and a transmitted wave B_2. Calculate B_1/A_1 and $\exp(j\phi)B_2/A_1$.

(Decompose $[M]$ into two projectors associated with the two eigenvalues $\pm j\phi$ and assume that there is very weak attenuation, so that x can tend to infinity.)

Exercise 8

Consider a surface wave electrical port to surface waves (V, I) and two piezoelectric ports (V_{a1}, I_{a1}) and (V_{a2}, I_{a2}). Show that the impedance matrix can be put into the form

$$
\begin{bmatrix} V \\ V_{a1} \\ V_{a2} \end{bmatrix}
=
\begin{bmatrix} Z_{11} & Z_{1a} & Z_{1a} \\ Z_{1a} & 0 & 0 \\ Z_{1a} & 0 & 0 \end{bmatrix}
\begin{bmatrix} I \\ I_{a1} \\ I_{a2} \end{bmatrix}
$$

Each of the two piezoelectric ports is loaded by the impedance $2R_0$. If the hexapole is nondissipative, show that

$$\frac{V}{I} = -\frac{Z_{1a}}{R_0} + Z_{11} = R + jX$$

Discuss the radiation resistance as a function of $Z_{1a} = jX_a$. Interpret the following impedance matrix:

$$
\begin{bmatrix} V \\ V_1 \\ V_2 \end{bmatrix}
=
\begin{bmatrix}
j\left(X - \dfrac{X_a^{\,2}}{2R_0}\right) & j\dfrac{X_a}{\cos\theta_1} & j\dfrac{X_a}{\cos\theta_2} \\[2mm]
j\dfrac{X_a}{\cos\theta_1} & 2jR_0\tan\theta_1 & 0 \\[2mm]
j\dfrac{X_a}{\cos\theta_2} & 0 & 2jR_0\tan\theta_2
\end{bmatrix}
\begin{bmatrix} I \\ I_1 \\ I_2 \end{bmatrix}
$$

Chapter 5

Frequency Filters

Frequency filtering is one of the principal applications of surface acoustic waves in signal processing: every linear process effects a filtering operation on the input signal. Let $x(t)$ and $y(t)$ be the input and output signals respectively. Let $X(j\omega)$ and $Y(j\omega)$ be the Fourier transforms of $x(t)$ and $y(t)$ respectively. The filtering operation with gain $H(j\omega)$ is defined in the frequency domain by the relation

$$Y(j\omega) \;=\; H(j\omega)X(j\omega) \tag{5.1}$$

In the time domain, we have the equivalent expression (called the *convolution*)

$$y(t) \;=\; \int_{-\infty}^{+\infty} h(\tau)x(t-\tau)\,d\tau \tag{5.2}$$

The function $h(\tau)$ is the impulse response of the filter and $H(j\omega)$ is the Fourier transform of $h(\tau)$. Causality implies that $h(\tau)$ is zero for $\tau < 0$.

5.1 Transformation effected by a surface-wave transducer

5.1.1 Single capacitance

Let V_l be the voltage applied to a piezoelectric transducer containing a single capacitance C_l with aperture W_l and thus with impedance given by

$$Z_l \;=\; \frac{1}{jC_l\omega} + R_l \tag{5.3}$$

where

$$C_l \approx \varepsilon W_l/2 \quad \text{and} \quad R_l \approx 1.4k^2/\varepsilon W_l\omega$$

(cf. Section 4.1, eqn 4.1)

For weak coupling, the current I_l flowing through the capacitance is

$$I_l = V/Z_l \approx jC_l\omega V = (j\varepsilon\omega/2)W_lV_l \tag{5.4}$$

The potential e_l induced at a distance T_l in a capacitance C_0 of aperture $W_0 \geqslant W_l$ is then (eqn 4.11)

$$e_l = Z_{0l}I_l$$

where

$$Z_{0l} \approx \frac{1.4k^2}{\varepsilon W_0 \omega} \exp(-j\omega T_l)$$

or

$$e_l \approx 0.7jk^2 \left(\frac{W_l}{W_0}\right) V_l \exp(-j\omega T_l) \tag{5.5}$$

5.1.2   Complex comb

To the first order in k^2, we can verify that the contributions of the respective elementary capacitances reinforce one another, so that

$$e = \sum_l e_l \tag{5.6}$$

The voltage V_l applied to the capacitance C_l is frequency equal to $\pm V$. More precisely, we have in an interdigital comb

$$V_l = (-1)^l V \tag{5.7}$$

If, in addition, the fingers of the comb are regularly spaced, we have

$$T_l = l\tau$$

It is convenient to put

$$\omega = \omega_0 + \Omega$$

where

$$\omega_0 \tau = \pi$$

We than obtain

$$e = \sum_l \frac{0.7jk^2}{W_0} (-1)^l \exp(-j\omega_0 T_l) \exp(-j\Omega T_l) V$$

$C_n C_{n-1}$

+ − + + − + −

Fig. 5.1 Successive capacitances C_n and C_{n-1} connected so that the weights have the same sign.

or

$$\frac{e}{V} \approx \left(\frac{0.7jk^2}{W_0}\right) \sum_l W_l \exp(-j\Omega T_l) \qquad (5.8)$$

We shall call the response given by eqn (5.8) the "prototype low-pass response". In practice, the alternating connection of the elementary capacitances is not the only possible one: two successive capacitances can have the same sign (Fig. 5.1). We can, however, retain the above model provided we allow negative coefficients W_l.

It is also convenient to put

$$A_l = W_l/W_0$$
$$X = V \qquad (5.9)$$
$$Y = e/0.7jk^2$$

so that, finally, we have the following low-pass prototype:

$$Y = \left(\sum_l A_l \exp(-j\Omega T_l)\right) X \qquad (5.10)$$

We recognize the definition of a (nonrecursive) transversal filter and note that this formulation is valid to the nearest approximation for weak coupling and for a single transducer. It is, however, useful because it enables us to use methods of synthesis studied in the theory of digital filters (see below).

5.2   Synthesis of transversal filters (FIR)

5.2.1   Generalities

5.2.1.1   Definition

A transversal filter is a *discrete-time* linear operator (i.e. one defined at discrete instants T_l) with *finite impulse response* (hence the acronym FIR) (Bellanger 1981; Boite and Leich 1982). If we again consider eqn (5.2) as the definition of a filter in the time domain, we have in this case

$$y(t) = \sum_{l=0}^{N-1} A_l x(t - T_l) \tag{5.11}$$

The integral is replaced by a *discrete* sum and there is only a *finite* number N of terms. The sampling instants T_l are usually equidistant, i.e.

$$T_l = l\tau \tag{5.12}$$

where τ is the clock period. In the time-harmonic state, $x(t) = X \exp(j\Omega t)$, $y(t) = Y \exp(j\Omega t)$ and

$$Y(\Omega) = \left(\sum_{l=0}^{N-1} A_l \exp(-j\Omega T_l) \right) X(\Omega) \tag{5.13}$$

which is identical with eqn (5.10).

Comparing this with Fig. 5.1, and taking account of the proportionality between the weight factors A_l and the apertures W_l of the comb, we obtain the following result:

RULE. To the first order in k^2, modulation of the comb reproduces in *amplitude* and in *time* the impulse response of the filter.

By way of example, Fig. 5.1 shows a sequence of apertures w_0, w_1, w_2, w_3, w_4, w_5, w_6. The corresponding impulse response is given in Fig. 5.2.

5.2.1.2   The z-transform

When the sampling instants T_l are equidistant, as in eqn (5.12), it is convenient to put

$$z = \exp(j\Omega\tau) \tag{5.14}$$

The response function $H(z)$ may then be written

$$H(z) = \frac{Y(\Omega)}{X(\Omega)} = \sum_{k=0}^{N-1} A_k z^{-k} = z^{1-N} P(z) \tag{5.15}$$

Up to the factor $z^{-(N-1)}$, this is a polynomial $P(z)$ of degree $N - 1$ in z, which can therefore by characterized by its zeros in the complex plane as well

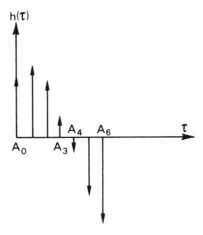

Fig. 5.2 Prototype low-pass impulse response of the comb of Fig. 5.1.

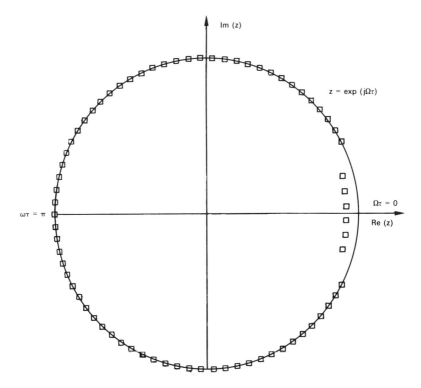

Fig. 5.3 Roots of the polynomial $P(z)$ associated with a low-pass filter.

as by its coefficients A_l. For example, Fig. 5.3 shows the zeros of a low-pass filter (which will be described later as a minimal phase-shift filter).

We can readily verify that the frequency response of Fig. 5.3 is indeed the low-pass response: eqn (5.14) shows that it is sufficient to follow the circumference of the unit circle. Starting with frequency $\Omega = 0$, for which $z = 1$, we observe first the zeros (in the interior of the circle) that correspond to ripples in the pass band response. Next, we find the zeros on the circumference of the circle itself: the polynomial $P(z)$ is then zero and these transmission zeros define the stop band. Since the polynomial has real coefficients, the traversal of more than half of the circle, i.e. when the frequency exceeds one-half of the clock frequency, gives us the complex conjugate image of the upper half-plane. We can therefore determine the response only between zero frequency and one-half of the clock frequency. Moreover, if we continue to go round the circle, we get the same values periodically. This aliasing of the spectrum is characteristic of sampled systems.

Finally, the problem of synthesis of a filter consists of finding the polynomial $P(z)$, described, as we desired, by the impulse response or by the transmission zeros in the complex plane of the filter.

5.2.1.3 Linear phase response

An important simplification is obtained when the impulse response is symmetric about the center of the filter, i.e. when (cf. Fig. 5.4)

$$A_k = A_{N-k-1}$$

In fact, we can then write $H(z)$ in the form

$$H(z) = z^{-(N-1)/2}Q(z) \tag{5.16}$$

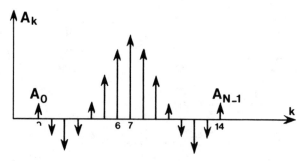

Fig. 5.4 Symmetric impulse response ($N = 15$).

where, if N is even,

$$Q(z) = \sum_{k=0}^{(N-2)/2} A_k(z^{(N-2k-1)/2} + z^{-(N-2k-1)/2}) \tag{5.17}$$

and, if N is odd,

$$Q(z) = \sum_{k=0}^{(N-3)/2} A_k(z^{(N-2k-1)/2} + z^{-(N-2k-1)/2}) + A_{(N-1)/2} \tag{5.18}$$

When z is on the unit circle, each term is a cosine, so that $Q(z)$ is real. The phase of $z^{-(N-1)/2}$ is equal to $(N-1)\omega\tau/2$, and is therefore a linear function of frequency. In other words, the transit time or group delay is seen to be constant and equal to $[(N-1)/2]\tau$. This type of filter is called a *linear phase filter*. The polynomial $P(z)$ has the same roots as $P(1/z)$, so that the roots other than ± 1 appear as pairs z_k, $1/z_k$, or even as groups of four roots z_k, z^*_k, $1/z_k$, $1/z^*_k$, when they are complex and outside the unit circle (Fig. 5.5). This constraint is the counterpart of the symmetry of the coefficients. It is thus very easy to obtain a constant group delay, i.e. independent of frequency and at a value of the order of $N\tau/2$, where τ is the clock period.

5.2.1.4 Minimal phase response

The impulse response of Fig. 5.4 shows that the propagation time corresponds to the passage of the largest coefficient in the middle of the filter (and hence has the value $N\tau/2$). In practice, this time is unfortunately relatively long, often too long to accommodate stringent specifications. However, there is another synthesis in which we are freed from the condition of linear phase. We can show that the minimal group delay is obtained when all the roots of the polynomial $P(z)$ lie in the interior of the unit circle. The diagram of Fig. 5.3 illustrates this case. It is then referred to as the *minimum phase filter*. The impulse response of Fig. 5.6 corresponds to such a filter: we notice immediately that the mean transit time (corresponding approximately to the largest coefficient) is considerably reduced and, moreover, becomes quite similar to the group delay of analog continuous-time filters. Note that it is convenient to add this internal propagation time to the external propagation time (corresponding to the transit time between the input and output transducers).

When a constant group delay is not required, the minimal phase response has additional important advantages: in general, *fewer coefficients* are needed to meet a given frequency response, or equally important, the minimal phase filter is *less sensitive* than the linear phase filter to errors in the coefficients (Feldmann and Hénaff, 1978b).

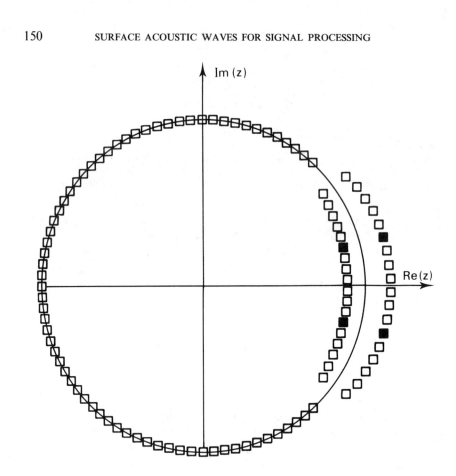

Fig. 5.5   Zeros of a linear-phase low-pass transversal filter.

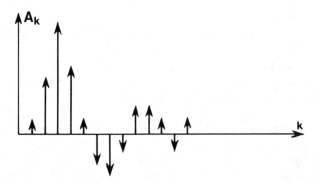

Fig. 5.6   Impulse response typical of the minimal phase filter.

5.2.1.5 Dispersive filters

In a dispersive filter, the amplitude $|H|$ of the required response is constant over the widest possible band. On the other hand, we are interested in the phase, or in the group delay whose variation is fixed. A common case (used in radar pulse compression) involves group delay that is a linear function of frequency

$$\tau_g \approx \tau_g^{\ 0}\,\frac{\omega}{\omega_0} \qquad \omega_1 < \omega < \omega_2$$

We shall see in Section 5.2.4 how this type of surface-wave filter can be conveniently constructed.

5.2.2 Synthesis of transversal filters by the window method

The synthesis of the transfer function of such as a filter, whether it be linear phase, minimal phase or any other, boils down in all cases to the determination of the set of coefficients $A_k(k = 0, 1, \dots, N - 1)$. There are several possible types of synthesis. First we recall that the set of coefficients A_k is simply the impulse response, so that, if we know the impulse response of a continuous time filter, we can sample over N values to synthesize an approximate response that differs to a greater or lesser extent from the original ideal response. More precisely, the sampling amounts to applying a comb with a finite number of fingers to the original function. It can be shown mathematically that the corresponding operation in the frequency domain is a convolution of the ideal response with the Fourier transform of the comb. We call this the "windowing", because the original impulse response is effectively observed through a window, namely, the sampling comb. Thereafter, the synthesis amounts to a choice of a "good" impulse response in conjunction with a "good" window.

5.2.2.1 Choice of windows

An all-pass window, i.e. a comb whose fingers all have the same length, has the disadvantage of leaving "scars", in the form of unwanted high-frequency oscillations in the frequency response. This effect is known as the Gibbs phenomenon and can be overcome by the use of more elaborate windows. As Fig. 5.7 indicates, the resulting response can be considered in the frequency domain as the prototype response regularized by the response of the window. A good window should contain a single lobe, as narrow as possible, and provide good rejection outside this lobe. The width $\delta\omega$ of the lobe is related to the duration ΔT of the impulse response by the well-known

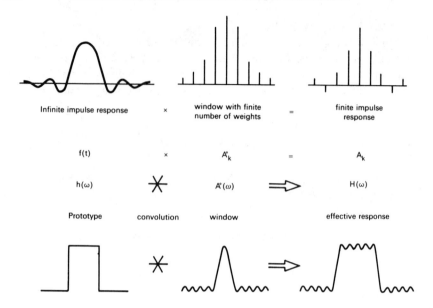

Fig. 5.7 Principle of synthesis by the window method.

uncertainty principle

$$\delta\omega\,\Delta T \approx 1 \qquad (5.19)$$

This shows that, whatever the waveform of the prototype, it is impossible to determine the steepness of the frequency response to better than $\delta\omega$. In a surface-wave transducer, the duration ΔT corresponds directly to the length $v\,\Delta T$ (where v is the velocity of the surface waves). Good frequency selectivity is associated with large dimensions of the crystal.

Hamming's window   Hamming's window (Temes 1962) is obtained by sampling the empirical function

$$y = 0.54 - 0.46\cos x \quad (0 < x < \pi) \qquad (5.20)$$

at

$$x_k = k\pi/(N-1) \quad (k = 0, 1, 2, \ldots, N-1) \qquad (5.21)$$

The advantage of this function, whose frequency response is shown in Fig. 5.8, is basically its great simplicity and acceptable behavior.

Dolph–Chebyshev windows   The Dolph–Chebyshev windows (Dolph 1946; Taylor 1960; Helms 1968) are calculated from the Chebyshev polynomials. They produce an optimum in the following sense: if the number N of weights and the width $\delta\omega$ of the principal lobe are known, these windows

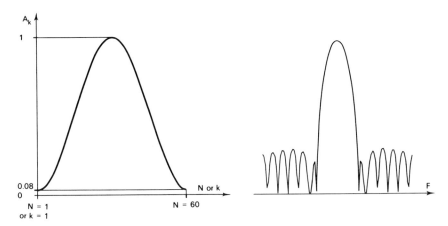

Fig. 5.8 Coefficients and frequency response of the Hamming window.

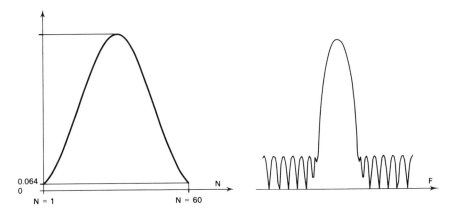

Fig. 5.9 A Dolph–Chebyshev window and its frequency response.

produce the response with the best possible rejection outside the lobe. Conversely, for a given rejection of the secondary lobes, the Dolph–Chebyshev window produces the narrowest possible principal lobe. Figure 5.9 shows the frequency response of such a window. Appendix C, page 309 gives a computer program for generating the corresponding coefficients.

Other windows There is a large number of other possible windows, whose advantages in the synthesis of surface-wave filters have not really be established. Interested readers should consult the literature (Kaiser 1966; Rossi 1967).

5.2.2.2 Symmetric impulse responses

There is an infinity of continuous-time impulse responses that can be used as prototypes, all the more since it is not necessary to limit ourselves to rational functions, nor even to causal impulse responses. When the response of a real bandpass filter is symmetric about the central frequency ω_0 (eqn 5.8), it is simpler to argue in terms of the associated low pass, but we can also synthesize directly a bandpass filter to meet asymmetric frequency responses.

In this section, we shall briefly consider some types of convenient impulse responses.

Rectangular response The null-phase response function defined by

$$H(j\Omega) = \begin{cases} 1 & |\Omega| \leqslant \omega_0 \\ 0 & |\Omega| \geqslant \omega_0 \end{cases} \tag{5.22}$$

has the (infinite) impulse response

$$h(\tau) = \frac{\sin(\omega_0 \tau)}{\tau} \tag{5.23}$$

This is a transcendental function that is symmetric in τ and noncausal (it is nonzero for $\tau < 0$). Its transcendental character is of no importance. To take account of its noncausal character, it is sufficient to center the window on a finite portion of this function.

This response function is perfectly steep: in practice, the selectivity will depend only on the window. It decreases with τ as $1/\tau$, i.e. the effect of truncation will therefore be relatively important because a perceptible fraction of $h(\tau)$ will thus be lost. This defect can be corrected by the use of rational approximations to the rectangle.

Rational responses Consider the noncausal maximally flat response

$$H(s) = \frac{1}{1 - s^2} \tag{5.24}$$

where $s = j\Omega$. This response is a special case of the more general response

$$H(s) = \frac{1}{1 + (-s^2)^n} \tag{5.25}$$

If we know an ordinary analog filter response defined by a *causal rational fraction* $S(s)$, we can generalize further by taking

$$H(s) = S(s)S(-s) \tag{5.26}$$

We shall see in eqn (5.24) that symmetric impulse responses can be deduced from this. In fact

$$H(s) \;=\; \frac{1}{1-s^2} \;=\; \frac{1}{2}\left(\frac{1}{1+s}+\frac{1}{1-s}\right) \;=\; f(s)+f(-s) \quad (5.27)$$

The response $f(s)$ is causal and, in addition, corresponds to the impulse response $\Upsilon(\tau)\exp(-\tau/2)$. The response $f(-s)$ can be interpreted as the same function *reversed in time*. Finally, the impulse response associated with eqn (5.24) is

$$h(\tau) \;=\; 0.5\,\exp(-|\tau|) \quad\quad\quad (5.28)$$

which is similar to eqn (5.23). The advantage of eqn (5.28) lies in its behavior at infinity, i.e. the exponential decrease, which means that truncation will be less drastic in its effect and the final function will be close enough to eqn (5.24). Exploiting the wide panoply of classical analog responses available to us (maximally flat, Chebyshev, elliptic, . . .), we obtain a fairly large variety of responses.

Combs modulated by all or nothing ("withdrawal" method)   A particularly interesting type of impulse response is obtained when it contains only the coefficients $+1$, -1 or 0 (Hartmann 1973). In digital filtering, these responses avoid all explicit multiplication. For surface waves, all the capacitances present have the same aperture (only their *branching* is different: we shall see that it is in general necessary in a two-transducer line that one of them should be of this type).

Consider the usual simple case of a symmetric three-lobe comb (Fig. 5.10). The response of such a transducer is

$$H \;=\; A_1 - 2A_2 \cos\phi \quad\quad\quad (5.29)$$

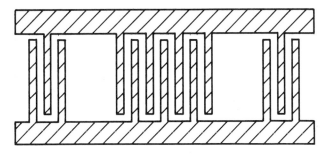

Fig. 5.10 Symmetric three-lobe comb modulated by withdrawal ($N_1 = 6$; $N_2 = 2$; $N_3 = 4$).

Let N_1 be the number of capacitances in the central lobe and N_2 the number of capacitances in each of the secondary lobes, separated from the first lobe by N_3 zero weights.

We have

$$A_1 \approx \frac{\sin N_1 \theta}{N_1} \qquad A_2 \approx \sin \frac{N_2 \theta}{N_2}$$

$$\phi = (2N_3 + N_1 - 3)\theta \quad \text{and} \quad \theta = \omega\tau/2$$

It can be shown that $H = N_1 - N_2$ at the central frequency and, in addition, the shape is maximally flat around this frequency if

$$\phi = N_1 \theta \left(\frac{1 - 2x^3}{24x} \right)^{1/2} \tag{5.30}$$

where

$$x = N_2/N_1$$

5.2.2.3   Minimal-phase impulse response

Apart from the rectangular response that has necessarily a linear phase, we have the same possibilities as in Section 5.2.2.2.

Rational responses   It will be sufficient to start with the response of a traditional causal analog filter $S(s)$ and calculate its impulse response using the inverse Laplace transform. For example, if

$$S(s) = \frac{1}{1 + s} \tag{5.31}$$

we have immediately

$$h(\tau) = \exp(-\tau)\, \Upsilon(\tau) \tag{5.32}$$

Withdrawal transducers   In the case of a two-lobe comb, the response can be written

$$H = A_1 - A_2 \exp(j\phi)$$

If N_1 is the number of capacitances in the central lobe, N_2 the number in the secondary lobe and N_3 the number of intervals between the lobes, we get to the second order in $\theta = \omega\tau/2$

$$|H|^2 \approx (N_1 - N_2)^2 + \tfrac{1}{3}\theta^2[(1 - x)^4 - 12x(a + 1)(a + x)]$$

where

$$x = N_2/N_1 \quad \text{and} \quad a = N_3/N_1$$

The behavior will be flat near the central frequency for a choice of N_1, N_2 and N_3 canceling the coefficient of the term in θ^2.

5.2.3   Algorithmic synthesis

When the number of weights in the comb is limited, it is advantageous to use algorithms devised for the synthesis of digital filters with finite impulse response. The most efficient program, first given by McClellan *et al.*, uses the Remez algorithm, according to which the extrema of the error function between the actual and the desired response are a minimum when they are equal in absolute value and alternate in sign. This program is given in Appendix D, page 313 (McClellan *et al.* 1973).

5.2.4   Phase-modulated filters

The bandwidth of the input transducer can be increased while keeping a sufficient number of fingers in the comb by using a parallel connection of two combs tuned to different frequencies (Fig. 5.11(a)).

We can choose F_1 and F_2 in such a way that the global response is approximately flat, account being taken of the number of fingers in each comb. It is actually more convenient to construct a single input transducer with two sets of fingers extending from the same contact pads (Fig. 5.11(b)). The two configurations give amplitude responses that are approximately the same, but the group propagation time is longer for one of the frequency groups (F_2) than for the other (F_1). We shall see later how this property is used in dispersive filters.

Finally, we can repeat the above procedure so as to have a comb whose maximum emission frequency varies continuously from F_1 to F_2 along the comb (Fig. 5.11(c)). This type of transducer is used particularly in dispersive filters. Such filters are said to be *phase-modulated* (Tancrell and Holland 1971; Hikita *et al.* 1980). For example, we can choose a group delay that is a linear function of frequency.

5.2.5   Double modulation filters

Capacitance *aperture* modulation (amplitude modulation) and *phase* modulation (Section 5.2.4) can of course be added. In practice, we almost always use smooth additional amplitude modulation in the form of the Hamming window or similar (Figs 5.8 and 5.9) to regularize the response of a phase-modulated transducer.

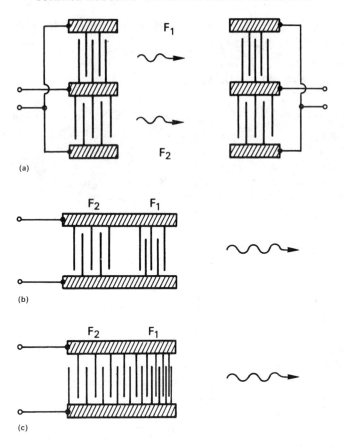

Fig. 5.11 Phase-modulated filters: (a) two parallel connected combs tuned to different frequencies F_1 and F_2; (b) single transducer approximately equivalent to two combs in parallel; (c) single phase-modulated transducer allowing continuous variation of frequency within bandwidth ΔF.

5.2.6   Other modulation procedures

A large number of modulation procedures have been proposed and used with a greater or lesser degree of success. They include amplitude modulation by variation of the distance between adjacent capacitances, multiple sources in the form of groups of capacitances connected in series and in parallel, phase modulation according to laws varying along the transducer and so on (Hikita *et al.* 1980; Yamanouchi *et al.* 1980; Ronnekleiv *et al.* 1973; Lakin *et al.* 1974; Malocha and Hunsinger 1977).

5.3 SWF design based on transversal filters

A surface-wave filter (SWF) consists of at least two transducers: a transmitter and a receiver. In addition, a matching circuit if often connected at the ports. The SWF is thus not only a filter meeting prescribed specification, but also a delay line. It is, of course, essential that the line is "clean", i.e. the useful impedances (active capacitances, radiation resistance) are large in comparison with "parasitic" impedances (parasitic capacitances, resistances of electrodes and so on). A very sophisticated synthesis that includes numerous secondary parameters often lays itself open to catastrophic results, because the parasitic impedances predominate, and we measure only their dispersion. Certain basic rules must therefore be observed.

5.3.1 Design rules

5.3.1.1 Bandwidth

A wide-band filter cannot be designed using an arbitrary material. The integral resistance relation given by eqn (3.15) can be written in the form

$$RC\Delta\omega \sim k^2\pi/2$$

where R is the mean series radiation resistance, C is the piezoelectric capacitance and $\Delta\omega$ is the bandwidth. If ω is the central angular frequency, $1/RC\omega$ can be interpreted as the Q factor of the susceptance $C\omega$.

$$Q = \frac{\omega}{\Delta\omega} \approx \frac{1}{RC\omega}$$

Hence

$$\frac{\Delta\omega}{\omega} \approx k \qquad\qquad (5.33)$$

This order-of-magnitude discussion shows that, in practice, it is very difficult to construct delay lines of relative bandwidth noticeably larger than k. Table 5.1 illustrates this limitation for some commonly used materials.

Table 5.1 Maximum practical bandwidth for different piezoelectric materials (%)

Lithium niobate	25
Lithium tantalate	10
Berlinite	8
Quartz	4
Bismuth germanium oxide	10
Gallium arsenide	3
Indium phosphide	2

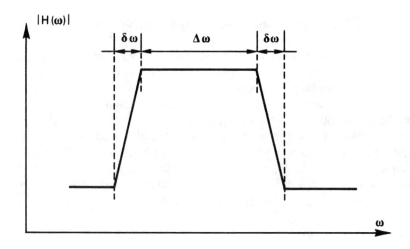

Fig. 5.12   Bandwidth $\Delta\omega$ and selectivity $\delta\omega$ of a filter.

5.3.1.2   Selectivity (cf. Fig. 5.12)

The selectivity $\delta\omega$ of a filter, or more generally, its frequency resolution, is determined by the uncertainty principle

$$T\,\delta\omega \approx 1 \tag{5.34}$$

where T is the total duration of the impulse response. One way of describing this is to say that "selectivity is paid for in centimeters of crystal". It is limited by parasitic capacitances, introduced to produce the small weightings of the tail of the impulse response, and by diffraction phenomena that make them imprecise. In practice, it is difficult to obtain filters for which the shape factor $(1 + 2\delta\omega/\Delta\omega)$ is less than 1.1.

For a line filter with $\delta\omega = \Delta\omega/2$, the width $\delta\omega$ is limited only by the length of the crystal and by higher-order effects, piezoelectric or mechanical, which we shall discuss below.

5.3.1.3   Piezoelectric overcoupling and sampling

We saw in Chapter 4 that, as the number of capacitances in a regular comb increases, the frequency response becomes appreciably distorted by recursive effects in the interior of the transducer. If the number of capacitances is $2N$, these effects become appreciable when

$$Nk^2 \sim 1 \tag{5.35}$$

(cf. Fig. 4.4). This limits the practical number of weights of a regular filter. When high selectivity is required, the weights are no longer introduced at half-wavelengths, but at a whole number $m > 1$ (preferably odd[†]) of half-wavelengths.

In fact, this sampling procedure amounts to working at a harmonic frequency, and the comb has several bandwidths. We select a unique band by sampling the input and output transducers at different values m_1 and m_2. Figure 5.13 shows the response of a regular comb with 40 weights, operating at the fundamental ($m = 1$), and for different samplings ($m = 3$ and 5).

5.3.1.4 Triple transit echo and insertion loss

From the design it is possible to evaluate both the so-called triple transit echo and the insertion loss as functions of the static capacitance of each of the transducers and of the radiation resistance. Actually, the impedance matrix of the filter can be written in terms of $\theta = \omega T$ as follows:

$$[Z] \approx \begin{bmatrix} 1/jC_1\omega + R_0 & R_0 \exp(-j\theta) \\ R_0 \exp(-j\theta) & 1/jC_2\omega + R_0 \end{bmatrix} \tag{5.36}$$

In the absence of matching, the transmittance S_{21} is given by

$$S_{21} = \frac{-2y^2 \exp(-j\theta)}{(1 + 2jy)^2 + y^2 \exp(-2j\theta)} \tag{5.37}$$

where R_0 is the source impedance and $C_1 = C_2 = C$.

We note that the transmittance oscillates as a function of $y = R_0 C\omega$ between the two values (Fig. 5.14)

$$|S_{21}|_{min} = \frac{2y^2}{1 + 5y^2} \tag{5.38}$$

$$|S_{21}|_{max} = \frac{2y^2}{1 + 3y^2} \tag{5.39}$$

The nominal value is

$$|S_{21}|_{nom} = \frac{2y^2}{1 + 4y^2} \tag{5.40}$$

The triple transit echo is given by

$$\frac{|S_{21}|_{max}}{|S_{21}|_{min}} = \frac{1 + 5y^2}{1 + 3y^2} \tag{5.41}$$

5.3.1.5 Mass loading effect

The presence of electrodes on the surface of the piezoelectric crystal produces a discontinuity that is partly due to the increase in inertia at the

[†]To avoid active parasitic capacitances between two successive weightings.

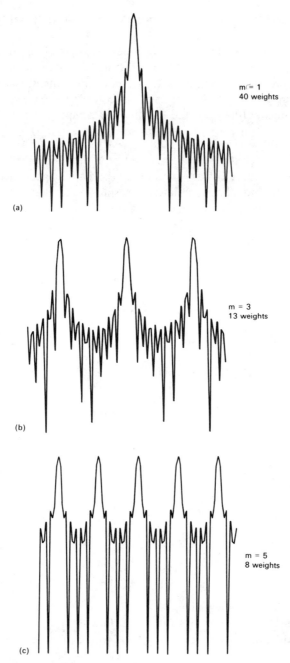

Fig. 5.13   Frequency response of a regular comb for different weights and sampling.

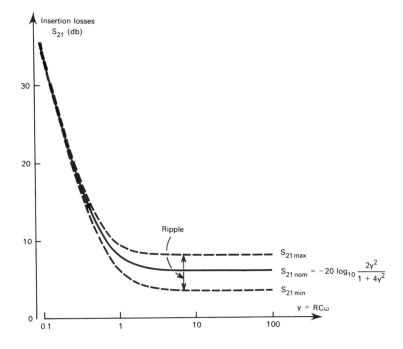

Fig. 5.14 Insertion loss and envelope of ripples due to multiple echoes in a line consisting of two identical regular combs, plotted against $RC\omega$: R = radiation resistance; C = capacitance; ω = central frequency.

interface (mass loading) and partly to its "stiffening". This effect can be evaluated approximately by the perturbation method outlined in Appendix 2.3. The result can be written (Datta and Hunsinger 1979) in the form of a relative change in velocity as a function of the product hK, where h is the thickness of the electrode and $K = 2\pi/\lambda$ is the wave number:

$$\frac{\Delta v}{v} = hK\left(a_1 - \frac{\rho_e}{\rho_p} a_2\right) = \eta hK \qquad (5.42)$$

where ρ_e is the density of the electrode and ρ_p is the density of the substrate. The term a_1 represents the stiffening effect, whereas a_2 describes the sensitivity to the extra load. The latter effect is in general the predominant effect in hard materials such as quartz or berlinite. The stiffening effect predominates in soft materials, such as gallium arsenide and indium phosphide. In practice, this effect should be compared with the change in velocity associated with the piezoelectric effect due to metallization

$$\frac{\Delta v}{v} \approx \frac{k^2}{2} \qquad (5.43)$$

The overloading of the electrodes is thus seen to occur mainly for weakly piezoelectric materials and at high frequencies.

5.3.2   Synthesis

A "clean" delay line having been defined in Section 5.3.1, we have been able to determine the material, the approximate number of weights and the dimensions of the crystal (it is also useful to take into account the dimensions of the packaging units available!).

At this stage the aim of synthesis is to determine the number of weights and to calculate their values. It is often sufficient to use windowing, which enables us rapidly to carry out a certain number of iterations until the target specification is met.

We can choose minimal phase synthesis or linear phase synthesis. A complete program of this kind (GENEFOS) is given in Appendix E, page 322. Program VERIFOS (Appendix F, page 333) enables us to verify the frequency response.

5.3.3   Simulation

The methods described in Chapter 4 are for checking the behavior of the filter as well as for calculating the influence of parasitic elements and, if the case arises, of matching. Program MAREFOS of Appendix G, page 336 implements this simulation. If the design is "clean", this verification stage need not involve a serious departure from what was anticipated. Nevertheless, in general, it implies a negative feedback in the design of the filter, and the result should settle down in one or two iterations.

5.4   Multistrip filters

The filter technology described in Section 5.3 exploits only interdigital transducers. In fact, we can first make a more complicated structure by adding multistrip couplers (MSCs) which improve the response. We can also use more complex multistrip arrays[†] that contribute directly to the response function. Finally, a different technology involving etching or implantation (cf. Chapter 8) enables us to obtain similar results by mechanical reflection. This idea—a reflector—will be taken up again in Section 5.5 to describe other filter designs.

[†]A multistrip reflector array (MRA) or a multistrip transmission array (MTA).

5.4.1 Multistrip array filters

Multistrip arrays can be used to act as filters either on their own, or (most commonly) as complementary filters, or as auxiliary devices.

Multistrip couplers

(a) The MSC is a wide-band device without natural selectivity. First of all, MSCs are used to separate bulk modes from the properly so-called surface mode. In this application, they suppress undesirable responses over the attenuated band and thus improve the *rejection of the filter*.

(b) The second application of the coupler is in shaping the wavefront: when two apodized transducers are placed face to face, the resultant response function is not equal to the product of the individual response functions, since some combinations of the weights of the two combs are not taken into account. However, the interposition of a coupler (Fig. 5.15) that collects all

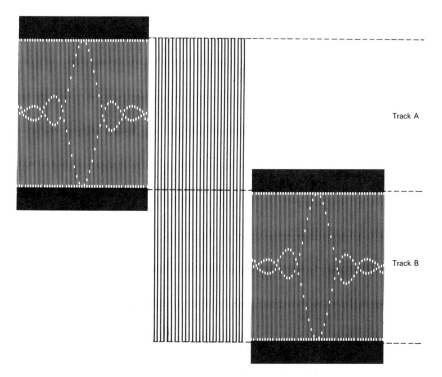

Fig. 5.15 Series connection of two apodized transducers.

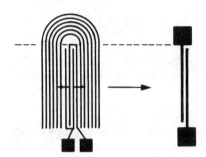

Fig. 5.16   Unidirectional MSC transducer (Marschall *et al.* 1971).

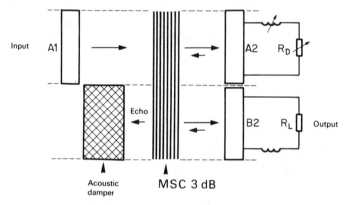

Fig. 5.17   Elimination of the triple echo (Marschall 1972).

the waves emitted by the first comb, and transmits them over the entire aperture of the second comb, compensates for this disadvantage. It is thus easy to *balance the apodizations of the two transducers*, so that the resultant response is equal to the product of the individual responses. The result is an improvement in the *selectivity* of the filter, since we then have at our disposal a greater number of weights (Marschall *et al.* 1973a).

(c) In the third application, the MSC is used to reduce triple transit echoes by various artifices: the transfer function between track A and track B is $j/\sqrt{2}$ when the number of strips is $N_{\text{opt}}/2$ (cf. Section 4.4.3.3). We can thus construct a unidirectional transducer by using a U-coupler (Marschall *et al.* 1971) (cf. Fig. 5.16) or collect the output signal on the transducer B2 of a pair (A2, B2) placed over the two paths (Marschall 1972) (cf. Fig. 5.17). This has the effect of eliminating echoes between the two ports. The matching of the transducers is critical.

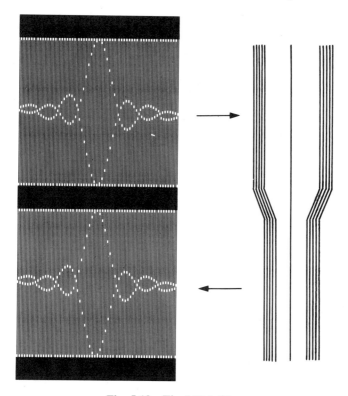

Fig. 5.18 The MRA filter.

MRA couplers

The use of MRA (Fig. 5.18) is advantageous in terms of the length of the crystal. The array has a natural selectivity, and the input and output transducers can be apodized simultaneously. The advantages of the MSC as regards the cancelation of bulk waves remain equally valuable.

A particular application of the MRA as a dispersive filter (the strips not being equidistant), enables us to make full use of the length of the crystal for long integration times (cf. Fig. 5.19).

MTA couplers

The MTA (Fig. 5.20) can be used (just like the MRA) as a complementary filter in a delay line with two apodized transducers. It is better adapted to wide-band devices and, in addition, there is a continuity between MSC and MTA (Feldmann and Hénaff 1977b; Solie 1977).

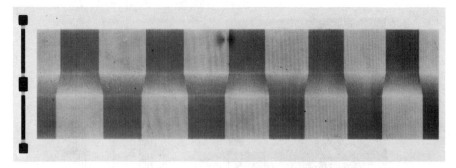

Fig. 5.19 Photograph of a dispersive MRA filter.

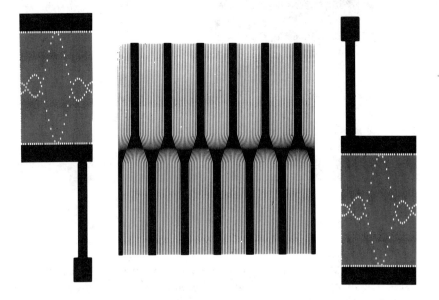

Fig. 5.20 MTA filter.

5.4.2 Slanted reflector array filters

A metallic layer deposited at an angle in the path of the acoustic wave produces partial reflection that can be collected by a second slanted reflector (Fig. 5.21).

In fact, there are reflectors other than in the form of the simple metal deposit. We can etch grooves or implant ions with the same result (these technologies will be described in Chapter 8).

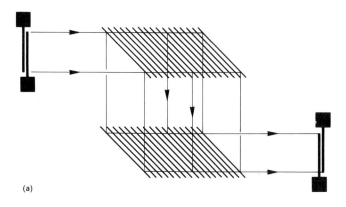

(a)

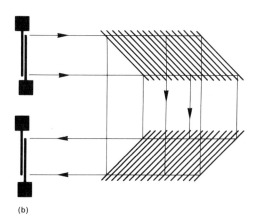

(b)

Fig. 5.21 Successive reflections by two slanted tracks: (a) without folding; (b) with folding.

The particular advantage of the etched groove is that it enables us to modulate the reflection coefficient. To the first approximation, the reflection coefficient A_k of groove number k is proportional to its depth h_k (or to the thickness of the deposited layer). The reflected wave $y(t)$ is given by

$$y(t) = \sum_{k=0}^{N-1} A_k x(t - \tau_k) \tag{5.44}$$

where $x(t)$ is the incident signal, τ_k is the differential delay due to groove k, and

$$A_k \approx K h_k \tag{5.45}$$

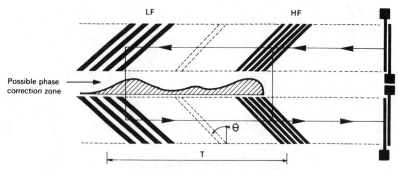

Fig. 5.22 Grooved dispersive filter.

$K = 2\pi/\lambda$ is the wave number and h_k is the thickness or depth. We can also modulate the reflection coefficient by varying the length W_k of the groove.

This type of filter has the disadvantage that it requires a supplementary step of technology. Moreover, the insertion loss is somewhat higher. By way of compensation, it has the following advantages:

(a) in principle, a nonpiezoelectric substrate can be employed;

(b) temperature compensation can be effected by a judicious choice of the two directions of propagation;

(c) dispersive filters are easy to fabricate (as indicated in Fig. 5.22) and there is the additional possibility of correcting the frequency-phase curve;

(d) photoetching is relatively easy (one groove per wavelength), and is not critical (a localized flaw has a slight influence on the response function).

5.5 Resonator filters

The design of the above filters is ultimately similar to that of digital filters. It is only more recently that the surface-wave resonator has been suggested as a means of simulating traditional analog filters. In practice, we can synthesize in this way only filters with very narrow bandwidth of low equivalent order (Coldren and Rosenberg 1979; Shreve 1975). The resonator has found its application more in the development of oscillators (cf. Chapter 6).

5.5.1 The concept of the resonator

5.5.1.1 Surface-wave reflector

Inductance We have already described in Chapter 4 (Section 4.3.3.1) how the ideal selective reflector could be constructed by placing a tuned inductance across a transducer (eqn 4.91). In practice, it is difficult to obtain appreciable reflection coefficients (> 0.7–0.8) in this way because of the resistance of the fingers and the finite Q of the inductance. In addition, the matching frequency depends on the thermal coefficient of the inductance.

Printed or grooved circuits   Actually, a comb (short-circuited or not), or simply a grooved circuit (as we have indicated in Section 5.4 above), is a relatively efficient surface-wave reflector. To evaluate these effects, we use a simplified model in which a scalar wave is reflected by a refracting medium. Let the velocity of the "free" surface waves be v_a and let the velocity perturbed by a layer or by a groove be $v_p = v_a + \Delta v_a$. The reflection coefficient can be defined by

$$r = \frac{v_p - v_a}{v_p + v_a} \approx \frac{\Delta v_a}{2v_a} \tag{5.46}$$

In general, Δv_a can be written as a function of the thickness h of the layer and of the wave number K as follows:

$$\frac{\Delta v_a}{v_a} \approx hK\eta$$

where η is calculated by a perturbation method as in Appendix 2.3.

Taking a groove of width $\lambda/4$, we find that the reflection coefficient per groove is as listed in Table 5.2. Reflection coefficients of the order of 0.9–0.95 can be obtained in this way for a few hundred grooves (conversion to bulk waves prevents us from exceeding these values).

5.5.1.2   One-port resonator

When a single transducer is inserted between two reflectors, it constitutes a one-port resonator as in Fig. 5.23.

Table 5.2   Reflectance per element (u) for small values of hK (the reflection coefficient is $r = ju \sin Ka$ where a is the length of the array)

Reflecting element	Material	Cut	Propagation	Reflectivity u
Metallic strip (Al)	Quartz	ST	X	$0.507\,h/\lambda$[a]
Metallic strip (Au)	Quartz	ST	X	$1.3\quad h/\lambda$[b]
Groove	Quartz	ST	X	$0.636\,h/\lambda$[a]
Groove filled with metal (Au)	Quartz	ST	X	$3\quad h/\lambda$[b]
Isolated metallic line (Al)	LiNbO$_3$	Y	Z	0.011[b]
Connected metallic line (Al)	LiNbO$_3$	Y	Z	0.018[b]
Groove	LiNbO$_3$	Y	Z	$0.678\,h/\lambda$[a]

[a] Datta and Hunsinger (1979).
[b] Dunnrowicz *et al.* (1976).

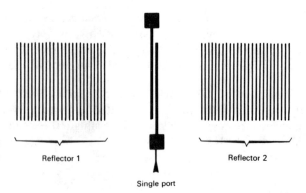

Reflector 1   Reflector 2

Single port

Fig. 5.23   One-port resonator.

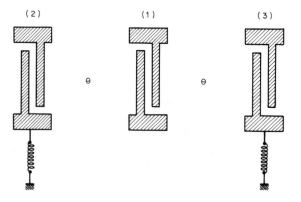

Fig. 5.24   Model of one-port resonator tuned with an inductance.

We can determine the input impedance of the dipole by assuming, for simplicity, that each of the reflectors is tuned by an inductance (Section 4.3.3.1).

The reader may wish to carry out the calculation as an exercise (Fig. 5.24).

We thus obtain a pure reactance at the resonance frequency. In practice, this procedure leads to a somewhat inconvenient synthesis because the resistance of the fingers is quite large in comparison with the characteristic impedance of the resonator. The actual driving point reactance is commonly capacitive at all frequencies! Accordingly, we generally use the ideas as given under the headings below.

5.5.1.3   Two-port network in the inside of a resonant cavity

We can place two transducers in the inside of a cavity. In the neighborhood of the resonance frequency, we then have transmission between the two

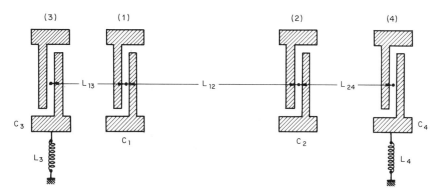

Fig. 5.25 Two-port resonator tuned with an inductance.

transducers, whereas the surface waves escape from the cavity well away from this frequency. The position of the transducers inside the cavity is critical. In particular, it depends on the sign of the reflection coefficient r in eqn (4.46). The two transducers must be in phase with the internal pattern of stationary waves.

EXAMPLE. Consider the reflectors loaded by inductances as in Fig. 5.25, and let L_{12}, L_{13}, and L_{24} be the distances between the transducers, where the two-port network consists of ports (1) and (2) in the figure. It can be shown that L_{13} and L_{24} must be minimal and equal to a quarter of a wavelength (modulo integral number of wavelengths), whereas L_{12} must be a maximum

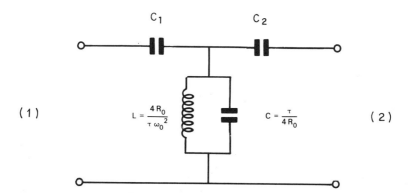

Fig. 5.26 Equivalent circuit of a two-port resonator inside a cavity (in the absence of a reflector, the rejector circuit would be replaced by the radiation resistance R_0).

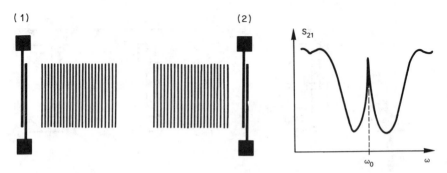

Fig. 5.27 Two-port network resonator with ports outside the cavity, and its frequency response.

and equal to half a wavelength (modulo integral number of wavelengths). If we denote by τ the transit time between transducers (3) and (4), we can show that in the neighborhood of the resonance frequency ω_0 we have the equivalent circuit of Fig. 5.26, where R_0 is the radiation resistance of the line (an analogous circuit, more classical but less convenient, can be obtained by the star–triangle transformation (Feldmann 1981, p. 165)).

5.5.1.4 Two-port network outside resonator cavity

We can also place the ports outside the cavity as in Fig. 5.27. The response of this configuration can be determined by analogy with the Fabry–Pérot *étalon* in optics: each array is replaced by a localized mirror, and the result is a periodic response whose frequency is limited in practice by the input transducers and the selectivity of the mirrors.

5.5.2 Filter synthesis

We can start with the equivalent circuit of a given configuration and insert the acoustic component into a traditional analog filter circuit (Feldmann 1981). In practice, this is only of theoretical value, because a number of significant effects have not been taken into account (resistance of the fingers, various losses, bulk waves), and most published systems are confined to stimulate a suitable single-cell analog filter conveniently matched.

Finally, it is worth noting an interesting procedure, involving piezoelectric coupling between two resonators, described by Rosenberg and Coldren (1976), and using an MSC (Section 4.4.3 and Fig. 5.28).

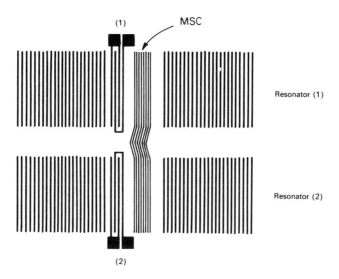

Resonator (1)

Resonator (2)

(2)

Fig. 5.28 Filter with resonators coupled by an MSC (Coldren *et al.* 1977).

Significant results have also been obtained by connecting in series several filters consisting of two-port resonators with ports inside the cavity (Cross *et al.* 1975).

5.6   Multiphase filters

The principle of multiphase transducers enables us to obtain unidirectional wide-bandwidth responses. The idea consists of placing three sources at least per wavelength, each of the sources being phased according to the traveling surface wave. Let

$$\alpha = \exp(-2j\pi/3) \qquad (5.47)$$

in the case of a three-phase transducer with three weights per wavelength, the weights at first being supposed equal. Then, if the signals applied to (1), (2) and (3) are phase shifted by 0, $2\pi/3$ and $-2\pi/3$ respectively, the cumulative signal obtained at (1) (point A in Fig. 5.29) after propagation is proportional to

$$1 + \alpha\alpha^* + \alpha^3 = 3 \qquad (5.48)$$

A delay of one-third of a wavelength corresponds to a phase factor of α.

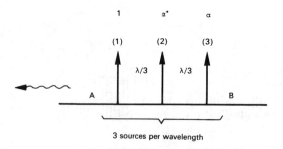

Fig. 5.29 Three-phase transducer: there is no radiation at B.

On the other hand, the signal obtained at B in Fig. 5.29 is

$$\alpha^2 + \alpha\alpha^* + \alpha = 0 \tag{5.49}$$

so that all the radiation is sent back to A.

While the principle of this method is simple, its implementation calls for two levels of circuitry separated by an insulator. This technology, used by Texas Instruments (Hays and Hartmann 1976), is illustrated in Fig. 5.30. It will be dealt with more fully in Chapter 8.

Three-phase electrical control presents no real problem, but increases the cost of the operation. As far as synthesis is concerned, it leads to non-recursive digital filters, at least as long as the weights are positive. The

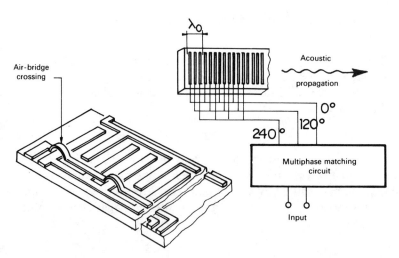

Fig. 5.30 Implementation of three-phase transducers (from Hays and Hartmann 1976).

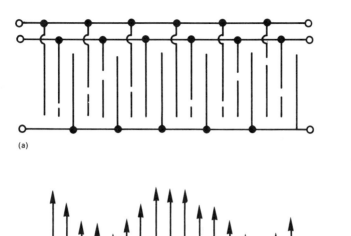

Fig. 5.31 Modulated three-phase transducer: (a) schematic; (b) weights.

topology of the connections also imposes certain constraints in the form of inequalities (cf. Fig. 5.31).

The calculation itself is carried out as follows. Let

$$\omega = \omega_0 + \Omega$$

If τ is the transit time between two successive sources, we can define ω_0 by

$$\omega_0 \tau = 2\pi/3$$

We can then verify that, as in Section 5.1.2 above, we obtain the equivalent of a low-pass filter in Ω (eqn 5.10).

5.7 Applications

We shall now enumerate some significantly successful applications of SWFs.

The first frequency filters to be used effectively in a professional way were carrier filters in carrier current telephone systems. The characteristics (good selectivity, least restrictive shape factors) called for a design free from problems (regular combs), allowing concentration on technological difficulties (Seguin *et al.* 1979).

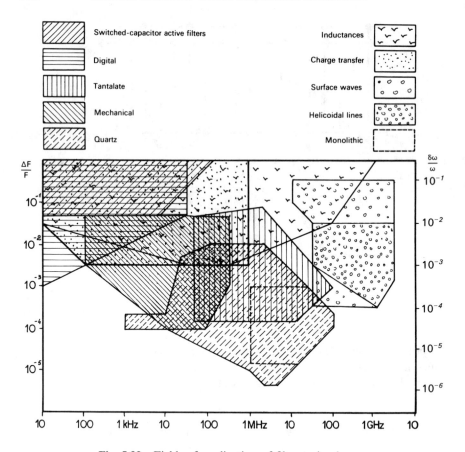

Fig. 5.32 Fields of application of filter technology.

Surface-wave filters are now used throughout their entire useful range. It is convenient to represent filter technology on the $(F, \Delta F)$ plane, where F is the central frequency and ΔF represents, on the one hand, the useful bandwidth and, on the other, the transition band δF of the filter (i.e. its selectivity). For each technology the two points must appear in a characteristic zone of the diagram (Fig. 5.32). This representation places surface-wave technology among all the technologies that are possible in the range between low frequencies and 2–3 GHz. The bandwidth ΔF is shown on the left-hand scale and the selectivity δF on the right.

It is useful to split up more precisely the zone between 30 MHz and 3 GHz, taking account of the principal materials used (quartz, lithium niobate, lithium tantalate, etc.) and the principal technologies (interdigital combs,

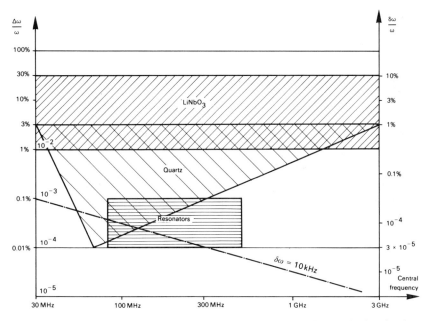

Fig. 5.33 Detail of Fig. 5.31 illustrating the choice of materials and of technology for different characteristics of the filter.

grooves, resonators). This is attempted in Fig. 5.33 which must be treated with caution because it does not take account of possible complexities of a particular implementation and is therefore to an extent rather arbitrary.

We recall that, at present, the optimum frequency of the SWF is around 70–100 MHz. The best-known commercial filter (the IF television filter)

Table 5.3 Performance of SAW filters

	Present limits	Typical values	Foreseeable limits
Central frequency	10 MHz–4.4 GHz	10 MHz–2 GHz	6 GHz
Bandwidth	50 kHz–$0.7F_0$	100 kHz–$0.5F_0$	$0.8F_0$
Minimum insertion loss	2 dB	3–20 dB	1 dB
Minimum shape factor	1.2	1.5	1.2
Minimum transition band	50 kHz	100 kHz	20 kHz
Rejection	60 dB	50 dB	70 dB
Phase difference/linear phase	$\pm 1°$	$\pm 2°$	$\pm 0.5°$
Ripples	0.01 dB	0.05–0.5 dB	0.01 dB

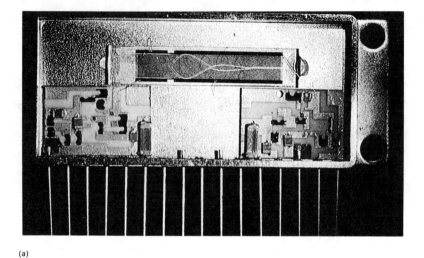

(a)

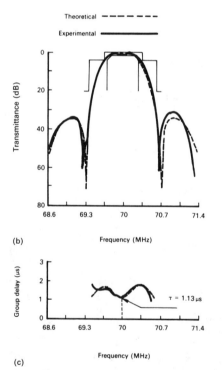

(b)

(c)

Fig. 5.34 Carrier recovery filter; Example (Hénaff and Brossard 1981). (a) Photograph of the device (dimensions of quartz crystal 25 × 5 × 1 mm); (b) theoretical and experimental transmittance; (c) theoretical and experimental group delay.

Table 5.4   Filter for carrier recovery in digital space communications, using phase-shift-keying modulation

Central frequency	70 MHz
Passband at 3 dB	700 kHz
Relative passband	1%
Insertion loss	25 dB
Rejection	35 dB
Piezoelectric material	*ST-X* quartz
Type of transducer and	Double-electrode fingers,
nature of modulation	amplitude modulation, noncausal
Form of amplitude response as	Rectangular
a function of frequency	
Form of phase response as	Minimal phase-shift
a function of frequency	

Source: CNET, Issy-les-Moulineaux, France.

corresponds to $\omega_0 = 30$ MHz with $\Delta\omega/\omega_0 \simeq 30\%$ and $\delta\omega/\omega_0 \simeq 1\%$. Its design is relatively delicate.

Table 5.3 indicates the present and the foreseeable performance of the SWF. The limits shown obviously cannot all be attained simultaneously: each implementation requires a compromise between the different parameters.

EXAMPLE 1. *Carrier filter*. Table 5.4 describes a selective filter obtained by weighting the fingers of a transducer. Its central frequency is relatively optimal for maximum performance and reproducibility. This filter (Fig. 5.34) is placed in a *phase-locked loop*, which means that the group delay must be reduced so that the locking region is as large as possible. The filter is therefore synthesized as a minimal phase filter.

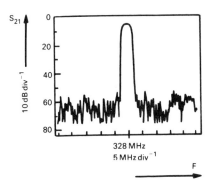

Fig. 5.35   Low-loss filter; Example (Hartmann *et al.* 1982).

Table 5.5 Intermediate frequency filter in a TV receiver. This filter is placed at the front end of the receiver: it has low insertion loss

Central frequency	328 MHz
Passband at 3 dB	3 MHz
Relative passband	0.9%
Insertion loss	6 dB
Rejection	50 dB
Piezoelectric material	*ST-X* quartz
Type of transducer and nature of modulation	3-phase unidirectional, phase modulation and withdrawal electrodes
Form of amplitude response as a function of frequency	rectangular ⎫ The design compensates for
Form of phase response as a function of frequency	linear ⎬ both TV set components and ⎭ TV transmitter predistortion

Source: Texas Inst., Dallas, USA.

EXAMPLE 2. *Low-loss filter*. Table 5.5 describes a filter (Fig. 5.35) with relatively low-loss (6 dB) and very small ripple within the passband, using the three-phase technique of Texas Instruments. Note that this performance is obtained at a relatively high cost (complicated technology, air bridges and multiphase excitation network).

EXAMPLES 3 AND 4. *High-frequency linear phase filters*. Of the following two examples with central frequency in the neighborhood of 1.5 GHz, one is of Japanese origin (cf. Table 5.6, Fig. 5.36) and the other American (cf. Table 5.7, Fig. 5.37). The poor insertion loss characteristics are due to the use of the SSBW mode by the Japanese, but better temperature stability is achieved.

Table 5.6 Filter for clock recovery for digital optical-fiber communications at $1.6 \, \text{Gbit s}^{-1}$

Central frequency	1.598 GHz
Passband at 3 dB	1.9 MHz
Relative passband	$1.2 \, 10^{-3}$
Insertion loss	24 dB
Rejection	50 dB
Piezoelectric material	$AT\text{-}\perp X$ quartz (SSBW mode)
Type of transducer and nature of modulation	Double electrode for 3rd harmonic operation
Form of amplitude response as a function of frequency	$\sin x/x$
Form of phase response as a function of frequency	Linear

Source: NTT, Musashino-shi, Tokyo, Japan.

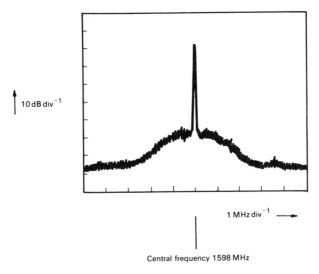

Fig. 5.36 Clock recovery filter; Example (Yamada *et al.* 1980).

EXAMPLE 5. *Very high frequency filter.* At 2.2 GHz and using the third harmonic, the device from Thomson-CSF shows that we can still obtain very acceptable performance as regards both rejection *and* phase distortion (Table 5.8 and Fig. 5.38).

EXAMPLE 6. *Pulse compression filter.* Consider a dispersive filter of length L, with linear modulation of group delay time between F_1 and F_2 (cf. Fig. 5.39).

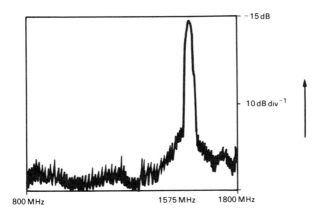

Fig. 5.37 *L*-band filter; Example (Potter and MacDonald 1981).

Table 5.7 *L*-band filter for the GPS (global positioning system) receiver. This filter is set in personal receivers (advantages: small dimensions and weight, as well as low price due to mass production)

Central frequency	1575.4 MHz
Passband at 3 dB	18 MHz
Relative passband	1.1%
Insertion losses	15 dB
Rejection	55 dB
Piezoelectric material	*ST-X* quartz
Type of transducer and nature of modulation	Unidirectional "group weighting", amplitude and withdrawal modulation
Form of amplitude response as a function of frequency	Rounded rectangle
Form of phase response as a function of frequency	Linear: $\Delta\psi < \pm 3°$ in the 1 dB bandwidth

Source: Texas Inst., Dallas, USA.

If the input transducer is short (a few fingers), and if we inject a short pulse at the input, we obtain at the output a signal of roughly constant amplitude and of duration $T = v_a/L$, whose "instantaneous frequency" varies from F_1 to F_2. Such a "chirp" signal is used in modern radars as a reference signal to increase the product $BT = (F_2 - F_1)T$ to some hundreds or thousands. A possible echo can be detected by sending the received signal

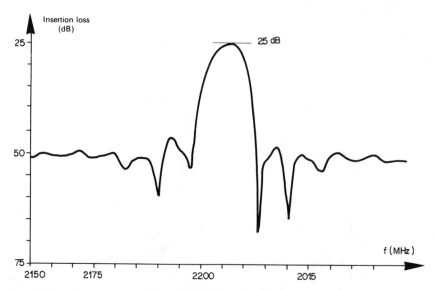

Fig. 5.38 Third harmonic of a SSBW delay line with double-electrode structure; Example (Thomson-CSF/DASM 1982).

Table 5.8 Narrow band filter for an oscillator used in radio links or space communications

Central frequency	2.2 GHz
Passband at 3 dB	7 MHz
Relative passband	0.32%
Insertion losses	25 dB
Rejection	25 dB
Piezoelectric material	AT-$\perp X$ (SSBW mode)
Type of transducer and nature of modulation	Double electrode for operation on 3rd harmonic and grooved reflectors
Form of amplitude response as a function of frequency	$\sin x/x$
Form of phase response as a function of frequency	Linear: $\Delta\psi \leqslant \pm 2°$

Source: Thomson-CSF, Cagnes-sur-Mer, France. Subcontract CNET.

through a filter that is similar but has its tuned frequency varying in the reverse direction, i.e. from F_2 to F_1 (we can take account of the Doppler effect by modifying these frequencies).

Figure 5.40 shows the amplitude response of a filter of this kind, studied by the Department of Specialized Acoustic Techniques at Thomson-CSF/DASM. This filter has the characteristics given in Table 5.9.

Figure 5.41 illustrates the technology of dispersive groove filters on YZ lithium niobate with a central frequency of 125 MHz, dispersion of 30 µs and useful bandwidth of 30 MHz.

EXAMPLE 7. *Intermediate-frequency TV filter*. The vast majority of color television receivers are now equipped with intermediate frequency (IF)

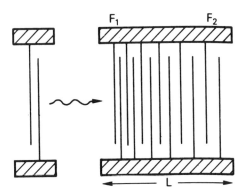

Fig. 5.39 Schematic diagram of a dispersive filter.

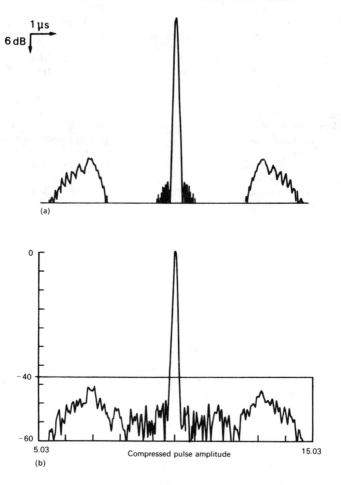

Fig. 5.40 Amplitude response of a dispersive filter on quartz, comprising a short transducer and a dispersive interdigital transducer: (a) theory; (b) experimental results (in the absence of the Doppler effect).

Table 5.9 Characteristics of a dispersive Thomson-CSF Filter (DASM 85/001/084 JYD) (Nonlinear frequency modulation; dispersion 5 μs; central frequency 75 MHz; useful frequency bandwidth $B = 15.4$ MHz; two combs deposited on quartz: one short, one dispersive; application: pulse compression)

	Without Doppler	With Doppler ± 120 kHZ
$\tau - 35\,dB/\tau - 4\,dB$	2.876	2.84
Level of sidelobes (dB)	42.7	38
Mismatch loss (dB)	0.9	0.927

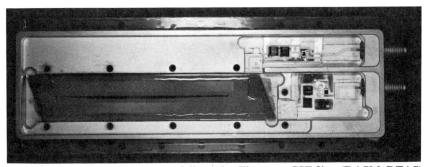

Fig. 5.41   Photograph of a grooved dispersive Thomson-CSF filter (DASM–DTAS).

surface-wave filters. Depending on the standards adopted and on the particular country, the characteristics differ for video and sound frequencies, and bandwidth and group delay. Each manufacturer offers at least 10 filters meeting these different specifications. The largest producers are in Japan (Toshiba, who report sales of 1.5×10^6 units per month, and Murata, who use thin films of ZnO as piezoelectric material). In Europe, Plessey and, especially, Siemens are the most important suppliers.

Example 7 is taken from the Toshiba TV–IF family. It deals with the F1028A with SECAM specifications, intended for France (video frequency of

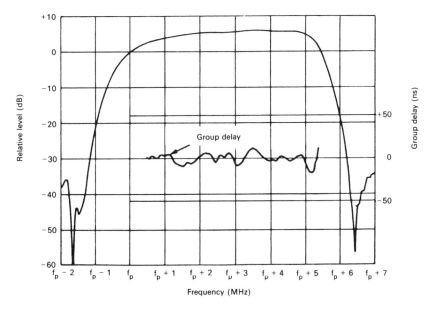

Fig. 5.42   Amplitude and group delay response of the F1028A filter.

Table 5.10 Television IF filter

		Min	Typical	Max	
Relative level	f_p + 11.15 (43.85 MHz)	—	−38	−32	dB
	f_p + 8.0 (40.7 MHz)	—	−38	−31	dB
	f_p + 6.5 (39.2 MHz)	—	−40	−34	dB
	f_p + 5.3 (38.0 MHz)	+2.7	+4.4	+6.1	dB
	f_p + 3.3 (36.0 MHz)	+5.8	+7.3	+8.8	dB
	f_p (32.7 MHz)	—	0	—	dB
	f_p − 1.5 (31.2 MHz)	—	−40	−35	dB
Ripples*		—	0.4	0.9	dB peak to peak
TCF		—	−18	−25	ppm K^{-1}
Spurious level[a] (8.7–32.7 MHz, 42.7–58.7 MHz)		—	−35	−25	dB
Input impedance	Rai (36 MHz)	—	16	—	kΩ
	Ci (1 MHz)	—	11.7	—	pF
	Rei (36 MHz)	—	5	—	Ω
Output impedance	Rao (36 MHz)	—	6	—	kΩ
	Co (1 MHz)	—	10.3	—	pF
	Reo (36 MHz)	—	3	—	Ω

*Using the measurement circuit described below.

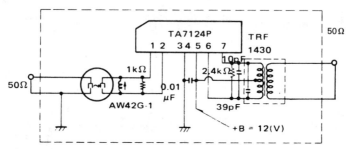

32.7 MHz). Its principal characteristics are summarized in Table 5.10. The choice of lithium tantalate as the substrate (X − 112°, Y) means that this filter has a small temperature coefficient and gives rise to few spurious signals.

Figure 5.42 shows a typical response of this filter in amplitude and in group delay (f_p = 32.7 MHz).

Matrix linear transformations Beyond the simple single-input, single-output filter, it is possible to use surface waves to effect more general transformations with several inputs X_i and/or several outputs Y_j.

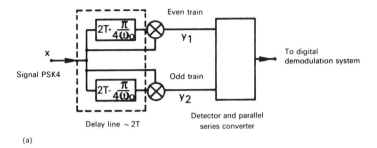

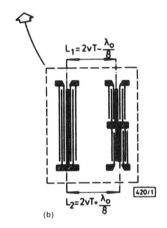

Fig. 5.43 PSK4 differential demodulator: (a) block diagram; (b) phase-shift cell (the transducers are unidirectional to avoid spurious reflections).

EXAMPLE 8. *Differential surface-wave demodulator for digital phase-shift-keyed signals.* This demodulator contains a unit with one input and two outputs out of phase by $\pi/2$ in four-phase shift-keyed modulation (PSK4). The demodulator (Fig. 5.43) (Hénaff *et al.* 1977) can be developed by phase shifting two delay lines by a quarter of a wavelength.

EXAMPLE 9. *Multidifferential demodulator for digital phase-shift-keyed signals.* Similarly, we can have one input and, for example, six outputs for a triple-differential system (Hénaff *et al.* 1977) (Fig. 5.44).

EXAMPLE 10. *Hadamard transformer.* In image processing, we are led to consider transformations of the video signal $i(t)$ of the form

$$I = [H]\,i$$

where i is the vector $i(t)$, $i(t - \tau)$, $i(t - 2\tau), \ldots, i(t - n\tau)$, τ being the sampling time and $[H]$ a $n \times n$ matrix called the Hadamard matrix of order

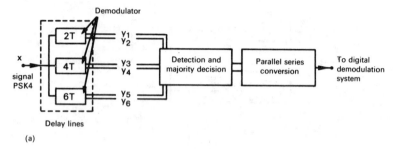

(a)

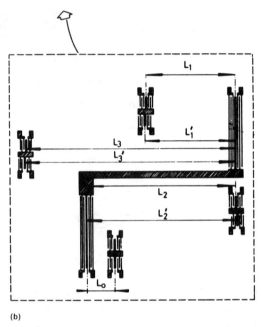

(b)

Fig. 5.44 PSK4—Triple-differential demodulator: (a) block diagram; (b) phase shifting cell: one-double input and six differential outputs.

n, characterized by the fact that it contains only components equal to ± 1. For example, the matrix of order 4 is

$$[H_4] = \begin{bmatrix} 1 & 1 & 1 & 1 \\ -1 & 1 & -1 & 1 \\ -1 & -1 & 1 & 1 \\ 1 & -1 & -1 & 1 \end{bmatrix}$$

This transformation is readily implemented by a sequence of identical taps connected in phase or out of phase depending on the sign to be reproduced

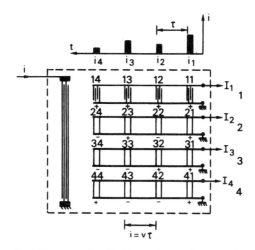

Fig. 5.45 Diagram of a Hadamard transformer of order 4.

(Fig. 5.45). This implementation is described in (Hénaff 1973) for processing videophone signals.

EXAMPLE 11. *UHF low-loss SAW filter.* For applications at the front end of modern UHF communication receivers (900 MHz band) in-line acoustically coupled two-pole SAW resonator filters can be used. This type of filter was originally developed by Siemens in Munich, West Germany (Zibis 1986) (see Table 5.11).

Table 5.11 UHF low-loss SAW filters

	Example a	Example b
Center frequency	914.5 MHz	914.5 MHz
Bandwidth (1 dB)	1.5 MHz	> 2.5 MHz
Bandwidth (30 dB)	< 20 MHz	40 MHz
Passband ripple	< 1 dB	< 1 dB
Insertion loss	< 6 dB	< 2 dB
Out-of-band rejection	> 45 dB	
Piezoelectric substrate	*ST*-cut quartz	*X*-cut 112.2° LiTaO$_3$
Transducer design	Fingergroups staggered in phase in the resonators	*X*-cut 112.2° LiTaO$_3$
Remarks	Excellent temperature stability	Allows self-matched filters
	Trap at 21.4 MHz below the center frequency for good image suppression in receivers with 10.7 MHz first $\perp$F	

EXAMPLE 12. *Saw notch filter*. Notch filter circuits are widely used in RF equipment. For example, the IF stages of RF receivers often use notch filters to eliminate discrete frequency regions where unwanted carriers appear from adjacent channel signals. The cable television industry uses millions of notch filters annually for providing access to premium signals to paying subscribers while denying access to basic service subscribers. Notch filters are used in satellite receivers to eliminate interference from terrestrial microwave signals. These filters are also used widely in RF transmitters to remove internally generated spurious signals from the output. They were developed by Hartmann Research Inc. and R.F. Monolithics in Dallas, Texas, USA.

SAW notch filters are based on quadrature hybrid couplers or on bridged-T all-pass networks. The demonstrated capabilities of these two kinds of SAW-based notch filters (quartz design) are summarized in Table 5.12 and compared with conventional LC circuits.

EXAMPLE 13. *High-performance SAW filters for cellular radio*. High-performance SAW filters with low insertion loss, sharp cut-off frequency response and high sidelobe suppression are becoming essential for RF circuit integration in communication equipment such as mobile telephone transceivers. Hikita *et al.* (1984) have designed SAW filters for this application and have realized a SAW antenna duplexer in the 800–900 MHz range. These filters use a new phase weighting technique and feature a laterally repeated structure implementing image–impedance connected interdigital transducers (IDTs), a $LiTaO_3$ substrate, a 36° *Y*-cut, *X*-propagating, surface shear wave with high k^2 (5%) and a rather good temperature coefficient (28 ppm °C^{-1}).

Table 5.12 SAW notch filters

	Bridged-T	Quad-hybrid	L–C
Passband width	> 10 : 1	Limited by quad-hybrid	> 10 : 1
Passband loss	< 2 dB	< 2 dB	< 2 dB
Stop band rejection	> 40 dB	> 20 dB	> 40 dB
Shape factor (3–30 dB)	2 : 1	2 : 1	30 : 1
Max stop band width	0.05%	1.5%	—
Min. frequency	150 MHz	150 MHz	< 1 MHz
Max. frequency	1.5 GHz	1.5 GHz	150 MHz

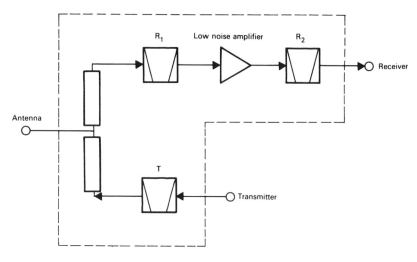

Fig. 5.46 Block diagram of antenna duplexer.

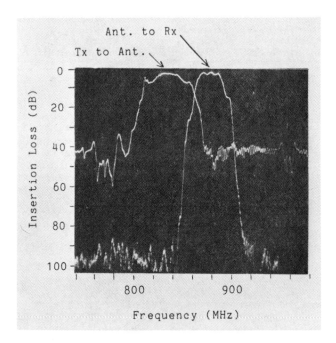

Fig. 5.47 Fundamental experimental results of SAW antenna duplexer for portable telephone transceiver (Hikita *et al.* 1984).

Figure 5.46 shows a block diagram for an antenna duplexer using two SAW filters (R_1 and R_2) in the receiver part and one SAW filter (T) in the transmitter part. Results are shown on Fig. 5.47; the losses of R_1, R_2 and T are approximately 2.5, 4 and 2 dB respectively. High sidelobe suppression of more than 100 dB for image frequency is achieved.

Conclusion

The SWF technology has now attained maturity. It has no serious rivals in the range 30 MHz to 3 GHz whenever appreciable Q is required. In this range, we encounter carrier or intermediate frequencies in, for example, television, radio links, satellite communication (Hénaff and Brossard 1981), optical communication (Yamada et al. 1980), and mobile cellular radio communication (Hikita et al. 1984). Through its ability to handle phase responses of almost any type, the SWF can process high-rate digital data. We can thus confidently predict a substantial industrial expansion of this technology, accompanying the development of video communication in all its forms.

Chapter 6

Oscillators

In this chapter we shall describe the principle and some applications of SAW oscillators. After frequency filters, they are the most important devices in signal processing. They provide standards that are stable in terms of frequency and of time.

At low frequencies (some tens of kHz), current technology uses essentially piezoelectric tuning-forks derived from watch quartz crystals. The best piezoelectric standards are still quartz plates, vibrating across their thickness in the region of 5 MHz. Similar technology can be used at higher frequencies, but the quality of the resonator deteriorates very rapidly. Frequency multiplication by purely electronic procedures is also limited by the increase in electrical RF noise, which rises as the square of the multiplication factor. This is why a technology such as SAW, which is capable of operation at frequencies between a few tens of MHz and several GHz, meets specific technological needs in areas where no other technology can seriously compete with it. The key to this technology lies in its ability to produce good surface resonators. As we shall see later, the Q of the resonator (or, in mathematical terms, the reciprocal of the fraction of stored energy that is dissipated per radian) is one of the important parameters that determines the stability of the device. It is now possible to construct SAW resonators with Q values of about 10^4. Moreover, the technology is compatible with simple and effective electronic frequency control. Surface acoustic waves are thus seen to be of great importance for the realization of oscillators in the frequency range between 50 MHz and about 5 GHz.

6.1   History

It all started at RSRE[†] where the first SAW oscillator was developed in 1969 (Maines *et al.* 1969) as a means of measuring the parameters of a delay line as functions of temperature. The same team subsequently developed a

[†]Royal Signals and Radar Establishment, Great Malvern, Worcestershire, England.

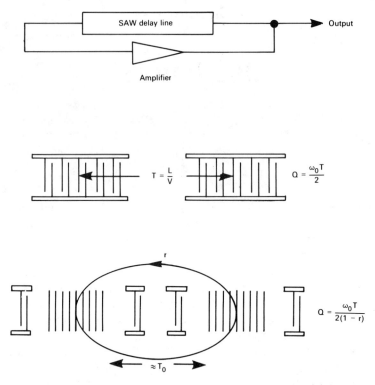

Fig. 6.1   Two-port SAW oscillator. T is the group delay.

great variety of oscillators, fixed and tunable, in which the acoustic component was a two-port network inserted in an electric circuit containing the amplifier (Fig. 6.1). The idea of a surface-wave resonator in the form of a reactive dipole (Fig. 6.2) was reported for the first time in 1970 by E. A. Ash (Ash 1970), who obtained a relatively disappointing Q factor ($Q < 100$). It is only quite recently that the advantages of these resonators have been demonstrated afresh with the implementation of structures with Q values of several thousand (Staples 1974). This was achieved with metallic or insulator arrays deposited on the surface, grooves or even by ionic implantation. The first published results are given in Table 6.1.

6.2   Principle of the acoustic surface-wave oscillator

6.2.1   Oscillator using true surface modes

Two approaches are possible to the realization of the SAW oscillators. They are based on the fact that there are two different SAW devices that can

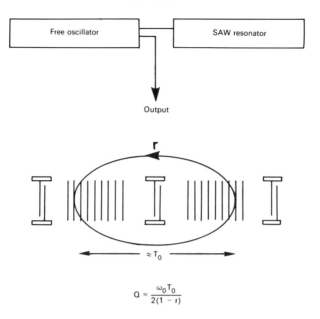

Fig. 6.2 One-port SAW oscillator.

be used as frequency stabilization elements, namely, the one-port SAW *resonator* and the two-port SAW *delay line*.

The one-port SAW resonator consists of an interdigital transducer inserted into an acoustic resonant cavity. It was described in Section 5.5.1.2 and is used, essentially, as a tank circuit (cf. Fig. 6.2). The two-port SAW delay line is connected to a wide-band amplifier in a feedback loop and provides stability through frequency-selective feedback (Fig. 6.1). As soon as the gain in the loop is sufficient, the device becomes unstable and oscillates at a frequency ω_0, determined by the phase condition

$$\phi = \omega_0 T + \phi_E = 2n\pi \qquad (6.1)$$

where n is an integer and ϕ_E is the additional phase shift due to the connections, the amplifier and (if present) the auxiliary phase shifter. The group delay T of the two-port SAW device, which is approximately equal to the ratio L/v of the length of the line to the wave propagation velocity, is defined first. This is obviously a multimode oscillator (several values of n satisfy eqn 6.1) whose effective working frequency must be selected by the transducers. It can be shown that the oscillator becomes a monomode device when the length of one of the interdigital combs is made equal to the distance between their centers (cf. Fig. 6.3) (Crabbe *et al.* 1973).

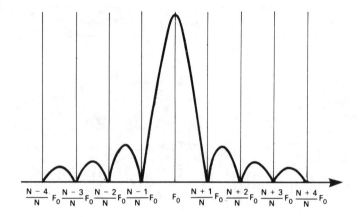

$$\frac{N-4}{N}F_0\quad\frac{N-3}{N}F_0\quad\frac{N-2}{N}F_0\quad\frac{N-1}{N}F_0\qquad F_0\qquad\frac{N+1}{N}F_0\quad\frac{N+2}{N}F_0\quad\frac{N+3}{N}F_0\quad\frac{N+4}{N}F_0$$

Fig. 6.3 Mode selection in a delay-line SAW oscillator.

Table 6.1 Comparison of first results obtained with SAW resonators

Type of resonator	Reference	Measured Q
Metallic arrays or interdigital combs on piezoelectric material	E. A. Ash, 1970 (Ash 1970) (University College, London)	80 at (30 MHz)
	E. J. Staples, 1974 (Staples 1974) (Texas Instruments, Dallas)	> 3 000 (from 50 to 500 MHz)
	K. M. Lakin, 1974 (Lakin *et al.* 1974) (UCLA, Los Angeles)	1 900 (at 34 MHz)
	J. Hénaff, 1975 (Hénaff 1976) (CNET, Issy-les-Moulineaux)	7 000 (at 100 MHz)
Mass loading	E. J. Staples, 1974 (Staples 1974) (Texas Instruments, Dallas)	9 000 (at 183 MHz) ZnO ST quartz
Mechanical strain by grooves etched or by ion implantation	R. C. M. Li, 1974 (Li *et al.* 1974) (MIT, Lincoln Lab)	> 6 000 (at 68 MHz)
	P. Hartemann, 1974 (Hartemann and Morizot 1974) (Thomson-CSF, Orsay)	1 800 (at 75 MHz)

We can show that the Q factor of this type of oscillator is defined by

$$Q = \frac{\omega_0}{2}\frac{\delta\phi}{\delta\omega} \approx \frac{\omega_0 T}{2}$$

The parameter T is thus redefined more precisely as the group delay of the two-port network (Feldmann 1981, p. 186). Therefore, Q is a parameter that can be fixed when the device is designed, in accordance with very flexible specifications. When the SAW interdigital transducer is placed in a resonant cavity, as described in Section 5.5.1.3, the group delay is increased and the Q factor becomes

$$Q = \frac{\omega_0 T_0}{2(1 - r)}$$

where r is the transmittance of the complete circuit (of the order of 0.8–0.9) and T_0 is the mean group delay of the circuit.

A simple SAW delay line is readily designed and implemented. The technology involves a thin metallic layer etched by standard photolithographic techniques. It is very reproducible and allows precise frequency adjustment. One- or two-port devices placed in a resonant cavity can be used to attain larger values of Q and lower insertion loss at intermediate frequencies. For example, at a fundamental frequency of 100 MHz it is possible to have $Q = 30\,000$–$40\,000$ (instead of only 4000–5000 for the simple delay line), but at the cost of a more complicated technology that generally requires two steps, namely, one for the interdigital transducers and the other for the reflectors of the acoustic cavity. The resonant cavity can be realized by different processes (cf. Table 6.1): metallic strips, zinc oxide arrays, etched grooves, dot arrays, ion-implanted arrays and so on. All these technological processes have given good results, especially in the lowest frequency range, but reduce the transmittance r with increasing frequency. The advantages of reflectors are lost as 1 GHz is approached.

6.2.2   Other oscillation modes

The structure of surface-wave oscillators containing a large number of gratings or electrodes and, thus producing total reflection of the wave, enables us to trap acoustic energy by using branches other than the true surface modes (cf. Section 2.2.4). Surface pseudomodes have the advantage of greater coupling and, often, lower temperature coefficients (cf. Chapter 8). Thus, the use of such modes, also called surface transverse waves (STW), has been proposed for high-Q high-frequency resonators, with moderate insertion loss, lower potential aging and greater power-handling capability than SAW resonators with comparable design parameters and electrical performance (Bagwell 1987; Auld and Thompson 1987).

6.3   Characterization of SAW oscillators

Frequency sources are generally characterized in terms of:

(a) *accuracy*, i.e. the degree of conformity between the measured or calculated frequency and the specified value;

(b) *reproducibility*, i.e. the degree of agreement across a set of independent devices based on the same design; and

(c) *stability*, i.e. the frequency and time-domain behavior of a given type of source (Cutler and Searle 1966).

Accuracy and reproducibility are primarily the concern of designers of specific applications but, for the user, the most important property is the stability of the frequency source. Following the conventional approach, we shall consider successively short-term (of the order of a second), medium-term (about an hour), and long-term (more than a year) stability.

6.3.1   Short-term stability

At first sight, the concept of a single frequency generated by an oscillator may seem clear enough, but it masks an underlying complexity that we shall now briefly describe. Let $x(t)$ be the signal (electric voltage) generated by the oscillator. To the first approximation, we have

$$x(t) \ = \ A \cos \phi(t) \qquad \phi(t) \approx 2\pi v_0 t$$

where A is the amplitude, ϕ the phase and v_0 the nominal frequency. It is more convenient to use the *fractional frequency*

$$y(t) \ = \ \frac{\dot{\phi}(t)}{2\pi v_0}$$

where $\dot{\phi}(t)$ indicates differentiation with respect to time.

To examine more thoroughly the stability of an oscillator, we have to consider the phase $\phi(t)$ and the reduced frequency $y(t)$ as *random functions*.

6.3.1.1   Time domain measurement of stability

The time domain measurement of stability usually involves counting the number of periods of the oscillator during a series of time intervals τ. In terms of the fractional frequency, we thus obtain a series of samples $\bar{y}_k (k = 1, 2, 3, \ldots)$ whose fluctuations may be described by

$$\sigma_y^2(\tau) \ = \ \left\langle \frac{(\bar{y}_{k+1} - \bar{y}_k)^2}{2} \right\rangle$$

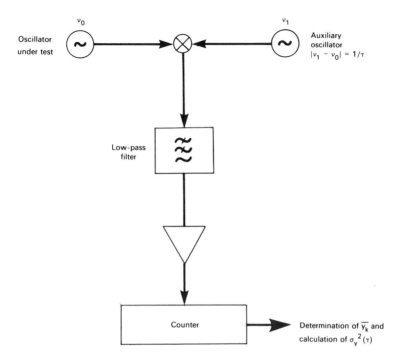

Fig. 6.4   Example of the measurement of the Allan variance (heterodyne method).

The quantity $\sigma_y^2(\tau)$ is called the Allan variance after its originator (Allan 1966). In practice, the mean frequencies $\bar{y}_k$ corresponding to consecutive time intervals τ are often measured only approximately. For example, the time τ can be determined by beating the frequency v_0 against the frequency v_1 of an auxiliary oscillator (cf. Fig. 6.4). This allows us to determine the variations of Allan variance as a function of the measurement time τ.

There are, of course, variances other than the Allan variance (Barnes *et al.* 1971), but the latter is sufficient to characterize SAW oscillators in the time domain. The other aspect to be studied is the spectral behavior.

6.3.1.2   Measurement of the spectral density of noise

The noise due to phase fluctuations can be measured near the nominal frequency v_0. In practical cases, where the amplitude can be considered constant, and where phase fluctuations are small, the signal from the oscillator can be mixed in quadrature with that of a reference oscillator tuned to v_0 (cf. Fig. 6.5).

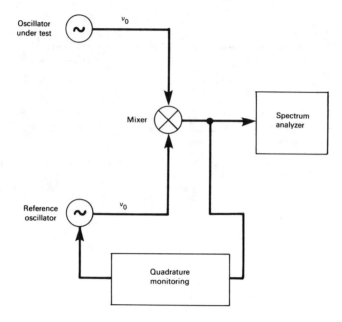

Fig. 6.5 Measurement of the phase fluctuation spectrum. The spectrum analyzer gives $S_\phi(f) = |V(f)/V_s|^2$, where V is the effective voltage ($\mathrm{Hz}^{-1/2}$) at the output of the mixer and V_s (in volts per radian) is the peak voltage of the two oscillators beating freely.

Measurement of the spectral density as a function of the frequency f, i.e. the Fourier frequency offset from the carrier, by means of a spectrum analyzer, gives us directly the function $S_\phi(f)$, called the one-sided spectral density of phase fluctuations (the quadrature monitoring of the reference oscillator must be sufficiently loose).

For the small values of f, the function $S_\phi(f)$ describes noise "close to the carrier", while high values of f relate to noise "far from the carrier". It is often more convenient to consider the quantity

$$S_y(f) \;=\; \frac{f^2}{v_0^2}\, S_\phi(f)$$

which involves the fractional frequency.

6.3.1.3 Relationships between Allan variance and noise spectral density

The two functions $\sigma_y^2(\tau)$ and $S_y(f)$ are related by an integral expression. It can be shown that

$$\sigma_y^2(\tau) \;=\; 2 \int_0^{f_h} S_y(f)\, \frac{\sin^4(\pi f \tau)}{(\pi f \tau)^2}\, \mathrm{d}f$$

where the limit of integration f_h is finite (and depends in practice on the measuring equipment).

For example, if we use the finite expansion for the spectral density

$$S_y(f) = \frac{h_{-2}}{f^2} + \frac{h_{-1}}{f} + h_0 + h_1 f + h_2 f^2$$

we can show from the above integral relation that the Allan variance is given by

$$\sigma_y^2(\tau) = h_{-2}\frac{4\pi^2}{6}\tau + h_{-1}2 \log 2 + \frac{h_0}{2\tau}$$

$$+ h_1 \frac{3.81 + 3 \log(2\pi f_h \tau)}{4\pi^2\tau^2} + h_2 \frac{3f_h}{4\pi^2\tau^2} \qquad (6.2)$$

where log denotes the natural logarithm.

6.3.1.4 Short-term stability of SAW oscillators

The measured spectral density of phase noise and the Allan variance are illustrated in Figs 6.6 and 6.7 respectively.

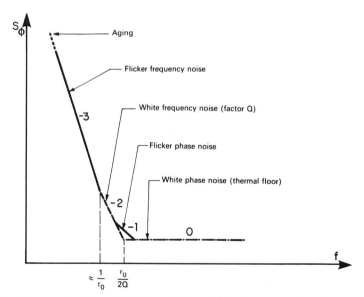

Fig. 6.6 Characterization of SAW oscillators in the frequency domain: one-sided spectral density of phase fluctuations.

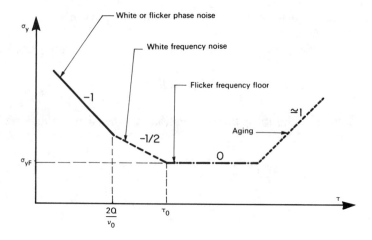

Fig. 6.7 Characterization of SAW oscillators in the time domain: Allan variance.

We have then, approximately, an expansion such as that given by eqn (6.2). Similarly, in terms of phase noise, we have

$$S_\phi(f) = \frac{v_0^2}{f^2} S_y(f) = \frac{v_0^2}{f^2} \left(\frac{h_{-2}}{f^2} + \frac{h_{-1}}{f} + h_0 + h_1 f + h_2 f^2 \right)$$

The most significant parameter in Fig. 6.6 is the *thermal level of white phase noise*. We can relate this floor physically to the energy stored in the oscillator cavity (Edson 1960; Leeson 1966). More precisely, we have

$$v_0^2 h_2 = \frac{2kT}{P_s}$$

where v_0 is the frequency of the oscillator, k is Boltzmann's constant, T is the absolute temperature, $P_s = P_0/FG^2$, P_0 is the output power, G is the linear gain of the amplifier and F is the noise factor of the amplifier.

Because of its dimensions and constitution, the SAW oscillator can operate at considerably higher power levels than bulk crystal oscillators at the same frequency and is therefore particularly advantageous in comparison with other technologies as far as this thermal floor is concerned.

EXAMPLE. $P_0 = 10\,\text{mW}$, $G = 10$, $F = 10$, $v_0 = 10^8\,\text{Hz}$; $v_0^2 h_2 = 10^{-15}\,\text{s}^{-1} = -150\,\text{dBc}\,\text{Hz}^{-1}$, i.e. 150 dB per Hz below the carrier.

For an output power of 2 mW, this thermal noise floor is very remarkable. Still lower values, reaching $-180\,\text{dBc}\,\text{Hz}^{-1}$ (Penavaire *et al.* 1980), can be achieved, which means that this type of oscillator is unique for certain applications in which noise far from the carrier is the decisive factor.

Another interesting parameter is the coefficient of the term in f^{-2} (white frequency noise) which represents the thermal noise filtered by the circuit. If Q is the Q factor of the loaded cavity, it can be shown that

$$h_0 = v_0^2 h_2 / 4Q^2$$

We recall that Q is of the order of 10^3–10^4. For values very much greater than this (10^5–10^6 for bulk waves), the corresponding segment of the curve does not appear in Figs 6.6 and 6.7.

In the time domain, Fig. 6.7 reveals a level of short-term stability associated with the term involving h_{-1} and called the *flicker frequency floor* σ_{yF}. In practice, the experimental value of σ_{yF} is of the order of 10^{-10}. Its dependence on components, temperature fluctuations, power supply and so on is complex and still not fully understood.

The final essential parameter is the term due to aging, which depends on the material, the electrodes, the fabrication procedures and so on. In practice, we have $h_{-2} \simeq 10^{-24}$, but we shall discuss aging at greater length in Section 6.3.3.

6.3.2 Medium-term stability

For many users, medium-term behavior is just as important. It depends on the stability of the delay time T as a function of the temperature. This dependence is linked, on the one hand, to the thermal expansion of the crystal and, on the other, to changes in its elastic properties. Some crystallographic orientations (cut and direction of propagation) minimize this effect over a fairly wide range of temperatures.

The parabolic behavior of the most commonly used piezoelectric substrate (ST cut quartz) leads to a frequency variation of only ± 4 parts per million (ppm) as the temperature varies from $+ 10\,°C$ to $+ 40\,°C$, but this variation reaches ± 13 ppm when the range of temperature is extended to between $- 10\,°C$ and $+ 50\,°C$.

The solid line in Fig. 6.8 shows the frequency variation of a SAW oscillator, operating at 98 MHz, on an ST quartz substrate, as a function of the temperature. The dotted line shows the theoretical variation for ST quartz alone. It is clear that the two curves are practically identical. The parabolic variation is similar to that of the BT cut quartz used for bulk waves, but this variation is much larger than that obtained for the AT cut. Hence the search for piezoelectric materials with zero temperature coefficients not only to the first order, but also to higher orders, remains a central pursuit. Unfortunately, no configuration meeting this criterion has yet been tested.

The principal parameters of the most interesting cuts of conventional piezoelectric crystals are given in Chapter 8.

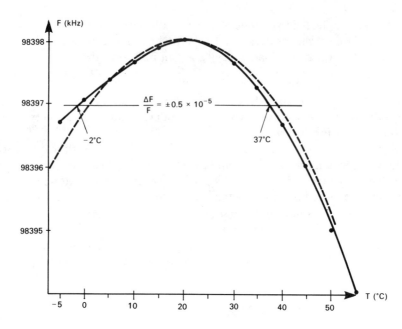

Fig. 6.8 Variation of oscillation frequency F as a function of the temperature T: (——) experimental results; (– – –) theoretical variation for ST quartz $F = F_0$ $[1 - 3.10^{-8}(T - T_0)^2]$ where $T_0 = 20\,°C$.

6.3.3 Long-term stability

A frequency drift, or aging, is observed for all crystal oscillators. In the case of SAW oscillators, the experimental results depend very much on the technological conditions (one- or two-port network structure, grooved or metallic arrays, annealing, nature of metallization, mounting, state of the surface and so on), but several laboratories (Shreve *et al.* 1978; Latham and Saunders 1978) agree on the figure of 1 ppm year^{-1}, and an example has even been reported in which the aging is less than 0.5 ppm in two years (Parker 1982).

6.4 Tunable oscillators

6.4.1 Principles

Alongside the fixed frequency oscillators described above, there is a very important class of oscillators whose frequency can be controlled electronically.

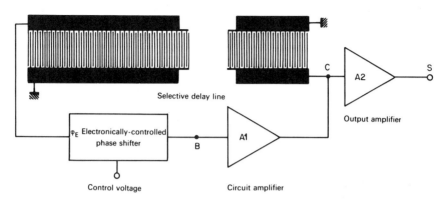

Fig. 6.9 Insertion of an auxiliary phase shifter in the loop of a two-port oscillator.

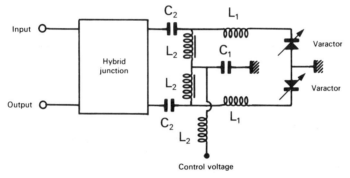

Fig. 6.10 Diagram showing an electronically controlled phase shifter.

Returning to the phase-matching equation (6.1)

$$\omega_0 T + \phi_E = 2n\pi \qquad\qquad (6.1)$$

we see that the oscillation frequency (cf. Fig. 6.9) can be modified by inserting an auxiliary phase shifter in the loop.

Such phase shifters are relatively easy to realize and to control electronically. The diagram of Fig. 6.10 represents a more or less classical type of phase shifter that has the advantage of keeping the amplitude of the signal constant for a total phase change close to π: it uses a hybrid junction and two varactors.

The capacitance of a varactor varies in accordance with the applied control voltage. This causes the phase of the output signal to vary relative to the input. The inductors L_1 are adjusted to provide a frequency variation that is a linear function of the control voltage, with the desired slope.

Examples of the application of such oscillators are given below (Examples 5 and 6 of Section 6.6).

6.4.2 Amplitude-to-frequency conversion

Tunable oscillators are extremely convenient in amplitude-to-frequency conversion. The video signal is applied at the input of an electronic phase shifter (for example, at the "control voltage" input in Fig. 6.10) in the loop of a tunable oscillator. The output is then a signal whose frequency is modulated in accordance with the variations of the video signal. Applications include coding of radar signals and spread spectrum communications.

More complex examples of the use of tunable oscillators include the analog-to-digital converter and the tunable filter described in Section 6.6 (Examples 7 and 8).

6.5 Summary of current performance

Table 6.2 summarizes the principal aspects of the performance attained at present by SAW oscillators.

Finally, SAW oscillators offer good performance over a range of frequencies extending from about 100 MHz (this limit is related to the size of the crystal at lower frequencies) to several GHz (this upper limit is related to technological constraints, e.g. the width of the fingers; the upper limit is continually increasing, the record being around 4 GHz; Lau *et al.* 1980; Mitsuyu *et al.* 1981). The most remarkable performance features are, on the one hand, the thermal noise level and, on the other, the range of frequency variation; it is clear that good performance cannot be attained in both these ways simultaneously. The first leads to interesting applications for fixed sources, in which the noise level close to the carrier is preponderant, and

Table 6.2 Summary of the performance attained at present by SAW oscillators

Frequency	0.1–4 GHz
Output power	10–100 mW
Range of frequency tuning	10^{-3} to 10^{-2}
Slope of frequency tuning	0.3–1 MHz V^{-1}
Thermal floor	-170 to -150 dBc Hz^{-1}
Temperature behavior 10–40 °C	± 4 ppm (quartz ST)
Aging	0.2 at 1 ppm year^{-1}

the second opens the way to numerous applications of voltage-controlled oscillators. We shall see some examples of this in the next section.

6.6   Notes on applications

The simplest applications involve fixed-frequency oscillators. At moderate frequencies, the advantages of robustness, low weight and reliability, combined with excellent spectral purity, are exploited in the following example of a pilot for a beacon in space.

EXAMPLE 1. Pilot for a satellite-borne beacon (CNET-France: study contract CNET–Thomson-CSF). The frequency of the pilot is 250 MHz and it generates, by successive multiplication, signals at 20, 30, 40 and 90 GHz. In addition, phase modulation at 20 and 30 GHz provides spectral line frequencies over a bandwidth in excess of 1 GHz.

This beacon can be used to carry out propagation measurements on an oblique path between the earth and the satellite in the 20, 30, 40 and 90 GHz frequency bands, including studies of attenuation, phase shifts, polarization decoupling and differential fading and phase shifting at 20 and 30 GHz.

Excellent dynamic range of measurement, even at 90 GHz, is obtained because of the spectral purity of the SAW pilot. This allows the use, in terrestrial receiving stations, of phase-locking loops with a narrow noise bandwidth. The rival bulk-wave device has virtually identical characteristics, but operates at lower frequencies, which means that supplementary multipliers are necessary and the device becomes more complicated.

Principal characteristics

(1) Frequency: 250 MHz;
(2) Initial setting: 5×10^{-6};
(3) Frequency stability:
    (a) per second: 5×10^{-9};
    (b) per day: 6×10^{-8};
    (c) in the range -10 to $+40\,°C$: $\pm 6 \times 10^{-8}$;
(4) Spectral purity:
    (a) $L(f)$ at 200 Hz: $-120\,dBc\,Hz^{-1}$;
    (b) $L(f)$ at 2 Hz: $-150\,dBc\,Hz^{-1}$;
    (c) Noise floor at 15 kHz: $-170\,dBc\,Hz^{-1}$.

The use of surface waves at "low" frequencies (near 100 MHz) is not incompatible with *mass production*. This is indicated by Example 2 (converter for a videotape recorder (VTR)).

EXAMPLE 2. An HF converter for a VTR (source: Toshiba). Two local oscillators working at 91.25 and 97.25 MHz ($\pm$ 100 kHz) are used in the HF converter of a VTR. The two (one-port) resonators are located on the same lithium tantalate crystal and are mounted in a single package. Production for the Japanese market is 10 000 units per month.

Nevertheless, at moderate frequencies, surface waves have a decisive advantage when the principal parameter is *spectral purity*. Example 3 describes such an application (Doppler effect radar).

EXAMPLE 3. Reference source for a Doppler effect radar (Thomson-CSF (Penavaire *et al.* 1980)). In this application, the resolution and range depend critically on the quality of the reference sources. The compromise between (i) low noise in the vicinity of the carrier, which requires a high-Q resonator (i.e. at relatively low frequency), and (ii) low thermal noise floor which demands a small multiplying factor, is achieved between 100 and 200 MHz. The source operates at 120 MHz and uses a SAW resonator (with etched grooves) of the two-port type.

Principal characteristics

(1) Frequency: 120 MHz;
(2) Initial resonator setting: $\pm 10^{-5}$;
(3) Adjustment of frequency: $< \pm 10^{-7}$;
(4) Spectral purity:
    (a) $L(f)$ at 1 kHz: -150 dBc Hz^{-1};
    (b) $L(f)$ at 20 kHz: -175 dBc Hz^{-1}.

For microwave sources (frequencies of several GHz), surface waves enable us to dispense with frequency multiplication. Example 4 shows such an oscillator, frequency-divided and set on an auxiliary low-frequency oscillator (a simple and cheap procedure). It is intended for digital radio links and satellite communication (Hénaff 1979a; Hénaff and Feldmann 1979).

EXAMPLE 4. Local oscillator for radio links and satellite communication (CNET-France). A low-consumption local oscillator (Fig. 6.11) can be devised according to the following scheme, which deploys a phase-locking loop locked not on the microwave signal itself, but on the frequency-divided signal, to bring it to the frequency of the bulk-wave reference quartz. The problem of spurious spectral lines is thus simplified, filtering is easier and power consumption is reduced. In this scheme, the 1 or 2 GHz source is a SAW oscillator. Moreover, the present performance of SAW oscillators is already suitable for digital radios links, and the bulk-wave quartz is no longer necessary.

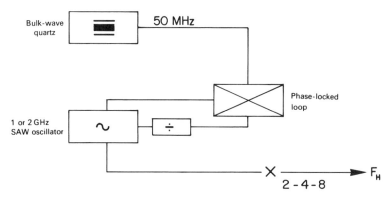

Fig. 6.11 Block diagram of the local oscillator.

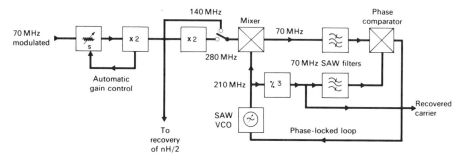

Fig. 6.12 Block diagram of carrier-recovery circuit.

SAW technology brings decisive advantages in the field of tunable oscillators (Hénaff and Brossard 1981). Example 5 illustrates an oscillator of this kind. It is tunable at around 210 MHz and is used for carrier recovery in coherent demodulation of digital signals. Example 6 involves a similar oscillator operating at approximately 280 MHz and used to recover the rhythm frequency in a digital 140 Mbit s^{-1} link (Hénaff and Feldmann 1979).

EXAMPLE 5. Carrier recovery in coherent demodulation (nPSK; CNET-France). The carrier-recovery circuit illustrated in Fig. 6.12 (compatible with 4PSK and 2PSK) uses two 70 MHz SAW filters and a 210 MHz voltage-controlled oscillator (VCO).

Using multiplication by 4 (or by 2), and starting with a 70 MHz signal modulated at 0, $\pi/2$, π, $3\pi/2$ (or 0, π) produces a 280 MHz (or 140 MHz) signal that is free from any phase jump. Mixing with a local 210 MHz signal gives, in both cases, a 70 MHz signal. The latter is filtered by a narrow-bandwidth SAW filter and is phase compared (Fig. 6.12) with the 70 MHz signal resulting from the division by three (by a digital divider) of the local 210 MHz and filtering by a SAW filter identical with the preceding one. We have chosen the SAW VCO because of its excellent intrinsic stability, associated with a frequency tuning range sufficient to follow variations due to the satellite Doppler effect and to the instabilities of frequency conversion in the satellite and terrestrial stations. The voltage-controlled phase shifter allows a range of electronic tuning that exceeds 600 kHz for a variation of less than 1 V.

The characteristics of this carrier-recovery loop for 0 dB E/N_0 ratio are as follows:

(a) Lock-in range: 70 MHz $\pm$ 50 kHz;
(b) Residual phase error (at 70 MHz $\pm$ 50 kHz): $\Delta_y < \pm 2°$;
(c) Mean phase deviation: $\sigma < \pm 2.5°$;
(d) Cycle slipping of recovered carrier: < 1 per day.

EXAMPLE 6. Recovery of rhythm frequency. When, in a digital transmission system, we connect in series several sections of the transmitting medium (several hops of radio links or lengths of cables with successive amplification), transmission errors are not multiplicative but simply additive if the digital signal is regenerated at each section and this regeneration implies sampling of the received signal, the useful signal being accompanied by thermal noise and intersymbol interference. This sampling is carried out by a rhythm signal with an appropriate phase. This rhythm signal must finally be generated from the received signal.

Figure 6.13 describes a rhythm-recovery circuit using a phase-locking loop that contains a SAW VCO whose frequency is compared with that of

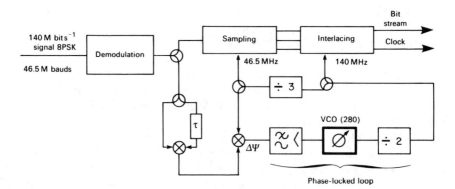

Fig. 6.13 Rhythm-recovery circuit.

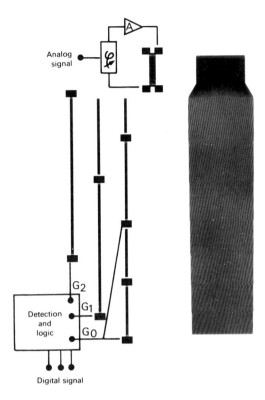

Fig. 6.14 Three-bit ADC using amplitude-to-frequency conversion, spatial dispersion by a fan-shaped MRA, and localization by a bank of transducers.

the signal received after passage through a band-pass filter at the rhythm frequency. The example chosen corresponds to digital transmission at 140 Mbit s^{-1} using an eight-state PSK modulation: this allows the use of a VCO at 280 MHz. For these high-rhythm frequencies, the use of SAW oscillators enables us to solve the problem easily and in a reliable and economic way, always because of their high fundamental frequency and their wide range of frequency tuning. On the other hand, to obtain short rise-time rhythm signals, it is advantageous to start with an oscillator operating at twice the rhythm frequency, followed by a digital divider by two.

Applications are of course encountered in high-rate digital transmission: radio links at 2 × 140 Mbit s^{-1}, circular wave-guides operating at 4 × 140 Mbit s^{-1}, and cables (including optical fiber cables) operating at 4 or 6 × 140 Mbit s^{-1}.

The following examples (7 and 8), describe more complex devices using the principle of amplitude-to-frequency conversion (cf. Section 6.4.2).

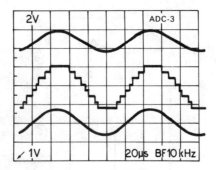

Fig. 6.15 Analog–digital–analog conversion: the input signal (top curve) is first digitized by the SAW ADC (middle curve) and is then reconstituted by a classical ADC and smoothed by a low-pass filter (bottom curve).

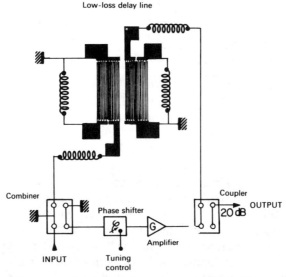

Fig. 6.16 Tunable narrow-bandwidth filter: the gain in the feedback loop is less than unity; the loop phase shifter controls the tuning frequency.

EXAMPLE 7. Analog-to-digital surface-wave converter (Feldmann and Hénaff 1978a). Using the amplitude-to-frequency conversion described in Section 6.4.2, we can construct an analog-to-digital converter (ADC) composed of a bank of filters arranged in the required manner. The most convenient configuration (cf. Fig. 6.14) consists of an MRA fan-shaped network (Section 5.4.1) which spreads out different frequencies in space along the network. A set of transducers facing the fan records digitally the position of the reflected beam, and therefore its frequency, which represents the amplitude of the input signal (cf. Fig. 6.15).

A device of this type is described in Feldmann and Hénaff (1978a) and is capable of providing fast ADC (1–100 MHz) while handling only a few encoding bits (3–5).

EXAMPLE 8. Tunable filters. When the amplitude-to-frequency conversion device of Fig. 6.11 is such that the circuit gain is less than unity, we obviously no longer have spontaneous oscillation. Nevertheless, the device can act as a *narrow bandwidth filter* (Fig. 6.16).

Different improvements can be made to smooth out the response as a function of tuning by a secondary filter, or to stabilize the frequency as a function of temperature. A filter of this kind is described in (Hénaff *et al.* 1981a) and can select a 30 kHz channel around a center frequency of 900 MHz for radiomobile communication systems.

The final example (9) is more forward-looking: it shows the implementation of tunable oscillators integrated on gallium arsenide and typically suitable for optical communication using semiconductor lasers (GaAs/GaAlAs).

EXAMPLE 9. Tunable source integrated on GaAs (United Technologies Research Center (Grudkowski *et al.* 1980). In 1980, Grudkowski showed that it was possible to produce tunable SAW oscillators in a monolithic circuit on GaAs. The structure was based on:

(a) a two-port resonator on semi-insulating GaAs ⟨001⟩ cut; (110) propagation (operation in the range 100–200 MHz);

(b) a SAW phase shifter using a Schottky barrier to deplete charges from the GaAs layer, grown epitaxially on the insulating substrate (variation of the applied electric field permits variation of velocity and therefore of the phase of the wave);

(c) gallium arsenide field-effect transistors in a loop amplifier and, eventually, an output stage.

Chapter 7

Nonlinear Effects and Applications

Alongside the linear phenomena described in the preceding chapters, important applications of SAWs result from nonlinear interactions. In this chapter, we describe first the principles of amplification of waves by the acoustic electric interaction, and then continue with the interactions between two or more surface waves as well as some applications (delay lines, convolvers, correlators, imagers and various processing devices). For completeness, we report briefly the existence of the "chirp-Z-transform" (CZT) transformation as well as acousto-optic interactions. While some of these applications (e.g. correlation) are mainly industrial plane, some others are still only at the laboratory stage.

7.1   Acoustoelectric interaction

The possibility of amplifying surface waves *in situ* would appear to allow a considerable extension of their field of application in the direction of long delay lines, nonreciprocal devices, large processing capabilities and so on. Research has led to significant results in the laboratory, but technological difficulties have so far precluded industrial applications. In this section we sketch a simple theory of amplification and the principles of devices as well as their potential applications. For further information, readers may consult Gulyaev and Pustovoit (1965) and Collins *et al.* (1968).

7.1.1   Principles

A piezoelectric surface wave can interact with a semiconductor on the top of a crystal, whether epitaxially grown or deposited as a thin layer, or simply laid down on the surface. In this last case, the mathematical analysis

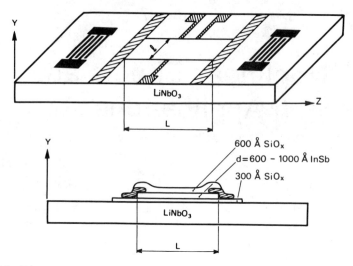

Fig. 7.1   Diagram of an acoustoelectric amplifier using a semiconductor in the form of a thin layer deposited on the crystal.

is particularly simple. All that needs to be done is to note that the permittivity of the external medium is no longer that of a vacuum ε_0 but rather (neglecting diffusion) (Kittel 1958)

$$\varepsilon_e = \varepsilon_m + \frac{\sigma}{j\omega} \tag{7.1}$$

where ε_m is the permittivity of the semiconductor and σ is its conductivity. In this configuration, the semiconductor can only attenuate the surface wave. To be able to amplify it, the electrons must be accelerated by an electric field (Fig. 7.1).

7.1.2   Electronic gain

When a continuous electric field is present, eqn (7.1) is still valid, provided the angular frequency ω of the piezoelectric wave is replaced with the apparent angular frequency $\omega\eta$ as seen by the electrons (because of the Doppler effect). The Doppler factor

$$\eta = 1 - \frac{v_0}{v_a} \tag{7.2}$$

depends on the average velocity v_0 of the electrons and on the velocity v_a of the acoustic wave. The acoustic wave and the electron flow may be said to approach synchronism as η tends to zero.

According to eqn (2.27), the propagation of the surface waves may now be described by

$$\varepsilon_s(v) = -\varepsilon_e \qquad (7.3)$$

As in Chapter 3, we can evaluate the function $\varepsilon_s(v)$, from the equation

$$\frac{1}{\varepsilon_s(v)} = \frac{1}{\varepsilon_p}\left[1 - \left(\frac{k^2}{1 - v^2/v_a^2}\right)^{1/v}\right] \qquad (7.4)$$

where $v = 1$ for Rayleigh-type waves and $v = 2$ for Bleustein-Gulyaev waves or surface-skimming bulk waves (SSBW).

Substituting in eqn (7.3) we obtain

$$\frac{v_a^2 - v^2}{v_a^2} = k^2\left(\frac{1 + jx\varepsilon_s/(\varepsilon_s + \varepsilon_p)}{1 + jx}\right)^v \qquad (7.5)$$

where

$$x = \omega\eta(\varepsilon_m + \varepsilon_p)/\sigma \qquad (7.6)$$

In practice, we have in most cases $k^2 \ll 1$, $\varepsilon_m \ll \varepsilon_p$, and $|x| \ll 1$. We obtain then, to the first order,

$$\frac{\Delta v}{v_a} \approx \frac{k^2}{2}(1 - jvx) \qquad (7.7)$$

The electronic gain is given by

$$g_0 \approx v\frac{k^2}{2}x \qquad (7.8)$$

This expression for the gain was established for the external permittivity given by eqn (7.1), but it can be generalized immediately to more complex electrical boundary conditions. It can be shown (Coldren and Kino 1971) that for a semiconductor-layer monolithic amplifier, it is sufficient to replace eqn (7.6) with

$$x = \eta v_a(\varepsilon_0 + \varepsilon_p)\sigma d \qquad (7.9)$$

where d is the thickness of the layer and ε_0 is the permittivity of vacuum. An air gap or a dielectric layer can similarly be taken into account in the definition of x. The electron velocity v_0 in eqn (7.2) depends on the drift mobility μ_D of the semiconductor and on the electric field $E = V/L$ between the electrodes (a distance L apart and held at a potential difference V). The *total gain* over the distance L is (in the case of the monolithic amplifier)

$$g \approx G_{SSD}(V - E_0 L) \qquad (7.10)$$

where

$$G_{SSD} = \frac{\partial g}{\partial V} = (v\omega\varepsilon k^2/2v_a)\frac{\mu_D}{\sigma d} \qquad (7.11)$$

is the small-signal differential gain. Note that the ratio $\sigma d/\mu_D$ is equal to the surface density Ne of electric charge in the semiconducting layer (N is in cm^{-2} and $e = 1.6 \times 10^{-19}$ Cb). The field

$$E_0 = v_a/\mu_D \qquad (7.12)$$

corresponds to wave-charge synchronism.

If l is the width of the layer of semiconductor, its ohmic resistance is given by

$$R = \frac{L}{l\sigma d} \qquad (7.13)$$

From this we can show that we can minimize dissipation for given gain g by choosing an optimum length and an optimum drift voltage

$$L_{opt} = \frac{g}{G_{SSD}E_0} \qquad (7.14)$$

$$V_{opt} = \frac{2g}{G_{SSD}} \qquad (7.15)$$

The minimum dissipation power is then given by

$$P_{min} = \frac{4l}{\pi}\left(\frac{\sigma d}{\mu_D}\right)^2 \frac{v_a \lambda}{\varepsilon v k^2} g \qquad (7.16)$$

where $\lambda = 2v_a\pi/\omega$.

7.1.3   Acoustoelectric current

The amplification or attenuation of waves by interaction with electrons results, by way of compensation, in the acoustoelectric current i_{AE}: which follows from the conservation of momentum. If P_a is the acoustic power, the conservation equation can be written in the form

$$\frac{i_{AE}}{\mu_D} + \frac{1}{v_a}\frac{\partial P_a}{\partial z} = 0 \qquad (7.17)$$

where z indicates the direction of propagation.

In addition, the ohmic current is

$$i_0 = -(l\sigma d)\frac{\partial V}{\partial z} \tag{7.18}$$

so that the total current is

$$I = i_{AE} + i_0 \tag{7.19}$$

Equations (7.13) and (7.17)–(7.19) can be incorporated in the formula

$$V = RI + V_{AE} \tag{7.20}$$

where

$$V_{AE} = \frac{\mu_D}{l\sigma d v_a}\Delta P_a \tag{7.21}$$

and ΔP_a is the variation in acoustic power across the semiconductor ribbon. Of course, these equations are valid even in the absence of amplification or when the semiconductor can only cause attenuation of the surface waves.

7.1.4 Technological implementation

Amplification of surface waves has been produced on several substrates, e.g. quartz and cadmium sulfide in the first attempts (Ingebrigtsen 1970; Maerfeld *et al.* 1971), but above all in lithium niobate because of its strong electromechanical coupling. If we leave on one side the case where the piezoelectric material is also a semiconductor (e.g. CdS), two technological solutions can be deployed:

(1) The semiconducting crystal is placed in close proximity to the piezoelectric crystal; they both have optically flat surfaces and are extremely close to each other ($< 500\,\text{Å}$) so as to ensure good coupling of the electric fields without affecting the small mechanical displacements of the surface of the piezoelectric crystal;

(2) The piezoelectric crystal is covered with a thin semiconducting film, which reduces polishing and positioning difficulties of the previous solution. Moreover, this monolithic structure is undoubtedly more reliable and more suitable for fabrication than that using physically separate semiconducting and piezoelectric crystals.

The first monolithic SAW amplifier (Coldren and Kino 1971), developed at the University of Stanford, consisted of a film of indium antimonide $\sim 1000\,\text{Å}$ thick, sandwiched between two thin films of silica and deposited on

YZ lithium niobate (cf. Fig. 7.1). Indium antimonide was chosen because of its high mobility and the relative ease with which it can be deposited by flash evaporation (Hénaff and Le Contellec 1974; Hénaff *et al.* 1974c). Its properties can be improved by subsequent annealing at temperatures below 500 °C.

7.1.5   Long delay lines

Applications that have been considered are principally long delay lines (Lewis and Patterson 1971; Marschall *et al.* 1973b). For example, Fig. 7.2 shows a helicoidal line in which acoustic waves follow a helicoidal path on this line. In principle, this configuration can be used to obtain very long delays. Lenses periodically refocus the acoustic beam, and amplifiers compensate for losses.

Technological advances will lead to many applications in filters, oscillators and even in complex signal processing.

7.1.6   Inverse acoustoelectric effect

Conversely, when a structure is monolithic or contains two separate materials, e.g. a semiconductor and a piezoelectric crystal, the electric charges in the semiconductor can be driven by the electric field of a SAW propagating

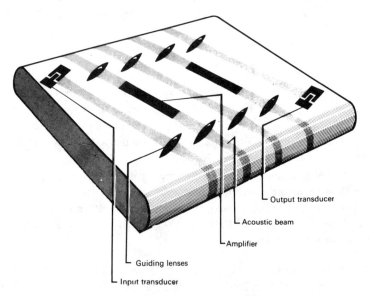

Output transducer

Acoustic beam

Amplifier

Guiding lenses

Input transducer

Fig. 7.2   Helicoidal delay line.

over the piezoelectric crystal. This principle is particularly interesting when the crystal is both semiconducting and piezoelectric (e.g. GaAs).

Applications

(1) Piezoelectric probe, used to determine the mobility and conductivity of the semiconductor by measuring the attenuation of the surface waves and of the acoustoelectric current.

(2) Control of charge transfer in charge-coupled devices. This mode of control is particularly advantageous at high frequencies at which we are free from the limitations of semiconductor technology.

EXAMPLES. Transversal filters (Feldmann 1980b, c) and programmable tapped delay lines (Guediri *et al.* 1987). The acoustic charge transport (ACT) device is a new type of high-frequency monolithic charge-transfer device (CTD) whose carriers are gathered by and transported within the traveling-wave electric field of the SAW propagating in a piezoelectric semiconductor such as GaAs.

7.2 Nonlinear interactions between acoustic surface waves

Interaction between several SAWs opens the way to relatively complex signal processing such as correlation and convolution. Photoconductivity and triboluminescence may even offer the hope of applications such as solid image sensors or flat displays. On the industrial plane, the convolution of two signals in a contradirected structure is the only application genuinely exploitable at present. It is employed mainly in the processing of radar signals.

7.2.1 Principle of nonlinear interactions

Consider a plane wave, propagating without change of form in a linear medium. When the medium ceases to be strictly linear, the plane waves interact with each other, but conservation of energy and momentum is preserved. For example, two waves (1) and (2) interact to give a wave (3), the conservation of momentum and of energy may be expressed in terms of wave vectors and angular frequencies as follows:

$$\boldsymbol{K}_1 + \boldsymbol{K}_2 = \boldsymbol{K}_3 \tag{7.22}$$

$$\omega_1 + \omega_2 = \omega_3 \tag{7.23}$$

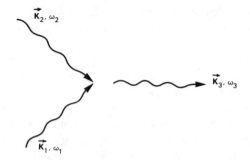

Fig. 7.3 The interaction of two waves with wave vectors K_1 and K_2 and angular frequencies ω_1 and ω_2 produces a wave with wave vector K_3 and angular frequency ω_3.

where K_1, K_2 and K_3 are the wave vectors and ω_1, ω_2 and ω_3 the angular frequencies of waves (1), (2) and (3) respectively (Fig. 7.3). These phase-matching conditions are necessary for the interaction to be cumulative. They can be generalized, of course, when more than three waves interact.

The strength of the interaction depends on the degree of nonlinearity of the medium. It has been suggested (Thompson and Quate 1971) that this nonlinear behavior can be described by the phenomenological equation

$$P_{3_{NL}} = \gamma S_1 S_2 \tag{7.24}$$

where $P_{3_{NL}}$ is the normal component of electrical polarization (expressed in coulombs per square metre) induced in wave (3) by the strains S_1 and S_2 (dimensionless) in waves (1) and (2) respectively. Alternatively, $P_{3_{NL}}$ can be written as a function of the energy flows Π_1 and Π_2 (in watts per meter) of the incident waves:

$$P_{3_{NL}} = h(F_1 \Pi_1 F_2 \Pi_2)^{1/2} \tag{7.25}$$

where F_1 and F_2 are the frequencies (in Hz) of waves (1) and (2) respectively.

A phenomenological equation of this type is valid only as a first approximation at low power levels. At higher power levels, saturation phenomena must be taken into account. The parameter h characterizes the nonlinearity of the medium (h is of the order of $10^{-17} \, \mathrm{Cs \, W^{-1} \, m^{-1}}$ in lithium niobate). It can be substantially increased in a semiconducting medium, in which case it depends (because of photoconductivity) on the ambient illumination, but saturation occurs more rapidly in this case.

7.2.2 Interaction between contradirected surface waves

It is easy to see that the interaction of collinear surface waves propagating in the same direction has no advantage over a classical nonlinear device (such

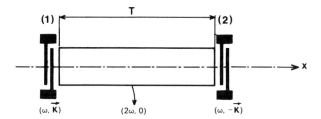

Fig. 7.4 Interaction of two contradirected surface waves.

as a diode). On the other hand, if the two waves propagate in opposite directions, the duration of the interaction is equal to one-half of the transit time T in the useful zone (Fig. 7.4). If the bandwidth is B, the product BT can reach several tens to several thousands—an exceptional value for this rhythm, T being the order of a microsecond. If a is the slowness vector in the direction of one of the waves, we have

$$K_1 = \omega_1 a$$
$$K_2 = -\omega_2 a$$

and therefore

$$K_3 = K_1 + K_2 = (\omega_1 - \omega_2)a$$

while conservation of energy requires that

$$\omega_3 = \omega_1 + \omega_2$$

Hence we deduce that the only solution with nonzero frequency is

$$\begin{cases} K_3 = 0 \\ \omega_3 = 2\omega \\ \omega_1 = \omega_2 = \omega \end{cases} \qquad (7.26)$$

Thus the only components that interact are those for which $\omega_1 = \omega_2$. Since $K_3 = 0$, it is sufficient to receive signal (3) on a central electrode placed between the two transducer combs (1) and (2) (Fig. 7.4).

In the frequency domain, the kernel of the interaction can be represented by the straight line $\omega_1 = \omega_2$ (Fig. 7.5).

We note that, in reality, the duration T of the interaction is finite, and the uncertainty principle then shows that it is impossible to separate two frequencies differing by less than $1/T$. Moreover, the bandwidth of the transducers is finite and equal to B. Figure 7.5 can therefore be made more realistic if we replace the straight line $\omega_1 = \omega_2$ by a finite segment of nonzero thickness of the order of $1/T$ (Fig. 7.6).

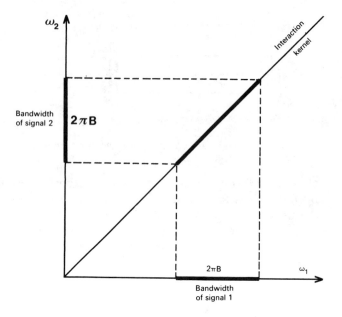

Fig. 7.5   Frequency kernel for convolution in the case of contradirected interaction.

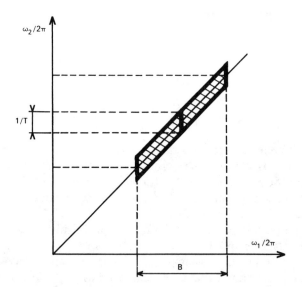

Fig. 7.6   Practical frequency kernel for convolution in the case of contradirected interaction.

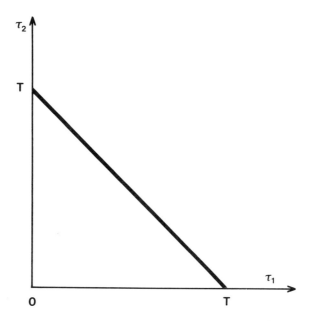

Fig. 7.7 Ideal-time convolution kernel in the case of contradirected interaction.

The number of the resolvable points in the band B is $B/(1/T) = BT$.

In the time domain, the central electrode receives a signal $s_3(t)$ which integrates all the products $s_1 s_2$ delayed by τ and $T - \tau$ respectively $(0 \leqslant \tau \leqslant T)$:

$$s_3(t) = \chi_{NL} \int_0^T s_1(t - \tau)s_2(t - T + \tau)d\tau \qquad (7.27)$$

where χ_{NL} is the nonlinear conversion factor, $s_1(t)$ is the input signal to port (1) and $s_2(t)$ is the input signal to port (2).

If we put $\tau_1 = T$ and $\tau_2 = T - \tau$, we see that the above integral is characterized by the "kernel" on the (τ_1, τ_2) plane and is represented in Fig. 7.7 by the straight line $\tau_1 + \tau_2 = T$ with $\tau_1 \geqslant 0, \tau_2 \geqslant 0$.

This notation enables us to write the equation in the form of the double integral

$$s_3(t) = \chi_{NL} \int\int \delta(\tau_1 + \tau_2 - T)s_1(\tau_1)s_2(\tau_2)d\tau_1 d\tau_2 \qquad (7.28)$$

where δ is the Dirac measure. In practice, this kernel must be "thickened" (by the order of $1/B$) to take account of the finite bandwidth of the transducers (Fig. 7.8).

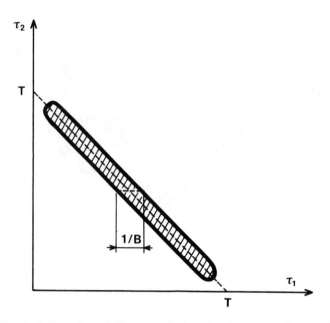

Fig. 7.8 Practical time kernel for convolution in the case of contradirected propagation.

Equations (7.27) and (7.28) prompt us to designate this nonlinear operation as a "kind of convolution". We shall call it simply a *convolution*, as in the figure captions, to simplify the writing. We recall that the true convolution would be

$$s_3(t) = \int_0^\infty s_1(t - \tau)s_2(\tau)\mathrm{d}\tau \qquad (7.29)$$

The principal difference between eqns (7.27) and (7.29) lies in the fact that the output $s_3(t)$ of eqn (7.27) contains a time period reduced by a factor of 2 relative to s_1 and s_2. If, for example, $s_1 = \delta(t)$, then $s_3(t) = s_2(2t - T)$! Conversely, the bandwidth of $s_3(t)$ is doubled and has the value $2B$. Hence the operation of such a device can only be sequential: signal samples of duration T are processed successively and are separated by "blanks" of the same duration.

Operation of the convolver
The configuration of the convolver shown in Fig 7.4 is the simplest possible. The current $J_{3_{NL}}$ received on the electrode of area $S = WL$ (width W, length L) is

$$J_{3_{NL}} = j\omega_3 S P_{NL} \qquad (7.30)$$

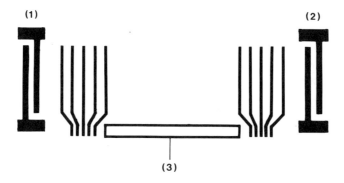

Fig. 7.9 Beam-compression convolver.

where P_{NL} is given by eqn (7.25), i.e.

$$P = \frac{h\omega_3}{2\pi} (\Pi_1 \Pi_2)^{1/2} \qquad (7.31)$$

The current injector $J_{3_{NL}}$ is loaded by the radiation resistance of the bulk wave perpendicular to the surface, which can be evaluated from (cf. Chapter 3)

$$R_3 = \frac{k^2 v_a}{\varepsilon S \omega_3^2} \propto \frac{1}{S \omega_3^2} \qquad (7.32)$$

The maximum available power is then

$$P_u = \tfrac{1}{4} R(J_{3_{NL}})^2 \propto \omega_3^2 S \Pi_1 \Pi_2 = \frac{L P_1 P_2 \omega_3^2}{W} \qquad (7.33)$$

where P_1 and P_2 are the acoustic powers emitted by combs (1) and (2). Since the length L is fixed, convolver output is inversely proportional to the width W of the electrode. Moreover, combs (1) and (2) must have apertures that are large enough for the surface-wave radiation resistance to be fairly high (of the order of $100\,\Omega$), so that the multistrip array beam compressor (described in Section 4.4) will find an essential application here (this was in fact the purpose for which it was invented). Finally, a good convolver, like that represented in Fig. 7.9, can contain a broad-band main line connected to a double beam compressor (of the order of 10–20) and a charge collector of long transit time T (a few microseconds to a few tens of microseconds).

Applications of convolvers
The main applications of convolvers are military: matched filtering for radar, sonar, or spread-spectrum communications. One of the signals is

programmed so that the convolution (eqn 7.27) is matched to the required signal. We can also conceive of radars emitting pseudorandom signals, or even (pseudo) white noise. This application constitutes one of the major industrial opportunities for surface waves.

7.2.3   Noncollinear interactions

Collinear waves admit only a single convolution-type interaction, described by Figs 7.5 and 7.7 in the frequency and time domains respectively. In fact, there are other solutions to the phase-matching equations (7.22) and (7.33), but the wave vectors are then no longer collinear. Apart from the advantages of using the whole surface of the crystal, which opens new perspectives in for displays, these solutions enable us to perform very complex functions the precise nature of which is still to be discovered.

Phase-matching rule

Let a_a, a_b and a_c be the slowness vectors of the three interacting waves, respectively. The phase-matching relations (7.22) and (7.23)

$$\omega_a + \omega_b = \omega_c$$

and

$$K_a + K_b = K_c$$

can be combined in the equation

$$\omega_a a_a + \omega_b a_b = (\omega_a + \omega_b)a_c \tag{7.34}$$

if we take into account the equation defining slowness (Chapter 2)

$$K = \omega a \tag{7.35}$$

Equation (7.34) states first that the slowness a_a, a_b and a_c are aligned on the slowness curve and also that a_c is the centre of gravity of a_a and a_b loaded by weights ω_a and ω_b.

THEOREM. *The necessary and sufficient condition for nonlinear and noncollinear interactions to exist in a material is that there exist three points aligned on the slowness curve.*

Examination of the figures of Chapter 2 shows that this situation is relatively exceptional. Nevertheless it exists in numerous materials with quadratic symmetry, but the corresponding modes admit quite large beam steering angles and often have weak coupling. If we are prepared to use pseudobranches, we can very easily find three aligned points but we must then also find very small attenuation (or accept perceptibly shorter processing time).

Bilinear signal processing

When a configuration with three slowness vectors has been chosen, it is possible to implement a processing "unit" allowing "convolution" and "correlation" type operations (Fig. 7.10).

Suppose that $\omega_a < \omega_b < \omega_c$, and let

$$m = \omega_b/\omega_a \qquad (7.36)$$

We can obtain an interaction of the form

$$s_3(t) = \int\int h(\tau_1, \tau_2)s_1(t - \tau_1)s_2(t - \tau_2)d\tau_1 d\tau_2 \qquad (7.37)$$

and a kernel of the type shown in Fig. 7.11a (similar to Fig. 7.7), with the central frequency ω_a applied to port 1, the central frequency ω_b applied to port 2, and output being taken at port 3 with central frequency $\omega_c = \omega_a + \omega_b$. If account is taken of the different slowness at ports (a) and

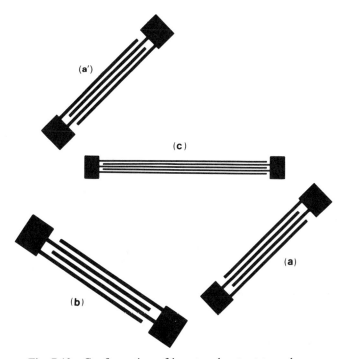

Fig. 7.10 Configuration of input and output transducers.

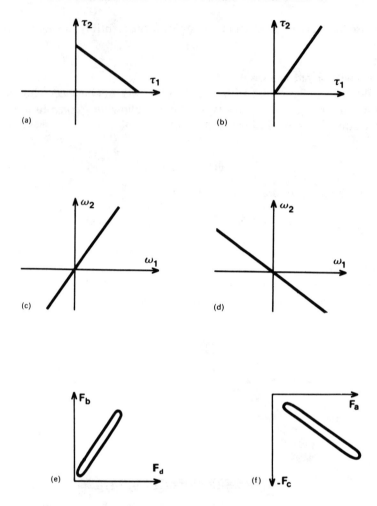

Fig. 7.11 Bilinear processing: (a) ideal-time convolution kernel; (b) ideal-time correlation kernel; (c) ideal frequency kernel—convolution; (d) ideal frequency kernel —correlation, (e) practical convolution kernel; and (f) practical correlation kernel.

(b), eqn (7.28) can have a slightly different kernel:

$$h(\tau_1, \tau_2) = \chi\delta(\tau_1 + m\tau_2 - T) \tag{7.38}$$

This kernel is still of the *convolution* type.

It is possible to obtain a very different time kernel, like that of Fig. 7.11b: all we need to do is to apply s_1 to port (a) and s_2 to port (c). We shall see that the kernel must be of the form

$$h(\tau_1, \tau_2) = \chi\delta(\tau_1 - m'\tau_2) \tag{7.39}$$

Physically, interaction is effected by subtraction of frequencies and of wave vectors:

$$\omega_b = \omega_c - \omega_a \tag{7.40}$$

$$\mathbf{K}_b = \mathbf{K}_c - \mathbf{K}_a \tag{7.41}$$

The signal $s_1(t)$ must be sent from port (a) of Fig. 7.10 and the signal $s_2(t)$ from port (c), the output being taken at (b). Taking into account the different slowness of the waves, we can substitute

$$m' = 1 + m \tag{7.42}$$

These results can be confirmed in the frequency domain: the Fourier transform of eqn (7.37) is

$$S_3(\omega_3) = \frac{1}{2\pi} \int \int H(\omega_1, \omega_2) S_1(\omega_1) S_2(\omega_2) \delta(\omega_1 + \omega_2 - \omega_3) d\omega_1 d\omega_2 \tag{7.43}$$

where S_1, S_2, S_3 and H are the transforms of s_1, s_2, s_3 and h respectively. For the convolution kernel (eqn 7.38), we obtain by a simple calculation

$$H(\omega_1, \omega_2) = \chi \frac{T}{m} \exp(-j\phi) \frac{\sin x}{x} \tag{7.44}$$

where

$$x = \frac{T}{2}\left(\omega_1 - \frac{\omega_2}{m}\right) \tag{7.45}$$

$$\phi = \frac{1}{2}\left(\omega_1 + \frac{\omega_2}{m}\right) T \tag{7.46}$$

The phase factor ϕ takes account of the propagation delay; it can of course be modified, depending on the geometry of the device.

When T is large, the term involving $\sin x / x$ enables us to recover the phase matching (eqn 7.36) when $\omega_1 = \omega_a$ and $\omega_2 = \omega_b$.

For the correlation kernel, we have an expression similar to eqn (7.44), but eqn (7.45) becomes

$$x = \frac{T}{2}\left(\omega_1 + \frac{\omega_2}{m'}\right) = \frac{T}{2}\left(\omega_1 + \frac{\omega_2}{1 + m}\right) \tag{7.47}$$

When T is large, eqns (7.44) and (7.47) define phase matching when $\omega_1 = \omega_a$ and $\omega_2 = \omega_c = (1 + m)\omega_a$.

We see, finally, that, to within a constant delay factor, we have the following approximate expressions for large T:

$$\text{(i) Convolution: } \omega_2 = m\omega_1 \tag{7.48}$$

$$S_3(\omega_3) \propto S_1(\omega_1)S_2(\omega_2) \qquad \omega_3 = \omega_1 + \omega_2 \tag{7.49}$$

$$\text{(ii) Convolution: } \omega_2 = (1 + m)\omega_1 \tag{7.50}$$

$$S_3(\omega_3) \propto S^*_1(\omega_1)S_2(\omega_2) \qquad \omega_3 = \omega_2 - \omega_1 \tag{7.51}$$

The special case of contradirected interaction corresponds to $m = 1$. Correlation is nevertheless hardly possible in view of the degeneracy of the frequencies ω_1 and ω_3, the power of S_3 being very small in comparison with S_1.

Efficiency of nonlinear conversion

It is interesting to compare the output power in the collinear case (eqn 7.33) with the present power. We must now write the piezoelectric equation for the emerging wave (3) in the form

$$\sigma_3 = |K_3|\varepsilon_s(v)\phi_3 + P_{NL} \tag{7.52}$$

where σ_3 is the electric charge per unit area, ϕ_3 is the surface potential, P_{NL} is given by eqn (7.31) and $\varepsilon_s(v)$ is the surface permittivity of mode (3).

Reception is effected by a regular interdigital transducer with radiation resistance

$$R_0 = \frac{1.4k^2}{\varepsilon W_3 \omega_3} \tag{7.53}$$

Taking eqn (7.30) into account, we can evaluate the available power in the form

$$P_u = \frac{1}{4}\frac{k^2 v_\infty h^2}{\varepsilon}\frac{\omega_3^2}{2\pi^2}\left(\frac{L}{W_3}\right)\left(\frac{L}{\lambda_3}\right)P_1 P_2 \tag{7.54}$$

where L is the length of interaction, W_3 is the width of the comb, λ_3 is the wavelength and P_1, P_2 is the acoustic power emitted by combs (1) and (2) respectively. Other things being equal, we note in relation to eqn (7.33) that the increase in output is in the ratio of L/λ_3. Nevertheless, W_3 cannot be reduced in this case.

Perspectives for signal processing

Unfortunately the ideal "unit", as described above, does not yet exist. Such a unit would enable us to implement complex adaptive signal processing in subensembles containing several such "units", or even tens of "units". To

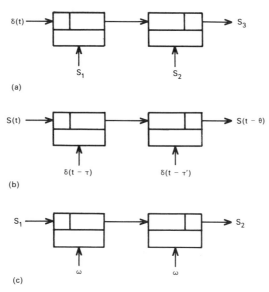

Fig. 7.12 Examples of nonlinear subensemble: (a) matched filtering: the signal s_3 is the correlation product of s_1 and s_2; (b) variable delay line: the delay is controlled by the phase difference between the two pulses; and (c) adjustable pass-band filter: the generator at frequency ω controls the central frequency of the filter.

illustrate some of the possibilities, we can represent each elementary cell by a rectangle divided into three subrectangles corresponding to the three ports, the areas being proportional to the central operating frequencies. By simply connecting two such units (Fig. 7.12), we can achieve matched adjustable filtering, a variable delay line or an adjustable pass-band filter.

7.2.4   Interaction between several branches

Consider the phase-matching conditions between four modes

$$\mathbf{K}_1 + \mathbf{K}_2 + \mathbf{K}_3 = \mathbf{K}_4 \qquad (7.55)$$

$$\omega_1 + \omega_2 + \omega_3 = \omega_4 \qquad (7.56)$$

When $\mathbf{K}_4 = 0$ (detection by a single electrode) and $\mathbf{a}_1$, $\mathbf{a}_2$ and $\mathbf{a}_3$ are the slownesses of the first three modes, we have

$$\omega_1 \mathbf{a}_1 + \omega_2 \mathbf{a}_2 + \omega_3 \mathbf{a}_3 = 0 \qquad (7.57)$$

If we take ω_4 as a parameter, the three linear equations (7.55)–(7.57) will in general have a unique solution:

$$\omega_1 = \alpha_1 \omega_4 \qquad \omega_2 = \alpha_2 \omega_4 \qquad \omega_3 = \alpha_3 \omega_4 \qquad (7.58)$$

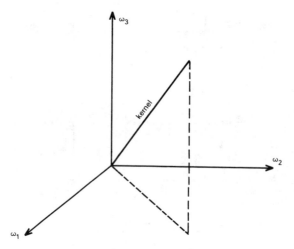

Fig. 7.13   Ideal frequency convolution kernel between three signals.

If, for example, the three transducers form an equilateral triangle in the principal plane of a crystal with trigonal symmetry, we have

$$a_1 + a_2 + a_3 = 0 \qquad (7.59)$$

and eqn (7.58) reduces to

$$\omega_1 = \omega_2 = \omega_3 = \frac{\omega_4}{3} \qquad (7.60)$$

Thus, relative to the axes ω_1, ω_2, ω_3, the convolution kernel in the frequency domain (the analog of Fig. 7.5) consists of the straight line shown in Fig. 7.13. By sending a broad-band recurrent pulse through one of the ports, we can realize the convolution and the correlation between the three other ports as in Section 7.2.3.

Another application of this four-mode system is the *designation of a point* inside the triangle formed by the transducers. Taking again the example of the equilateral triangle (Fig. 7.14), if we transmit three recurrent chirped signals with linear frequency variation

$$\omega_1 = \omega_2 = \omega_3 = \omega_0 + \mu t \qquad (7.61)$$

we see that only the "center of gravity" of the triangle is phase matched. If we delay differently the three frequency ramps, we displace the phase-matched point inside the triangle. By modifying the slopes and periods of the ramps, we can even scan the interior of the triangle according to a predetermined program. If the interior of the triangle consists of a photoconductive electrode

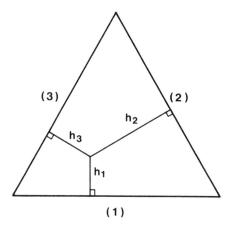

Fig. 7.14   Equilateral triangle.

(a semiconductor, for example) whose nonlinearity depends on illumination, we have a solid image sensor. We note that it may be possible to produce a flat display by using the nonlinear properties of triboluminescent phosphors excited by surface waves.

Phase matching between five modes
We can add a fixed supplementary plane wave to obtain five-mode interaction. The advantage lies in the supplementary degrees of freedom which free us from certain geometric requirements.

7.3   General survey of the CZT transformation and spectral analysis

7.3.1   Principle of the CZT transformation

Nonlinear SAW transform devices are of interest in relation to discrete nonlinear components because the nonlinear product is integrated over a long time T and gives a large BT (a measure of the complexity of the transformation). Nevertheless, when we can separate an instantaneous nonlinear fraction (and therefore implementable by discrete components) and a linear fraction for integration over a long interval, we can realize nonlinear surface-wave transformations in which the waves come into play only linearly. An example is the use of a dispersive linear filter with large product BT in

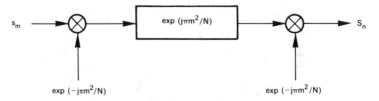

Fig. 7.15 Definition of the "chirp-Z-transform" (CZT).

conjunction with instantaneous multiplication, before and after filtering, by a "frequency ramp". This is called the "chirp-z-transform" or CZT (Fig. 7.15).

The dispersive filter implements a convolution which, to simplify the calculation, we can consider to be discrete

$$S_n = W^{-n^2}[(S_n W^{-n^2}) * W^{n^2}] \qquad (7.62)$$

where

$$W = \exp(j\pi/N) \qquad (7.63)$$

and where the asterisk denotes the convolution product

$$S_n = W^{-n^2} \sum_{m=0}^{N-1} (W^{(n-m)^2} s_m W^{-m^2}) \qquad (7.64)$$

or

$$S_n = \sum_{m=0}^{N-1} s_m W^{-2nm} = \sum_{m=1}^{N-1} s_m \exp(-2j\pi nm/N) \qquad (7.65)$$

We recognize this as the discrete Fourier transform (Bellanger 1981).

To understand this transformation intuitively, we note that a dispersive filter transmits successively the low and then the high frequencies of the signal (or vice versa, depending on the design of the filter). Premultiplication by a frequency ramp selects from the signal the frequency band to be explored, matched to the dispersive comb that extracts this fraction of the signal. Postmultiplication then restores the phase.

This transformation, like other similar transformations, is used principally in military applications. Interested readers are referred to specialized papers (Rabiner *et al.* 1969; Butler 1977; MacFall *et al.* 1977; Jack *et al.* 1980).

7.3.2 Implementation

The basic component for this type of transformation is the dispersive filter. These necessary devices can be constructed from phase-modulated

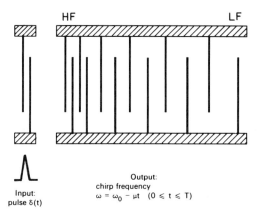

Fig. 7.16   Realization of a frequency ramp by a dispersive filter.

transducers (Section 5.2.4 Fig. 5.10), groove arrays (Section 5.4.2, Fig. 5.21; Section 5.7, Example 6, Figs 5.38–5.40), or multistrip reflector arrays (MRAs: Fig. 5.18). The filter is characterized by its bandwidth B and transit time T. When we feed a pulse into the input of a line consisting of a wideband transducer and a chirped transducer, the instantaneous frequency at the output is of the form (Fig. 7.16)

$$\omega = \omega_0 - \mu t \quad (0 \leqslant t \leqslant T)$$

i.e. a frequency *ramp* of slope μ.

The impulse response of such a line is then of the form $\exp(-j\mu t^2)$, in conformity with eqn (7.62). In practice, we need two signals reversed in time, of slope $+\mu$ and $-\mu$, respectively. We can realize this inversion exactly by heterodyning with a local oscillator and filtering, so that the final block diagram is as given by Fig. 7.17, with three identical dispersive lines (Tortoli and Andreucceti 1986).

7.3.3   Discussion and other forms of spectral analysis

The third dispersive line, used to restore the phase, can be suppressed provided we pick up the signal after filter F_1 (Fig. 7.17) and suitably delay it (without dispersion). When the phase is not significant, we can suppress this stage completely. The use of a single line (but of longer duration) has been proposed (Tortoli and Andreucceti 1986).

In addition, SAWs are particularly well suited to spatial separation of the spectral components of a signal: it is sufficient to use a bank of filters as

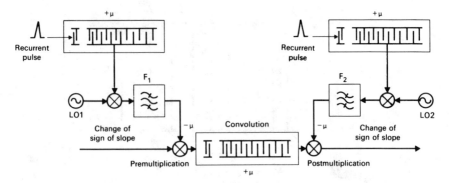

Fig. 7.17   Spectral analysis using three identical dispersive lines.

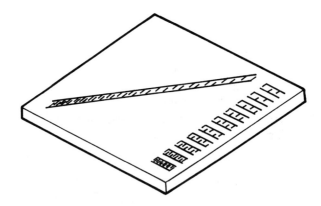

Fig. 7.18   The slanted chirped transducer spectrum analyzer (from Barnard *et al.* 1986).

in Fig. 4.20 (Feldmann and Hénaff 1976). We can also use a slanted chirped transducer as in Fig. 7.18 (Barnard *et al.* 1984, 1986).

A final possibility is offered by the construction of an electronically tunable narrow-bandwidth filter, constructed as an oscillator, but with loop gain less than unity (Fig. 7.19) (Hénaff and Feldmann 1980) (cf. Example 8, Chapter 6).

7.3.4   Conclusion

Surface acoustic waves are particularly well suited to processing the Fourier spectrum of a signal at frequencies inaccessible by other means,

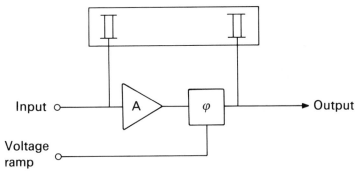

Fig. 7.19 Spectral analysis obtained by a narrow-bandwidth filter tuned electronically by a voltage ramp (Hénaff and Feldmann 1980).

especially by digital techniques. They can also be combined with digital or CCD post-processors to produce specialized routines, especially for military applications.

7.4   General survey of acousto-optic interactions

Acousto-optic surface interactions (Fig. 7.20) are produced by guiding an optical beam into a thin slice on the surface of a crystal such as lithium niobate, onto which a SAW is also directed (Kuhn *et al.* 1970).

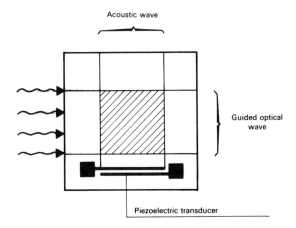

Fig. 7.20 Acousto-optic interaction.

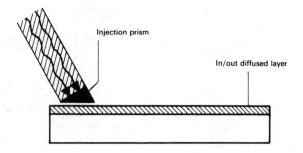

Fig. 7.21 Injection of an optical beam into an in-diffused (or out-diffused) layer by a prism.

An optical guide on lithium niobate can be produced by in-diffusion of titanium (or other metal) or out-diffusion of oxygen (Fig. 7.21) (Schmidt and Kaminow 1974; Schmidt 1975; Kaminow and Carruthers 1973).

We thus have at our disposal a thin slice whose optical refractive index on the surface is higher than the bulk index of the crystal. It follows from this that the optical wave, directed, for example, by a prism or grating (Dakss *et al.* 1970), is trapped between two less refractive layers, i.e. vacuum (or air) and the interior of the crystal, and remains on the surface.

The photon–phonon interaction is essentially nonlinear: the nonlinearity can be characterized by a phenomenological parameter (a tensor) called the acousto-optic coefficient. For surface waves, it is a relatively complicated combination of the relevant components of the tensor, and we can consider that a simple scalar χ_{NL} specifies the strength of the interaction.

In terms of signal processing, the complexity of the interaction can be characterized by the product BT (B the bandwidth of the acoustic signal, T the transit time of the acoustic signal across the optical field). The time T rarely exceeds $1\,\mu s$ and the bandwidth B is of the order of 10^7–10^8 Hz. The product BT is therefore still of the order of some 10–100 which limits this type of interaction to relatively modest complexity. Moreover, the strength of the interaction, related to the acousto-optic tensor, is never very great. For all these reasons, we are usually limited to the so-called first-order interactions, in which the emerging optical wave has a single wave vector defined by the law of conservation of momentum and energy:

$$\boldsymbol{K}_a + \boldsymbol{K}_o = \boldsymbol{K}_o' \qquad (7.66)$$

$$\Omega_a + \omega_o = \omega_o' \qquad (7.67)$$

where a refers to acoustics and o to optics, and $\boldsymbol{K}_a$, $\boldsymbol{K}_o$, $(\boldsymbol{K}_o')$ are the incident (emerging) wave vectors and Ω_a, $\omega_o(\omega_o')$ are the incident (emerging) angular frequencies.

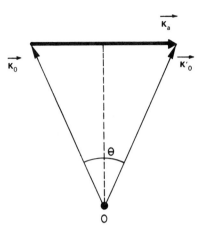

Fig. 7.22 Geometric representation of the conservation of momentum.

In practice

$$\Omega_{\mathrm{o}} \ll \omega_{\mathrm{o}}, \omega'_{\mathrm{o}} \tag{7.68}$$

$$|K_{\mathrm{a}}| \ll |K_{\mathrm{o}}|, |K'_{\mathrm{o}}| \tag{7.69}$$

From this we deduce that, when $|K_{\mathrm{o}}| = |K'_{\mathrm{o}}|$, the angle of deviation of the optical wave is (Fig. 7.22)

$$\theta \approx \frac{K_{\mathrm{a}}}{K_{\mathrm{o}}} = \frac{\Omega_{\mathrm{a}} v_{\mathrm{o}}}{v_{\mathrm{a}} \omega_{\mathrm{o}}} \tag{7.70}$$

where v_{a} and v_{o} are the phase velocities of the acoustic and optical waves respectively.

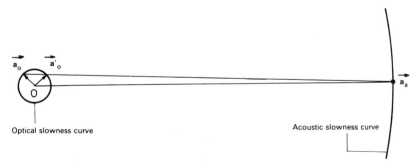

Fig. 7.23 Phase-matching ($|a_{\mathrm{a}}|/|a_0| \approx 10^5$).

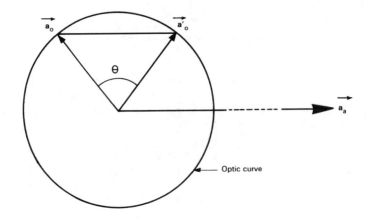

Fig. 7.24   The Bragg angle.

Phase-matching

As in purely acoustic nonlinear effects, the waves are nondispersive (a property already implicitly incorporated in eqn 7.71), so that phase-matching is obtained if the three slowness points are aligned on the slowness chart. If we take into account the very different velocities of optical and acoustic waves, the corresponding diagram is as shown schematically in Fig. 7.23 (and repeated in Fig. 7.24). If the optical curve is a circle, we have $|K_o| = |K'_o|$, and eqn (7.70) reappears. These phase conditions are called *Bragg conditions*, and the angle of incidence of the optical waves on the acoustic wave-front is called the *Bragg angle*.

Under Bragg conditions the interaction is cumulative by construction. Thus, despite the fact that the elementary interaction is weak, a complete deflection can be produced, and this can be used as a base for, say, a switching device.

In conclusion, the surface-wave acousto-optic effect is relatively limited in the product *BT* (number of separable points) and is relatively low in intensity. In practice this restricts its use to the Bragg conditions. With certain materials, e.g. lithium niobate, optical guides can readily be produced by in-diffusion.

7.5   Conclusion

Nonlinear effects have been deployed exclusively in the military field, particularly in the processing of radar signals. Their extension to the civil field is certainly only a question of time, because of their unique properties. It is nonetheless true that a large part of the study of the nonlinear effects is destined to remain in the area of research for some time to come.

Chapter 8

Materials and Technology

We propose in this chapter to describe the technological aspects of SAWs. The technology proper is quite similar to that of microelectronics, and it is this that has determined the rapid industrial development of the technique. The original material is in general different, since we are concerned with piezoelectric insulators (certain semiconductors, e.g. GaAs, can however be used). We shall first review possible materials and then deal with the technological processes.

8.1   Materials for surface waves

The qualities required for a good surface-wave material can be classified as follows:

(a) availability at moderate cost;
(b) good mechanical properties and resistance to environmental effects (e.g. humidity);
(c) fair electromechanical coupling;
(d) good temperature stability.

At present, availability at moderate cost is really achieved only for the most commonly used materials, e.g. quartz, lithium niobate and lithium tantalate. As far as the piezoelectric properties and temperature stability are concerned, the situation can be summarized as follows: there are good piezoelectric materials, i.e. materials with good electromechanical coupling, such as lithium tantalate and especially lithium niobate, but the corresponding known cuts have very high temperature sensitivity (of the order of 90 ppm K^{-1}), which sometimes prevents these devices from performing their function.

There is, on the other hand, a material with poor coupling, i.e. quartz, which has the advantage of a cut with zero first-order temperature coefficient. This is the so called ST cut.

In this section, we assess several known materials for possible configurations in terms of the *piezoelectric coupling coefficients* and *frequency temperature coefficients*.

8.1.1 Computer program

8.1.1.1 Principles

There is really no sure prescription for finding cuts with a zero temperature coefficient. We can say, however that the temperature coefficient can vanish only if there are bulk-wave temperature coefficients of both signs. This criterion eliminates lithium niobate as a possible candidate. Otherwise, tabulation of temperature coefficients seems to be the only practical method. The number of points to be explored for surface waves is very large (we must note both the cut and the direction of propagation). For a step of 5°, there are 1650 directions on a sphere and 72 on a circle, needing 118 800 calculations for a single exploration at a given temperature. Since a temperature coefficient requires two different calculations, each lasting about 0.1 min (on the HB6000 computer), we see that a complete tabulation would require about 10 days' computation!

Fortunately, we can take advantage of symmetries and use a larger step, except for ambiguous zones. The examination of a given material such as quartz needs at least 10 hours of computation (without counting the time taken to construct the program).

8.1.1.2 Computation

There is nothing original about the principle of the calculation itself. The flow chart (Fig. 8.1) is similar to that used by Campbell and Jones (1968).

The computation is carried out as follows. We choose an adequate tabulation with a fairly coarse step (10°), taking into account the symmetry of the materials studied and the Kramer degeneracy (in view of reciprocity) in the velocities. For each point to be tabulated, we fix a reference temperature (20°) and calculate the phase velocities for two temperatures $T - \Delta T$ and $T + \Delta T$. We write the tensors of constants relative to canonical axes for the particular cut, and proceed according to the algorithm described in Chapter 2. The corresponding computer program is given in Appendix J.

8.1.1.3 Presentation of results

The results can be summarized by considering the zero FTC line (when it exists) on the stereographic projection of the normals to the different

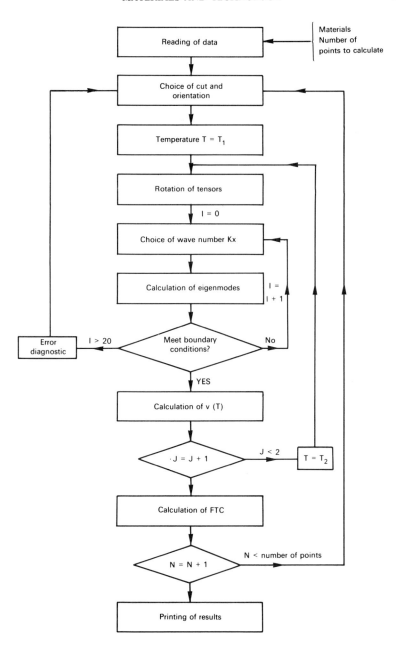

Fig. 8.1 Flow diagram for calculating the FTC (frequency temperature coefficient).

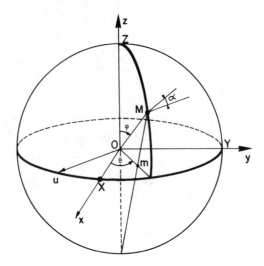

Fig. 8.2 Definition of cut and orientation. The normal to the plane is defined by the angles θ and ϕ. The direction of propagation in the plane is referred to the intersection Ou of this plane with the (x, y) plane.

cuts. In fact, each stereographic projection is associated with one direction of propagation on a cut, relative to a reference direction which can be taken as the intersection of the plane of the cut and the XOY plane (Fig. 8.2); we take OX as the reference direction for the cut Z).

Finally, we need three real parameters to represent a cut and a direction of propagation, and the resulting set of points can be represented by a volume in three dimensions. The three parameters being angles, their periodicity enables us to imagine this volume as a torus whose transverse section represents the stereographic projection of the cuts (Fig. 8.3) and whose parallels correspond to the directions of propagation within each cut. Within this toroidal volume, we seek surfaces of equal FTC and of equal coupling constants.

8.1.2   Results for quartz

The torus representing the different configurations contains a surface of zero FTC, which must pass through the so-called ST configuration. The points with largest coupling coefficient ($k^2 > 0.3\%$) are concentrated on the $\alpha = 0°$ and $\alpha = 10°$ sections. Unfortunately, these coupling constants do not correspond to zero FTC. The ST cut with coupling constant $k = 0.13\%$ is still one of the most favorable.

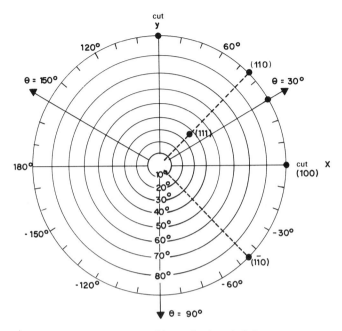

Fig. 8.3 Stereographic projection defining cuts.

However, the optimum is a doubly rotated cut with $\alpha = 20°$, $\theta = 45°$ and $\phi = 45°$, and a coupling constant 30% greater than that of the ST cut. In certain cases, this can compensate for the difficulty of cutting the corresponding crystal plates. The characteristic parameters of these two cuts are summarized in Table 8.1.

The chart of Fig. 8.4 corresponds to $\alpha = 20°$, and the full lines represent constant values of the coupling coefficient; on the broken lines, the first-order temperature coefficient is zero. Point A represents the chosen cut ($\alpha = 20°$, $\theta = 45°$, $\phi = 45°$).

In practice, ST quartz is almost exclusively employed. Its frequency is shown as a function of temperature in Fig. 8.5 (cf. Section 6.3.2). Nevertheless, the cut is sometimes modified slightly so as to adjust the temperature inversion point (20 °C).

There does not seem to be a cut of quartz whose surface behavior is a cubic function of temperature (and not simply parabolic as in Fig. 8.4). Nevertheless, on the first pseudomode surface shell, there are SSBW modes in the neighborhood of the AT cut, which is well known for bulk waves (Cady 1946) and displays more favorable (parabolic) behavior.

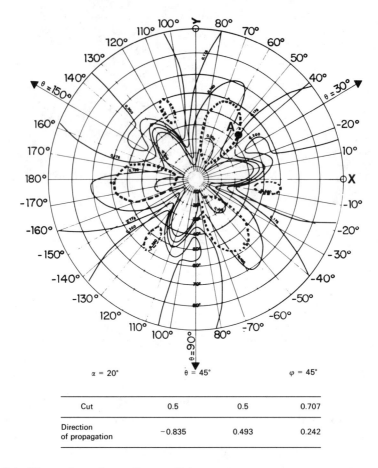

	$\alpha = 20°$	$\theta = 45°$	$\varphi = 45°$
Cut	0.5	0.5	0.707
Direction of propagation	−0.835	0.493	0.242

Fig. 8.4 Lines of equal coupling coefficient and zero temperature coefficient for $\alpha = 20°$ in quartz. Point A indicates the optimum and corresponds to a doubly rotated cut ($\theta = 45°$, $\phi = 45°$).

8.1.3   Results for lithium tantalate

The same procedure can be applied to lithium tantalate. We note first that there is no orientation with zero FTC (the temperature coefficients range from about 30 to 60 ppm).

The piezoelectric coupling coefficients are defined according to the same convention as for quartz, but there is much greater uncertainty in the values

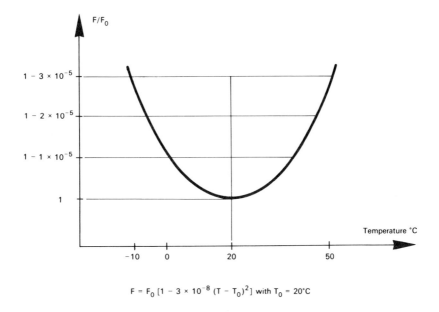

$$F = F_0 [1 - 3 \times 10^{-8} (T - T_0)^2] \text{ with } T_0 = 20°C$$

Fig. 8.5 The relative frequency of ST quartz as a function of temperature.

Table 8.1 Principal parameters of interesting cuts of quartz

	Angles			Cut			Propagation		
	α	θ	φ	X	Y	Z	X	Y	Z
Quartz: ST^a	0°	90°	47° 25	0	0.734	0.679	−1	0	0
Quartz: maximum k^2 at FTC = 0	20°	45°	45°	0.500	0.500	0.707	−0.835	0.493	0.242

	v (m s^{-1})	k^2 (%)	Ψ^b (d°)	β^c (10^{-8} K^{-2})	FTC (ppm)	$\varepsilon_{LF}/\varepsilon_0$
Quartz: ST^a	3159.2	0.14	0	−4	0	4.56
Quartz: maximum k^2 at FTC = 0	3493.9	0.17	3° 86	−8.7	0	4.56

[a]Schulz *et al.* (1970).
[b] Ψ: beam steering angle (power flow angle).
[c] β: second-order temperature coefficient.

Table 8.2   Principal parameters of interesting cuts of lithium tantalate

	Angles			Cut			Propagation		
	α	θ	φ	X	Y	Z	X	Y	Z
LiTaO$_3$: (A)	90°	30°	80°	0.853	0.492	0.174	-0.150	-0.087	0.985
LiTaO$_3$: (B)	20°	25°	35°	0.520	0.242	0.819	-0.651	0.733	0.196

	v (m s^{-1})	k^2 (%)	Ψ[a] (d°)	β[b] (10^{-8} K^{-2})	FTC (ppm)	$\varepsilon_{LF}/\varepsilon_0$
LiTaO$_3$: (A)	3298.6	1.36	0	—	31	47.29
LiTaO$_3$: (B)	3423.8	1.52	1° 33	—	49	48.25

[a] Ψ: power flow angle.
[b] β: second-order temperature coefficient.

of the e_{ij} coefficients in the coupling matrix. This uncertainty is due to the influence of Li/Ta stoichiometry in commercial samples.

With these reservations, we note among the most favorable zones the rotated Y cut ($\alpha = 90°$, $\theta = 30°$ and $\phi = 80°$) with a coupling coefficient of 1.4% and FTC of 30 ppm. The maximum coupling exceeds 1.5% for the doubly rotated cut ($\alpha = 20°$, $\theta = 25°$ and $\phi = 35°$) (cf. Table 8.2).

It is also possible to obtain satisfactory temperature dependence by using a substrate of LiTaO$_3$ (Y cut, propagation in the Z direction), and a silica overlay (Parker and Schulz 1975). For example, for an oscillator operating at 825 MHz (Hénaff et al. 1978), a variation of 0.6 ppm K^{-1} has been obtained in the range 0–40 °C in place of 38 ppm K^{-1} for the uncompensated tantalate. Finally, an improvement in the temperature behavior can be achieved by using temperature-compensated oscillators (Hénaff and Feldmann 1978).

8.1.4   Results for lithium niobate

Lithium niobate is not expected to have a cut with zero temperature coefficient. This is confirmed by calculation. In fact, the FTC is almost constant at high values of the order of 75–95 ppm.

As regards piezoelectric coupling, the strongest coupling amounts to 5.5%, compared with 4.45% for the classical YZ cut. The corresponding orientation ($\alpha = 0°$, $\theta = 30°$, $\phi = 40°$) gives, in addition, a low FTC (72 ppm) for a Y cut simply rotated through 130°. This cut has been reported for $\phi = 41.5°$ by Slobodnik and Conway (1970) (cf. Table 8.3).

Table 8.3 Principal parameters of interesting cuts of lithium niobate

	Angles			Cut			Propagation		
	α	θ	φ	X	Y	Z	X	Y	Z
LiNbO$_3$: YZ	90°	90°	90°	0	1	0	0	0	1
LiNbO$_3$[a]	0°	30°	41°5	0.574	0.331	0.749	−0.500	0.866	0

	v (m s^{-1})	k^2 (%)	Ψ[b] (d°)	β[c] (10^{-8} K^{-2})	FTC (ppm)	$\varepsilon_{LF}/\varepsilon_0$
LiNbO$_3$: YZ	3491.1	4.86	0	—	94	45.84
LiNbO$_3$[a]	4003.6	5.57	0	—	72	55.19

[a] Slobodnik and Conway (1970).
[b] Ψ: power flow angle.
[c] β: second-order temperature coefficient.

We note that the SSBW modes with strong coupling (up to 17%) discovered by Yamanouchi and Shibayama (1972) and Takayanagi et al. (1970) have been used in acoustoelectric amplification (Hénaff et al. 1974a; Hénaff and Feldmann 1974). Figure 8.6 illustrates the characteristic behavior of the surface permittivity.

8.1.5 Results for berlinite

Berlinite (AlPO$_4$) is a crystal very similar to quartz as far as structure, mechanical properties and piezoelectric properties are concerned. The importance of this material has been emphasized by Carr and O'Connell (1976) and Jhunjhunwala et al. (1976).

Compared with quartz, the piezoelectric coupling constant of berlinite is greater by a factor of almost 4, but its temperature coefficient, which is zero to the first order, has second-order values that are perceptibly higher (Detaint et al. 1979) (cf. Table 8.4).

The practical importance of this crystal could become quite considerable if the material becomes commercially available.

Figure 8.7 gives the berlinite map for $\alpha = 0°$. Point B indicates the ST cut ($\alpha = 0°$, $\theta = 90°$, $\phi = 87.1°$).

8.1.6 The thallium chalcogenides

Two chalcogenides of thallium, Tl$_3$VS$_4$ and Tl$_3$TaSe$_4$, have been studied from the piezoelectric viewpoint (Weinert and Isaacs 1975; Hénaff and

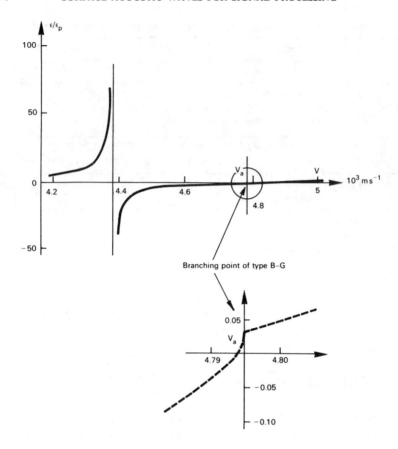

Fig. 8.6 Pseudomode surface permittivity $(Y + 41°, X)$ in lithium niobate: the insert shows that the branching point is typical of a Bleustein–Gulyaev mode.

Feldmann 1977a, b, 1982). These materials have very large coupling coefficients and zero temperature coefficients (cf. Tables 8.5 and 8.6), but low velocities and poor mechanical properties (they are too "soft") which makes them usable only at low frequencies ($< 70\,\text{MHz}$).

8.1.7 The "banana"

The word "banana" is used for the crystal with the formula $Ba_2NaNb_5O_{15}$. It belongs to a family called tungsten bronzes (its structure has been examined for electro-optical effects and nonlinear optical properties).

Table 8.4 Principal parameters of interesting cuts of berlinite

	Angles			Cut			Propagation		
	α	θ	φ	X	Y	Z	X	Y	Z
A	6° 75	90	90	0	1	0	−0.993	0	0.117
B	22° 3	0	90	1	0	0	0	−0.925	−0.379
C	6° 875	45	45	0.5	0.5	0.707	0.762	0.642	0.085
ST	0	90	87.1	0	0.999	0.050	−1	0	0
D	0	90	90	0	1	0	1	0	0

	v (m s^{-1})	k^2 (%)	$\varepsilon_{LF}/\varepsilon$	Ψ[a]	β[b] (10^{-8} K^{-2})	T_i^c (°C)
A	2752.6	0.57	6.14	4° 36	1.34	20
B	2756.6	0.55	6.11	0° 76	0.7	18
C	3060.6	0.86	6.04	4° 36	1.25	20
ST	2736.5	0.56	6.14	0	2.06	19
D	2739.6	0.58	6.14	0	2	25

[a] Ψ: power flow angle.
[b] β: second-order temperature coefficient.
[c] T_i: inversion temperature.

It is not very well known in piezoelectricity, but it seems to combine very desirable properties, i.e. good mechanical behavior, easy growth, appreciable coupling (1.3%) and good temperature stability ($\sim 10^{-6}$ K^{-1}), as indicated in Table 8.7 (Hénaff and Feldmann 1983). The large differences between measured and calculated values are due to the fact that the theoretical coefficients are quite old and refer to crystals from different sources (and therefore probably of different composition).

8.1.8   The III–V semiconductors

The importance of III–V semiconductors lies in the great variety of their properties. They are the basic materials used in semiconductor lasers, and often serve as substrates in monolithic optoelectronics and integrated optics. The combination (on the same plate) of optics, electronics and acoustics can lead to complex devices. So far, only piezoelectric components of this kind (e.g. monolithic oscillators (Grudkowski *et al.* 1980) have been tested.

The main crystal of this family is gallium arsenide (GaAs) which has very weak piezoelectric coupling on the surface branch (Campbell and Jones

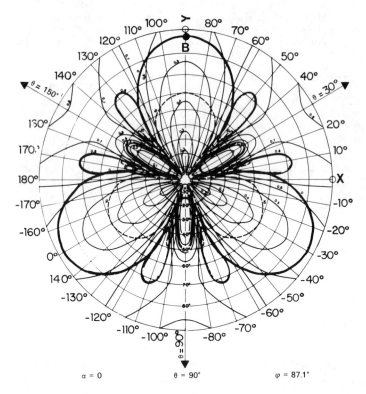

Fig. 8.7 Lines of equal coupling coefficient and zero temperature coefficient for $\alpha = 0$ in berlinite. Point B represents the ST cut ($\alpha = 0°$, $\theta = 90°$, $\phi = 87.1°$).

1970; Szabo and Slobodnik 1973; Swierkowski *et al.* 1973), a pseudo-mode with a coupling of 0.11% has been demonstrated (Hénaff *et al.* 1981b Table 8.8). The second material is indium phosphide (InP) which is slightly less favorable from the piezoelectric viewpoint (Hénaff *et al.* 1982).

8.2   Design of masks for SAW devices

8.2.1   Device design

The design of SAW devices consists of the following stages:

Table 8.5 Principal parameters of interesting cuts of thallium tantaloselenide

	Angles			Cut			Propagation		
	α	θ	φ	X	Y	Z	X	Y	Z
D	9	30	60	0.750	0.433	0.500	−0.562	0.816	0.135
E	51	60	45	0.354	0.612	0.707	−0.820	−0.161	0.550
F	60	40	68	0.710	0.596	0.375	−0.570	0.174	0.803
G	60	45	39.5	0.450	0.450	0.772	−0.826	−0.119	0.551
H	70	25	60	0.785	0.366	0.500	−0.570	0.111	0.814
J	70.75	32	38	0.522	0.326	0.788	−0.806	−0.115	0.581
K	50	0	62.75	0.889	0	0.458	−0.351	0.643	0.681

	v (m s^{-1})	k^2 (%)	$\varepsilon_{LF}/\varepsilon$	Ψ^a	β^b (10^{-8} K^{-2})	T_i^c (°C)
D	847.1	4.17	11.40	14.57	−10.7	25
E	847.4	4.01	11.59	13.59	10.7	23
F	852.5	4.01	11.56	−12.74	−11.3	17
G	843.6	4.16	11.33	15.68	−10	24
H	846.8	4.17	11.26	−15.93	−9.5	30
J	849.9	4.17	11.24	16.57	−8.9	21
K	870.8	4.12	11.44	0	−11.2	20

[a] Ψ: power flow angle.
[b] β: second-order temperature coefficient.
[c] T_i: inversion temperature.

(a) specification of bandwidth, selectivity and temperature stability;
(b) choice of central frequency, material and dimensions;
(c) transducer specification, calculation and possible matching;
(d) simulation, evaluation of side-effects and final choices;
(e) computer-aided design of masks.

Programs for the fabrication of masks differ from other microelectronics computer software by:

(a) greater simplicity due to the limited number of transducers, simple interconnections and the fact that, in general, only a single level of masking is employed; however, two, three or more masks have to be used for multiphase transducers, or when different technologies are combined (etched arrays and transducers, for example);
(b) greater precision, especially of geometric dimensions, because analog operation requires absolute and not just relative specification;

Table 8.6 Interesting parameters of the principal cut of thallium vanadosulfide

Angles			Cut			Propagation			v	k^2	$\varepsilon_{LF}/\varepsilon_0$	Ψ^a	β^b	T_i^c
α	θ	φ	X	Y	Z	X	Y	Z	$(\mathrm{m\,s^{-1}})$	(%)			$(10^{-8}\,\mathrm{K^{-2}})$	(°C)
0	45	73	0.676	0.676	0.292	−0.707	0.707	0	959.26	3.12	37.8	0	−22.9	20

^{a} Ψ: power flow angle.
^{b} β: second-order temperature coefficient.
^{c} T_i: inversion temperature.

Table 8.7 Principal parameters of interesting cuts of the "banana"

	Angles			Cut XYZ	Propagation XYZ	v_0 $(\mathrm{m\,s^{-1}})$		k^2	$\dfrac{\varepsilon_{LF}}{\varepsilon_0}$	ψ	FTC $(\mathrm{ppm\,K^{-1}})$	
	α	θ	φ			Calculated	Experimental	(%)			Calculated	Experimental
A	90°	0	45°	101	101	3270	3335^a 3337^b	1.35	108	0	176	1.5^b
B	90°	90°	45°	011	011	3273	3341^b	1.19	110	0	68	3^b

^{a} Experiment at 273 MHz.
^{b} Experiments at 822–823 MHz.

Table 8.8 Principal parameters of interesting cuts of gallium arsenide (GaAs) and indium phosphide (InP)

	Angles			Cut XYZ	Propagation XYZ	Velocity (m s^{-1})		Coupling coefficient (%)		
	α	θ	φ			Calculated	Experimental	Calculated	Experimental	
GaAs										
A	90°	45°	0°	001	$\bar{1}10$	2863		0.09		
B Surface mode	0°	45°	54°7′	111	$\bar{1}10$	2426		—		
B Pseudomode	0°	45°	54°7′	111	$\bar{1}10$	3240		0.11		
InP										
A	90°	45°	0°	001	$\bar{1}10$	2639	2267	0.0384	0.02	R^a
B	0°	45°	54°7′	111	$\bar{1}10$	2133		5.6×10^{-5}		
C	0°	45°	54°7′	111	$\bar{1}10$	2992		0.056		
D	90°	45°	90°	110	001	2595	2576	0.013	0.012	R^a
E	0°	45°	90°	110	$\bar{1}10$	3113	3089	2×10^{-5}		B^b

[a] R = Rayleigh.
[b] B = Bleustein–Gulyaev.

(c) the use of relatively large patterns, which limits the possibilities of photocomposition of one pattern on a single mask.

8.2.2   Program for fabricating transducer masks

This program is written in FORTRAN and is given in Appendix K. It generates a sequence of weights w_1, w_2, w_3, . . . , by limiting spurious capacitances and allowing for possible changes of sign. By way of example, Fig. 8.8 illustrates the method of producing a change of sign in the sequence $(2, 6, -2, -7, -6)$ (cf. Section 5.1.2).

Moreover, it is desirable to add "dummy fingers" as in Fig. 8.9 to maintain a constant metallization ratio of 50% and thus avoid distortion of wave-fronts.

8.2.3   Necessary equipment

The design of a device is usually carried out on a large computer, so that the advantages of peripherals such as hard disks, VDUs, magnetic tapes and connection to the telephone network can be exploited. The device is designed

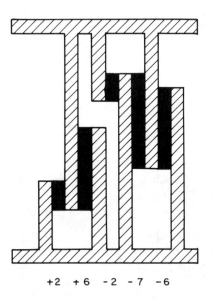

+2   + 6   - 2   - 7   - 6

Fig. 8.8   Realization of a set of weights $(2, 6, -2, -7, -6)$ with a change of sign (the active zones are shown in black).

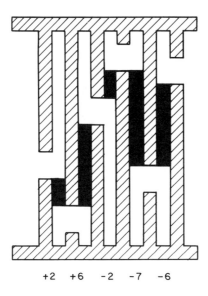

+2   +6   -2   -7   -6

Fig. 8.9 Comb equivalent to that in Fig. 8.8, but with "dummy fingers" used to avoid distortion of wave-fronts.

and tested, and the lay-out programs are stored on magnetic tape for a plotting table, or a "pattern generator", or indeed scanning electron beam lithography. The mask (or masks) is then made by the same techniques as in microelectronics, and is used for photolithographic operations.

8.3   Techniques for fabricating SAW devices

Usually, SAW devices are produced by the planar fabrication method illustrated in Fig. 8.10, or a variant thereof. (For further information, readers are referred to Smith (1974, 1977).) The polished surface of the substrate is covered by a film of polymer that is sensitive to certain wavelengths. The sandwich is then exposed to suitable radiation on which a pattern has been imposed by a mask representing the design of the SAW device.

The exposed (or unexposed, according to its polarity) polymer is then removed in a development stage, leaving the required pattern in relief on the surface of the substrate. One can then etch the substrate (a), dope it chemically (b), or deposit another metal in the interstices of the polymer relief pattern (c).

A variation of this process (cf. Fig. 8.11) that is generally used consists of depositing a metallic layer on the polished surface of the substrate before

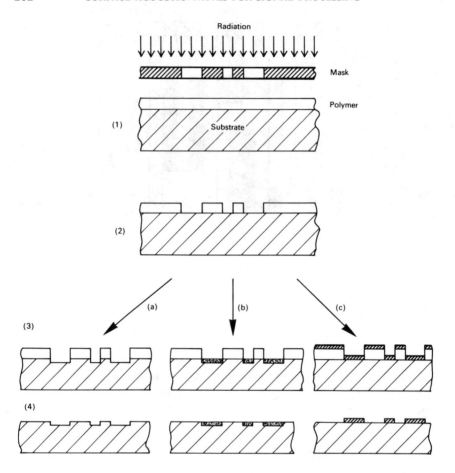

Fig. 8.10 Different techniques for the manufacture of SAW devices: (a) etching of the substrate; (b) chemical doping of the substrate; (c) selective deposit of metal ("inverse etching").

covering it with the polymer film. After exposure and removal of the resin, the metallic layer is etched as in (a).

8.3.1 Exposure

Exposure is the operation in the course of which the polymer film is illuminated through the appropriate mask by radiation of suitable wavelength. Several procedures can be used.

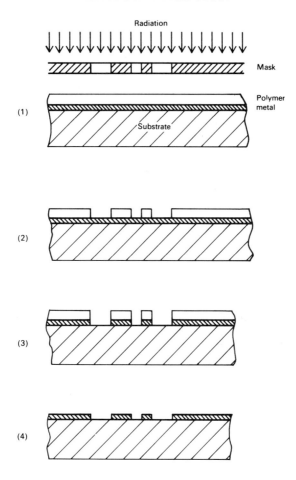

Fig. 8.11 Classical etching technique for a metallic layer: (1) deposition of metal, coating with photoresist resin, exposure; (2) after development; (3) after chemical treatment; (4) after cleaning.

8.3.1.1 Optical printing

An optical system forms the image of the mask on the substrate coated with a *photoresist* (e.g. Shipley's AZ1350) with a demagnification factor of 1/5 or 1/10. The main advantage of this method is that neither the mask nor the substrate is destroyed; its principal disadvantage is that its resolution is inferior to that of the other procedures. It is therefore reserved for mass-produced devices with linewidths exceeding 1 μm.

8.3.1.2   Contact printing

This is the most widely used photolithographic technique for SAW devices. The mask is placed in contact with (or very close to) a photoresist layer on the substrate and collimated ultraviolet radiation is used to transfer the pattern of the mask to the photosensitive layer. The results are excellent up to linewidths of 0.8 μm if the air gap between the mask and the resin-coated substrate is thin enough to eliminate diffraction effects. This is achieved by evacuating the space between the mask and the substrate after they have been aligned.

Smith et al. (1971, 1974) and Melngailis et al. (1975) have proposed an improvement of this procedure in which very thin photomasks (0.2 mm) can be slightly deformed so as to fit as well as possible over the whole surface. This method has a resolution of the order of 0.4 μm over very large areas (up to 100 cm^2), provided the substrate is very well polished and dust free. It is not used in production at present, because it requires great skill on the part of the operator.

8.3.1.3   Holographic recording

Although little used, holographic techniques appear to be ideal for recording gratings in photoresist films (Shank and Schmidt 1973) gratings are produced by interference between two plane waves issuing from the same laser, emitting in the region between the visible and the ultraviolet ranges (e.g. at $\lambda = 3250$ Å for the He–Cd laser). Given the difficulties of alignment of these gratings relative to the substrate, and especially to the transducer already deposited on them, the holographic technique is used mainly to fabricate masks that are used later as other photomasks.

8.3.1.4   Scanning electron-beam lithography

A finely focused electron beam can be scanned over the substrate (covered with a polymer film sensitive to electrons), the scanning in X and Y being controlled by the pattern to be reproduced (Broers and Hatzakis 1969). The first systems were produced by modified scanning electronic microscopes (Wolf et al. 1973). The principal advantage of electron-beam lithography is its excellent resolution (approximately 1000 Å). The disadvantages include the limited field (approximately 1 mm^2) and certain problems connected with the charging up of the surface to be treated. Moreover, the first noncommercial devices were slow, complex and costly. This has now been remedied and there are numerous specialized electronic mask makers marketed by Cambridge, ETEC (Perkin-Elmer), Varian, JEOL, Philips and so on. Advances toward greater and greater speeds have been achieved by generating images with:

(a) the "raster scan" in which the object to be irradiated moves continuously in the Y-direction while scanning in the X-direction is being carried out electronically (over some hundreds of microns); the final image is produced by the juxtaposition of strips of this width;

(b) enlarged spots or spots of definite shape (generally rectangular and adjustable).

8.3.1.5 X-ray lithography

The principle employed is the same as that of contact photolithography (cf. Section 8.3.1.2), but the wavelength of the radiation used is in the range 4–44 Å, which greatly reduces the diffraction effects (Spears and Smith 1972).

The essential problem is the realization of a mask presented in the form of a fine membrane, semitransparent to the X-rays, on which the pattern is made with an absorbing material. For example, 4000 Å of gold can be deposited on a film of mylar, 6 μm thick, or a wafer of silicon, 3 μm thick (at $\lambda = 8$ Å).

The principal advantage is the excellent resolution (approximately 500 Å) combined with simplicity and low cost (it is not necessary, as with the electron beam to irradiate in vacuum).

Possible distortions are the major disadvantage (geometric distortion and distortion of the mask).

8.3.2 Etching

The oldest method, and still the most widely used in mass production, is aqueous chemical etching. It has numerous versions, but essentially involves the deposition in vacuum of the desired metal film (e.g. 2000 Å of aluminium) as uniformly and homogeneously as possible, on the piezoelectric crystal that has been previously oriented, polished, carefully cleaned and cleared of grease (Smith 1977). The metal is then coated with a photoresist which is exposed by one of the methods described above. Finally, after appropriate development and baking of the photoresist, the unprotected metal is etched.

8.3.2.1 Aqueous etching

Aqueous chemical etching has to be fitted to the metal–substrate combination, i.e. the chemical agent must attack the metal, but not the photoresist or the crystal. A dozen etching agents suitable for most commonly used metals, e.g. aluminium, can be found in Smith (1977). They include:

(a) 80 ml phosphoric acid, 10 ml water, 5 ml nitric acid;
(b) one part of concentrated hydrochloric acid in four parts of water;

(c) a solution of soda in water (but this is incompatible with the Shipley AZ1350 photoresist).

Generally, these etching agents can be used without problems on quartz and lithium niobate, but they must be tested beforehand and adjusted for other, less inert, substrates.

Depending on dimensions of the material, nature of the substrate, thickness and nature of the metal and so on, the concentration of the etching agent, its temperature, the time of application and so on, may have to be modified, but once the process has been optimized it is very fast, cheap and suitable for a large number of identical pieces. The method is therefore very well adapted to mass production of SAW devices as long as the dimensions of the fingers are larger than 2 μm.

8.3.2.2   Plasma etching

This is also chemical etching, but no longer in an aqueous medium: RF plasma of the etching gas is used. The technique is very widely used in the semiconductor industry for the etching of silicon, silica and silicon nitride. It has been adapted, among other things, to the etching of gratings for quartz SAW resonators.

8.3.2.3   Ion etching

Ion bombardment of a surface gives rise to the emission of atoms from the surface as a result of momentum transfer. Any material can be treated in this way, but in the case of insulators, charge build-up on the surface must be avoided by using RF or ion-neutralization techniques. The system consists of an ion source (argon plasma), an ion extractor that communicates the required energy to the ions and a target on which the element to be etched is placed. The surface of the element is protected by a metal film and/or photoresist layer the thickness of which depends on the depth of etching required.

This method is used principally to etch out grooves in the reflection gratings of SAW resonators. It gives excellent results, the only problem being the overheating of the element despite the presence of a cooling system. This overheating can lead to an expansion of the element and, subsequently, to difficulties in superposition of masks, as used with metallic transducers.

8.3.2.4   Lift-off technique

This is a variant of the preceding methods in which certain operations are interchanged. The photoresist is deposited directly on the substrate, an "inverted" mask is exposed, unwanted photoresist is removed and metal is deposited over the entire surface of the crystal. Finally, the photoresist is dissolved with a solvent (in general, acetone). All that remains is the metal lodged between the photoresist tracks (cf. Fig. 8.10c). This is possible only if there is no continuity between the metal deposited on the surface of the crystal and that deposited on top of the photoresist. It is therefore necessary, on the one hand, that the side walls of the photoresist be strictly vertical and, on the other, that the metal being deposited must arrive in the form of a vertical parallel beam. One of the problems encountered is that of good adhesion of the metal. This is achieved only if the substrate is perfectly clean. The advantages of the lift method are:

(a) chemically reactive substrates can be used;
(b) there is a greater choice of metals;
(c) very good resolution ($\simeq 0.7$–$0.8\,\mu\text{m}$);
(d) a high fabrication yield.

8.3.3 Mounting and matching

As with microelectronic integrated circuits, it is possible for SAW devices to proceed to multiple fabrication (or "batch processing"), i.e. to the use of a large crystalline substrate and a mask on which the desired pattern is repeated many times by a photographic process (cf. Fig. 8.12). This technique obviously allows an appreciable reduction in cost through mass production. It is thus necessary, before the crystals are mounted, to divide the plate into elementary devices.

In any case, it is useful to scratch the reverse face roughly beforehand (a precaution to be taken before finally polishing the front face, so as not to disturb it later) and to bevel the edges so as to avoid spurious SAW reflections.

The crystal is mounted on a metallic or ceramic unit (type TO5, TO8 or flat-pack) and firmly attached to its base. The transducers are then connected to the terminals of the unit (or to the metallized parts of the ceramic) by an aluminium wire, $50\,\mu\text{m}$ in diameter, soldered ultrasonically or, less commonly, by thermal compression. An acoustically absorbing material is then placed on the edges of the crystal to absorb the acoustic waves and avoid all spurious reflections.

This manufacturing procedure makes obvious certain advantages of these devices:

(a) the planar form allows mass production by techniques that will be quite standard from now on;

(b) the characteristics of the device are defined by the photomask, which ensures good reproducibility;

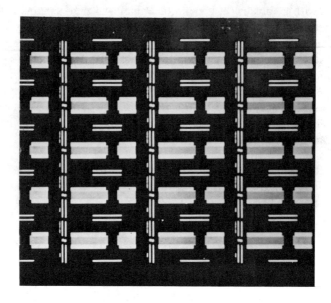

Fig. 8.12   Photographically produced multiple mask.

(c) adhesion of the delay line and of its soldered connections ensure great mechanical strength, as well as good heat dissipation, which allows high power levels in the devices.

Figures 8.13–8.16 illustrate some mountings of elementary isolated crystals. It is also possible, as Figs 8.17 and 8.18 show, to mount the SAW device directly on a ceramic bearing a hybrid amplifier.

Except for the last case, the SAW device is placed between two matching networks that connect it to the circuits. These networks are in general necessary to avoid reflections, to reduce insertion loss and to introduce complementary filtering beyond the useful band.

In the frequency range in which SAW devices operate most satisfactorily, the input impedances of the systems into which these devices are integrated and the input impedances of the measuring instruments are often purely resistive and equal to $50\,\Omega$. It is therefore often advantageous to match the SAW devices to this impedance, which also guarantees their interchangeability. A computer program for calculating the necessary matching elements (inductive and capacitive) to fit any comb, taking account of parasitic elements, is given in Appendix L (program PEIGNE).

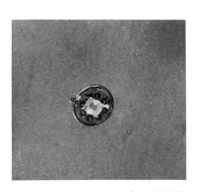

Fig. 8.13 Mounting of a 300 MHz filter in a TO5 package.

Fig. 8.14 Mounting of a wide-band (20%) 70 MHz filter in a TO8 unit.

Fig. 8.15 Mounting of a filter for an oscillator on gallium arsenide.

Fig. 8.16 Mounting of a 70 MHz IF filter in a TO8 unit between two hybrid amplifiers: this arrangement allows interchangeability of the IF filter according to the desired bandwidth (Hénaff and Brossard 1981).

Fig. 8.17 Examples of SAW oscillators: the SAW delay line is welded directly to the midpoint of the amplifier.

 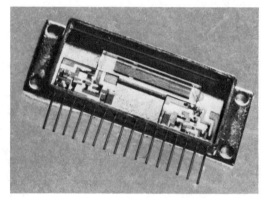

Fig. 8.18 Examples of SAW filters mounted between two amplifiers (Hénaff and Brossard 1981).

8.4 Example of device design

Finally, we propose to give in detail the different stages of the design of a particular device, chosen quite simply in the interests of clarity, but complex enough to illustrate, in a nontrivial way, the various techniques.

8.4.1 Specification

Suppose it is required to produce a SAW filter operating at a central frequency of 70 MHz with a 3 dB bandwidth of 5 MHz, a ripple of $\leqslant 0.5$ dB

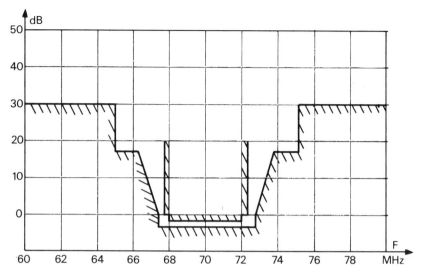

Fig. 8.19 Specification of a filter.

within 4.25 MHz and rejection level $\geqslant 30\,\mathrm{dB}$ (Fig. 8.19). Insertion losses are to be $\leqslant 25\,\mathrm{dB}$.

The required frequency stability is $\pm\,200\,\mathrm{kHz}$ ($\leqslant \pm\,3.10^{-3}$) swing for a $\pm\,25°$ from the ambient temperature. If aging and the drift of the other components give rise to effects comparable with those of temperature variation, frequency stability demands that the FTC must be

$$\mathrm{FTC} \leqslant \frac{200\,\mathrm{kHz}}{70\,\mathrm{MHz}} \times \frac{1}{3} \times \frac{1}{25} = 40\,\mathrm{ppm}$$

8.4.2 Technological choices

Examination of Table 5.1 shows that the choice of the piezoelectric material falls on lithium niobate, lithium tantalate and berlinite. The availability of berlinite is still inadequate, and considerations of temperature stability point to the use of YZ lithium tantalate. The attenuation in the pass-band may not force the matching of the transducers (perhaps it will be necessary to compensate their capacitance by a series inductance), and the simple technology of two two-phase combs should be sufficient. The required rejection, given the bandwidth, does not justify recourse to an MSC (its technology is still rather delicate and it uses a large crystal surface).

8.4.3   Filter synthesis

A rough treatment of the problem is effected by the window method (cf. Section 5.2.2).

The use of two apodized transducers complicates the problem of synthesis because the correspondence between the effective impulse response and the overlap length of electrodes is valid only when there is a second

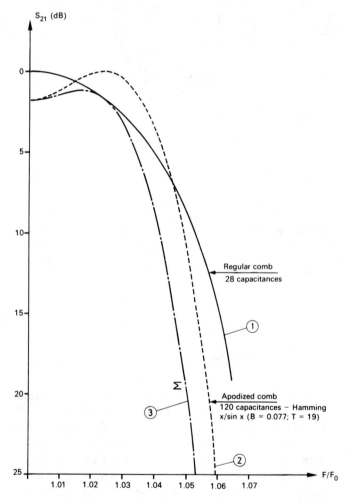

Fig. 8.20 Frequency response of a regular comb (1), an apodized comb (2) and the sum of (1) and (2) = (3).

transducer of uniform aperture (otherwise it is necessary to couple the two apodized transducers with an MSC). It is therefore convenient to take a simple regular comb for one of the transducers. Given the choice of lithium tantalate as substrate (Section 8.4.2, $k^2 = 0.9\%$ for the YZ cut), we find a large insertion loss if the transducer has few fingers. We therefore choose the number of capacitances to be between 25 and 30, but then the frequency response behaves as $(\sin x)/x$. The second comb must therefore compensate for the convexity of this response and its behavior must be $x/\sin x$. This

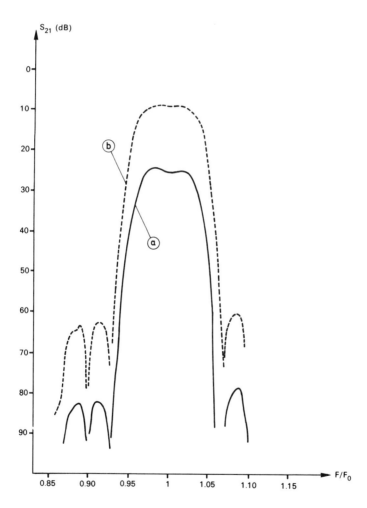

Fig. 8.21 (a) Unmatched ports; (b) compensation of the capacitance of each port by an inductance.

specification is incorporated in the menu of program GENEFOS in Appendix E.

For example, trials give the following results:

(a) regular comb: 28 capacitances;
(b) $x/\sin x$ comb: 120 capacitances; Hamming window; $B = 0.077$; $T = 19$.

Figure 8.20 shows the frequency response of the regular comb (1), the apodized comb (2), and the result (3) obtained by adding (1) and (2), which is not therefore the global frequency response, but gives a first approximation to it.

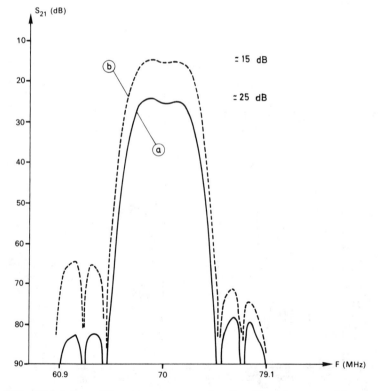

Fig. 8.22 Simulation of frequency response by S_{21}: (a) without matching; typical parasitic impedances; (b) capacitances compensated by series inductances; typical parasitic impedances.

8.4.4   Simulation and final design

Simulation involves the physical and electrical characteristics, the dimensions, the coupling coefficients, velocity, permittivity and matching conditions.

8.4.4.1   Simulation

We use program MAREFOS of Chapter 5 (given in Appendix G) in two cases.

(a) Ports unmatched, which corresponds approximately to the amplifier mounting shown in Fig. 8.16.

(b) Compensation of the capacitance of each port by an inductance.

The results are given in Figs 8.21a and b.

In case (a) the insertion loss is about 25 dB, the ripple is ± 0.8 dB, the rejection is 55 dB and the 3 dB bandwidth 6.5%. We note that there is a slight asymmetry in the frequency response (the high frequencies being slightly more attenuated than the low frequencies).

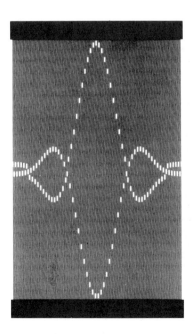

Fig. 8.23   Filter mask corresponding to the example studied in text.

In case (b) inductances compensate port capacitances, the insertion loss is reduced to 9 dB, the rejection is 50 dB and the ripple within the band remains within ± 0.3 dB with the response flatter than in case (a). However, this simulation is unrealistic to the extent that it does not take account of parasitic impedances.

This is why we prefer to follow MAREFOS with program S_{21}, the results of which are given in Fig. 8.22.

8.4.4.2   Definition of parameters

Since the GENEFOS-simulated matching corresponds to equal of the radiation resistances of comb and source, we may be tempted to choose the radiation resistance $R_0 = 50\,\Omega$, and width $W = 1.2$ mm for the regular comb. In reality, the width must be a compromise: at the chosen frequency, 1.2 mm corresponds to 26 wavelengths, i.e. diffraction effects will be appreciable. Moreover, the total capacitance of the regular comb is then 6.7 pF, which is rather low compared with the parasitic capacitances (1–2 pF). It is therefore better to increase W, while remaining within reasonable limits for the dimensions of the tantalate crystal and the resistance of the transducer

Fig. 8.24 Photograph of the filter constructed on a 5 × 8 mm lithium tantalate crystal and mounted in a TO8 unit (diameter ≃ 10 mm).

fingers. This is why we have chosen $W = 4\,\text{mm}$, which is equivalent to 86 wavelengths.

We take the distance between the comb centers to be equal to 90 wavelengths, large enough to limit electrical leakage between the two ports and small enough to ensure that diffraction losses are negligible. The results are:

(a) nominal wavelength $\lambda = 46.3\,\mu\text{m}$;
(b) number of fingers in regular comb: $N_1 = 29$;
(c) number of fingers in apodized comb: $N_2 = 121$;
(d) width of fingers (electrodes with split fingers are used to minimize reflections): $\lambda/8 = 5.8\,\mu\text{m}$;
(e) width or aperture: $W = 4\,\text{mm}$;

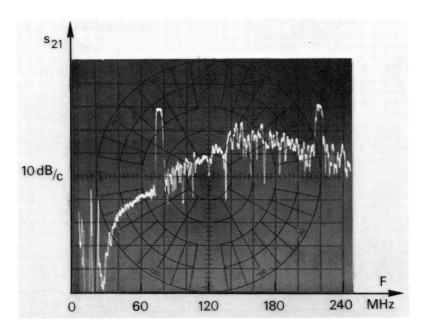

Fig. 8.25 The measured frequency response of a single filter mounted in the TO8 unit (not matched) in the range 0–240 MHz (Hewlett-Packard network analyzer, No. 8505A). Note the rise in parasitic effects at high frequencies (due to the capacitance of the mounting) and the response of the filter to the third harmonic (210 MHz), which is as large as to the fundamental (due to the use of split fingers), but is unimportant in the application envisaged, in which the filter is mounted between two amplifiers that reject this frequency.

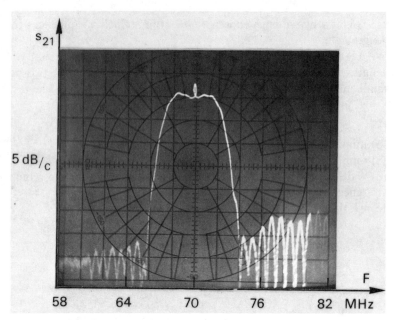

Fig. 8.26 Measurements performed as in Fig. 8.25, but in the frequency range 70 ± 12 MHz (insertion loss 25 dB).

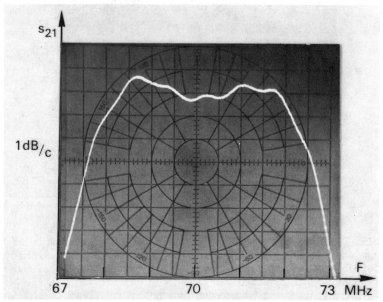

Fig. 8.27 Detail of Fig. 8.25 in the range 70 ± 3 MHz with sensitivity of 1 dB div⁻¹. There is a clear asymmetry in the response, as indicated by MAREFOS.

(f) distance between comb centers: $d = 90\lambda$;
(g) overall dimensions of the crystal: 5 mm × 8 mm.

8.4.5   Comb layout

The program for comb tracing is given in Appendix K. The table of weights and of the different geometric parameters defined above, and the choice of scale for the trace, are sufficient to provide an outline of the corresponding mask (cf. Fig. 8.23).

8.4.6   Fabrication

Fabrication techniques were described in Section 8.3. Given the dimensions of the crystal and the design, we apply the classical etching technique

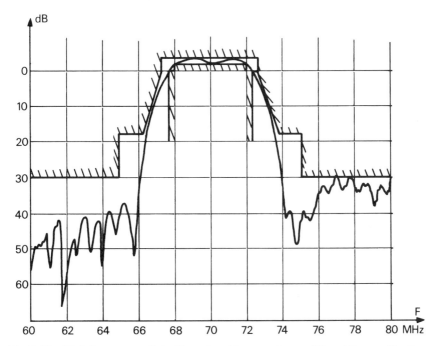

Fig. 8.28   Global response of the filter placed between its amplifiers. The specification is also shown.

to an aluminium layer, as explained in Fig. 8.11. A photograph of this filter, mounted in a TO8 unit, is shown in Fig. 8.24.

8.4.7 Measurements

Figures 8.25–8.28 summarize the results obtained for different situations.

Chapter 9

Conclusion and Perspectives

Surface acoustic wave technology has now reached maturity. The basic principles have been identified and methods of manufacture, derived from those of microelectronics, have been perfected.

The technoeconomic advantages of this technology are important in several respects:

(1) The SAW operating frequencies lie in a range (Fig. 5.32) that is relatively poor in high-quality components: the very high frequency components are at their lower limit and traditional components at their upper limit. Fortunately, the SAWs fill a gap in the technology, in a frequency range that is now more commonly used.

(2) These acoustic components allow levels of performance in signal processing that have been unattainable hitherto. This is particularly true in the case of radar, for which values of the product BT (bandwidth × processing time) of several thousand are called for (cf. Chapter 7); in simpler applications such as filtering, exceptional values of the bandwidth–selectivity combination are possible; in the case of oscillators, the thermal noise spectral density (Chapter 6) is remarkably low, while allowing very generous margins in electronic tuning.

(3) Finally, SAWs benefit from the technology of microelectronics, with the same potential advantages in terms of density and reliability (Chapter 8).

These advantages have important industrial consequences.

Among applications for the general public, the entire field of moving pictures makes use of this frequency range: over and above the mass production of filters for television sets, the whole area of video communications is involved, whether it be by cable, optical communication, or broadcasting by satellite. Direct reception of transmission by satellite, particularly with modulation of MAC-packets-type and/or high-definition television (HDTV), can benefit from this technology. In the longer term, there is no doubt whatever that the deployment of wide-band will make extensive use of SAWs.

In another sector, that of communication with mobiles, the 900 MHz wave band makes extensive use of acoustic components. Since the rapid expansion in the number of terminals has given rise to massive demands, Japanese firms (particularly Hitachi) have already shot ahead in this market.

In the field of military equipment, complex processing of radar signals and wide-band communications rely routinely on SAWs. Moreover, there are direct spin-offs in civil radar, where the forms of signals are becoming more sophisticated.

Looking more to the future, we can see that optical communications and the SAW technology are to some extent complementary. The integration of semiconductor components (lasers, detectors, logic) and acoustic components (signal processing) can contribute greatly to price reductions, thus stimulating the spread of wide-band circuits, both professional (local area network) and domestic (smart house).

In the laboratory, we note, on the one hand, more fundamental basic research along traditional lines (filtering, signal processing, materials, technology) and, on the other, the emergence of new areas of research such as *piezoelectronics* in which piezoelectric semiconductors perform more complex functions that combine surface waves and electronic processing. This is a very promising line for the future. The combination of SAWs with other techniques could also open up unexpected avenues, e.g. spin waves in nonlinear effects or superconducting electrodes in resonators or oscillators, and so on.

In the industrial domain, the emergence of hundreds of companies on the fringes of the market, among the current users of SAWs, is symbolic of the economic importance of this technology. For example, in the telecommunication sector, it is significant that, alongside the AT & T laboratories (who were pioneers in the subject) and CNET, there are firms like Hitachi, Siemens and BT, who have understood the importance of SAWs.

In conclusion, SAWs are now part of a high technology that is indispensable to the development of advanced communication systems. However, much remains to be done in the integration of these components into new systems, in the development of new methods of signal processing that will profit from some of the original features of phenomena already used, and, more fundamentally, in the improvement of our basic understanding of the subject.

References

Adler, R. (1971) Simple theory of acoustic amplification, *IEEE Trans. Son. Ultrason.*, **SU-18**, 115–118.

Allan, D. W. (1966) Statistics of atomic frequency standards, *Proc. IEEE*, **54**(2), 221–230.

Amstutz, P. (1959) Sur un problème d'approximation qui se présente en théorie des réseaux, *Ann. Télécommun.*, **14**(5–6), 111–121.

Angot, A. (1961) *Compléments de Mathématiques*, *Revue d'Optique*; also Masson, Paris, 1972.

Ash, E. A. (1970) Surface wave grating reflectors and resonators, *IEEE Symp. on Microwave Theory and Techniques*, Newport Beach, Calif., USA.

Ash, E. A. (1978) Fundamentals in signal processing devices, *Topics in Applied Physics*, vol. 24, ed. by A. A. Oliner, Springer-Verlag, Berlin.

Ash, E. A. and Morgan, D. (1967) Realization of microwave circuit functions using acoustic surface waves, *Electron. Lett.*, **3**(10), 462–464.

Ash, E. A., Dieulesaint, E. and Rakouth, H. (1980) Generation of surface acoustic waves by means of a C.W. laser, *Electron. Lett.*, **16**(12), 470–472.

Auld, B. A. (1973) *Acoustic Fields and Waves in Solids*, Wiley Interscience, New York.

Auld, B. A. and Kino, G. S. (1971) Normal mode theory for acoustic waves and its application to the interdigital transducer, *IEEE Trans. Electron. Devices*, **ED-18**(10), 898–908.

Auld, B. A. and Thompson, D. F. (1987) Temperature compensation of surface transverse waves for stable oscillator applications, *Proc. IEEE Ultrason. Symp.*, cat. 87CH492-7, 305–312.

Auld, B. A., Renard, A. and Hénaff, J. (1982) STW resonances on corrugated plates of finite thickness, *Electron. Lett.*, **18**(4), 183–184.

Bagwell, T. L. and Bray, R. C. (1987) Novel surface transverse wave resonators with low loss and high Q, *Proc. IEEE Ultrason. Symp.*, cat. 87CH2492-7, 305–312.

Ballman, A. A., Carruthers, J. R. and O'Bryan, H. N. Jr. (1970) Growth of uncracked baryum sodium niobate crystals, *J. Cryst. Growth*, **6**, 184–186.

Barnard, M. E., Lancaster, M. Y. and Paige, E. G. S. (1984) A novel spectrum analyser based on the slanted chirped transducer, *Proc. IEEE Ultrason. Symp.*, cat. 84CH2112-1, 103–105.

Barnard, M. E., Lancaster, M. Y. and Paige, E. G. S. (1986) The exponentially chirped SCT spectrum analyser, *Proc. IEEE Ultrason. Symp.*, cat. 86CH2375-4, 143–146.

Barnes, J. A. *et al.* (1971) Characterization of frequency stability, *IEEE Trans. Instrumentation and Measurement*, **IM-20**, 105–120.

Bellanger, M. (1981) *Traitement Numérique du Signal*, Collection technique et scientifique des télécommunications, Masson, Paris.

Bernacki, S. E. and Smith, H. I. (1975) Fabrication of silicon MOS devices using X-ray lithography, *IEEE Trans. Electron. Devices*, **ED-22**(7), 421–428.

Bert, A. G., Epsztein, B. and Kantorowicz, G. (1973) Signal processing by electron-beam interaction with piezoelectric surface waves, *IEEE Trans. Microwave Theory and Techniques*, **MTT 21**(4), 255–263.

Bleustein, J. L. (1968) A new surface wave in piezoelectric materials, *Appl. Phys. Lett.*, **13**, 412–413.

Bleustein, J. L. (1969) Some simple modes of wave propagation in an infinite piezoelectric plate, *J. Acous. Soc. Amer.*, **45**, 614–620.

Boite, R. and Leich, H. (1982) *Les Filtres Numériques*, Collection technique et scientifique des télécommunications, 2nd edn, Masson, Paris.

Born, M. and Huang, K. (1954) *Dynamical Theory of Crystal Lattice*, University Press, Oxford.

Born, M. and Wolf, E. (1964) *Principles of Optics*, Pergamon Press, New York.

Born, M. and Wolf, E. (1970) *Principles of Optics*, 4th edn, Pergamon Press, New York.

Bridoux, A., Moriamez, M., Rouvaen, J. M. and Dieulesaint, E. (1972) Determination of a nonlinear parameter for acoustic-surface-wave convolution in $LiNbO_3$, *Electron. Lett.*, **8**(10), 257–258.

Brillouin, L. (1960) *Les Tenseurs en Mécanique et en Elasticité*, Masson, Paris.

Brillouin, L. and Parodi, M. (1956) *Propagation des Ondes dans les Milieux Périodiques*, Masson, Paris.

Broers, A. N., Lean, E. G. and Hatzakis, M. (1969) 1.75 GHz acoustic-surface-wave transducer fabrication by an electron beam, *Appl. Phys. Lett.*, **15**(3), 98–101.

Brossard, P. and Hénaff, J. (1976) Circuits de récupération des fréquences porteuses et rythme dans des systèmes de transmission numérique, French patent no. 76 30 684.

Butler, M. B. N. (1977) Development and application of an SAW chirp-Z transformer, *AGARD Conference Proc.* (230), 5.1.1–5.1.10.

Cady, W. G. (1946) *Piezoelectricity*, McGraw-Hill, New York.

Campbell, J. J. and Jones, W. R. (1968) A method for estimating optimal crystal cuts and propagation directions for excitation of piezoelectric surface waves, *IEEE Trans. Son. Ultrason.*, **SU-15**(4), 209–217.

Campbell, J. J. and Jones, W. R. (1970) Propagation of piezoelectric surface waves on cubic and hexagonal crystals, *J. Appl. Phys.*, **41**, 2796–2801.

Carr, P. H. (1971) Mixing of noncollinear elastic surface waves in $LiNbO_3$, *J. Appl. Phys.*, **42**(13), 5330–5332, 1971.

Carr, P. H. and O'Connell, Lt R. M. (1976) New temperature compensated materials with high piezoelectric coupling, *Proc. 30th Frequency Control Symp.*, 129–131.

Casimir, H. B. G. (1945) On Onsager's principle of microscopic reversibility, *Rev. Mod. Phys.*, **17**, 343–350.

Chambers, J., Mason, I. M. and Turner, C. W. (1972) Acoustic-surface-wave convolution on crystals of CdS, $LiNbO_3$ and $Bi_{12}GeO_{20}$, *Electron. Lett.*, **8**(12), 314–316.

Chauvin, D., Coussot, G. and Dieulesaint, E. (1971) Acoustic-surface-wave television filters, *Electron. Lett.*, **7**(17), 491–492.

Coldren, L. A. and Kino, G. S. (1971) Monolithic acoustic surface wave amplifier, *Appl. Phys. Lett.*, **18**, 317–319.

Coldren, L. A. and Kino, G. S. (1973) CW monolithic acoustic surface wave amplifier incorporated in a $\Delta v/v$ waveguide, *Appl. Phys. Lett.*, **23**, 117–118.

Coldren, L. A. and Rosenberg, R. L. (1979). Surface-acoustic-wave resonator filters, *Proc. IEEE*, **67**(1), 147–158.

Coldren, L. A., Rosenberg, R. L. and Rentschler, J. A. (1977) Monolithic transversely coupled SAW resonator filters, *Proc. IEEE Ultrason. Symp.*, cat. 77CH1264-1SU, 888–893.

Collins, J. H., Lakin, K. M., Quate, C. F. and Shaw, H. J. (1968) Amplification of acoustic surface waves with adjacent semiconductors and piezoelectric crystals, *Appl. Phys. Lett.*, **13**, 314–316.

Coquin, G. A. and Tiersten, H. F. (1967) Analysis of the excitation and detection of piezoelectric surface waves in quartz by means of surface electrodes, *J. Acoust. Soc. Am.*, **41**(4), 921–939.

Coussot, G. (1973) Rayleigh wave guidance on $LiNbO_3$, *Appl. Phys. Lett.*, **22**(9), 432–433.

Crabb, J., Lewis, M. F. and Maines, J. D. (1973) Surface acoustic wave oscillators: mode selection and frequency modulation, *Electron. Lett.*, **9**(10), 195–197.

Cross, P. S., Smith, R. S. and Hydl, W. H. (1975) Electrically cascaded surface-acoustic-wave resonator filters, *Electron. Lett.*, **11**(11), 244–245.

Curie, J. and Curie, P. (1880) Développement, par pression, de l'électricité polaire dans les cristaux hémièdres à faces inclinées, *Comptes Rendus de l'Académie des Sciences*, 2 August 1880, and *Bull. Soc. Min. de France*, **3**, 90–93.

Cutler, L. S. and Searle, C. L. (1966) Some aspects of the theory and measurement of frequency fluctuations in frequency standards, *Proc. IEEE*, **54**(2), 136–154.

Dakss, M. L., Kuhn, L., Heidrich, P. F. and Scott, B. A. (1970) Grating coupler for efficient excitation of optical guided waves in thin films, *Appl. Phys. Lett.*, **16**(12), 523–525.

Datta and Hunsinger, B. J. (1979) First-order reflection coefficient of surface acoustic waves from thin-strip overlays, *J. Appl. Phys.*, **50**(9), 5661–5665.

Detaint, J., Feldmann, M., Hénaff, J., Poignant, M. and Toudic, Y. (1979) Bulk and surface acoustic wave propagation in berlinite, *Proc. 33rd Frequency Control Symp.*, 70–79.

Devries, A. J. and Adler, R. (1976) Case history of a surface wave TV IF filter for color television receivers, *Proc. IEEE*, **64**(5), 671–676.

Dieulesaint, E. (1970) Lignes à ondes élastiques: application au traitement des signaux électriques, *Onde Electrique*, **50**(11), 899–907.

Dieulesaint, E. and Hartemann, P. (1973) Acoustic surface wave filters, *Ultrasonics*, **11**(1), 24–30.

Dieulesaint, E. and Royer, D. (1974) *Ondes Elastiques dans les Solides*, Masson, Paris.

Dieulesaint, E. and Royer, D. (1976) Lignes à ondes élastiques de surface, *Onde Electrique*, **56**(4), 180–185.

Dieulesaint, E. and Royer, D. (1978) Acoustic surface waves, *Handbook of Surfaces and Interfaces*, vol. 2, pp. 65–190, ed. by Leonard Dobrzynski, Garland STPM Press, New York.

Dieulesaint, E., Royer, D. and Ballegeer, J. C. (1976) SAW co-ordinate sensor, *Electron. Lett.*, **12**(22), 586–587.

Dieulesaint, E., Mattiocco, F. and Royer, D. (1978) Excitation et détection d'ondes de Rayleigh à l'aide d'une feuille de polymère piézoélectrique, *C.R. Acad. Sci.*, **287**(8), 171–173.

Dieulesaint, E., Royer, D. and Rakouth, H. (1982) Optical excitation of quartz resonators, *Electron. Lett.*, **18**(9), 381–382.

Dolph, C. L. (1946) A current distribution for broadside arrays which optimizes the relationship between beamwidth and sidelobe level, *Proc. IRE*, **34**, 335–348.

Dunnrowicz, C., Sandy, F. and Parker, T. (1976) Reflection of surface waves from periodic discontinuities, *Proc. IEEE Ultrason. Symp.*, cat. 76CH1120-5SU, 386–390.

Durand, E. (1953) *Electrostatique et Magnétostatique*, Masson, Paris.

Edson, W. A. (1960) Noise in oscillators, *Proc. IRE*, **48**, 1454–1466.

Engan, H., Ingebrigtsen, K. A. and Tonning, A. (1967) Elastic surface waves in α-quartz: observation of leaky surface waves, *Appl. Phys. Lett.*, **10**, 311–313.

Engan, H., Hanebrekke, H., Ingebrigtsen, K. A. and Jergan, E. (1969) Numerical calculations on surface waves in piezoelectrics, *Appl. Phys. Lett.*, **15**(8), 239–241.

Farnell, G. W. (1970) Properties of elastic surface waves, *Physical Acoustics*, vol. 6, ed. by W. P. Mason, Academic Press, New York.

Farnell, G. W. (1978) Types and properties of surface waves, *Topics in Applied Physics*, vol. 24, edited by A. A. Oliner, Springer-Verlag, Berlin.

Farnell, G. M. and Adler, E. L. (1972) Elastic wave propagation in thin layers, *Physical Acoustics*, vol. 9, pp. 35–127, ed. by W. P. Mason and R. N. Thurston, Academic Press, New York.

Feldmann, M. (1971) Modes in general gaussian optical systems using quantum-mechanics formalism, *J. Opt. Soc. Am.*, **61**, 446–449.

Feldmann, M. (1973a) Les ondes piézoélectriques dans les isolants, *Onde Elect.*, **55**(5–7).

Feldmann, M. (1973b) Analyse des transducteurs a ondes piézoélectriques de surface, *Ann. Telecommun.*, **28**(9–10), 352–370.

Feldmann, M. (1974) Réflecteur d'ondes élastiques de surface et filtres comprenant un tel réflecteur, French patent no. 74 395 74.

Feldmann, M. (1979) Direct synthesis of minimum phase transversal filters, *Proc. IEEE ISCAS*, cat. 79CH1421-7CAS, 15–18.

Feldmann, M. (1980a) Le filtrage en télécommunications: une évolution rapide vers la miniaturisation, *l'Echo des Recherches*, no. 101, 3–10.

Feldmann, M. (1980b) French patent no. 80 12868.

Feldmann, M. (1980c) French patent no. 80 12870.

Feldmann, M. (1981) *Theorie des Réseaux et Systèmes Linéaires*, Collection technique et scientifique des télécommunications, Eyrolles, Paris.

Feldmann, M. and Hénaff, J. (1972) Non linear interaction using leaky surface waves, *Proc. IEEE Ultrason. Symp.*, cat. 72CH0708-8SU, 310–313.

Feldmann, M. and Hénaff, J. (1974) A new multistrip acoustic surface wave filter, *Proc. IEEE Ultrason. Symp.*, cat. 74CH0896-ISU, 157–160.

Feldmann, M. and Hénaff, J. (1975) Procédé de balayage bidimensionnel d'une image au moyen d'ondes élastiques de surface, French patent no. 75 12 728.

Feldmann, M. and Hénaff, J. (1976) An ASW filter using two fan-shaped multistrip reflective array, *Proc. IEEE Ultrason. Symp.*, cat. 76CH1120-5SU, 397–400.

Feldmann, M. and Hénaff, J. (1977a) Propagation des ondes élastiques de surface, *Revue de Physique Appliquée*, **12**(11), 1775–1788.

Feldmann, M. and Hénaff, J. (1977b) Design of multistrip arrays, *Proc. IEEE Ultrason. Symp.*, cat. 77, CH 1264-1SU, 686–690.

Feldmann, M. and Hénaff, J. (1978a) A new A/D converter using surface acoustic waves, *Proc. IEEE Microwave Theory and Techniques Symp.*, cat. 78CH1355-7MTT, 456–458.

Feldmann, M. and Hénaff, J. (1978b) Design of SAW filter with minimum phase response, *Proc. IEEE Ultrason. Symp.*, cat. no. 78CH1344-1SU, 720–723.

Feldmann, M. and Hénaff, J. (1980a) Filtre transversal à transfert de charges commandé par une onde élastique de surface et procédé de fabrication, French patent no. 2 507 027.

Feldmann, M. and Hénaff, J. (1980b) Filtre récursif à double transfert de charges commandé par une double onde élastique de surface et procédé de réalisation, French patent no. 2 484 152.

Feldmann, M., Hénaff, J. and Carel, M. (1976) ASW filter bank using a multistrip reflective array, *Electron. Lett.*, **12**(5), 118–119.

Gagnepain, J. J. (1983) Phase and frequency noises in oscillators, *Noise in Physical Systems and 1/f Noise*, pp. 309–317, North Holland, Amsterdam.

Gagnepain, J. J. and Besson, R. (1975) Non linear effects in piezoelectric quartz crystals, *Physical Acoustics*, vol. XI, Academic Press, New York.

Gautier, H. and Tournois, P. (1981) Very fast signal processors as a result of the coupling of surface acoustic wave and digital technology, *IEEE Trans. Son. Ultrason.*, **SU-28**(3), 126–131.

Gautier, H., Maerfeld, C. and Tournois, P. (1978) Acoustic memory correlator using GaAs Schottky diodes, *Appl. Phys. Lett.*, **3.2**(9), 517–518.

Gautier, H., Maerfeld, C. and Tournois, P. (1979) Theory of the light-sensitive diode acoustic airgap convolver, *J. Appl. Phys.*, **50**(1), 333–339.

Geckinli, N. C. and Yavuz, D. (1978) Some novel windows and a concise tutorial comparison of window families, *IEEE Trans. Acoustics, Speech and Signal Processing*, **ASSP-26**(6), 501–507.

Glowinski, A. (1972a) Microacoustique et télécommunications, *Onde Electrique*, **52**(2), 54–67.

Glowinski, A. (1972b) Vibrations d'épaisseur des lames piézoélectriques, *Ann. Télécommun.*, **27**(3–4), 147–158.

Glowinski, A. and Feldmann, M. (1970) Piezoelectric plate vibration analysis using Maxwell's equations, *IEEE Ultrason. Symp.*, San Francisco.

Greebe, C. A. A. J., Van Dalen, P. A., Swanenberg, T. J. B. and Wolter, J. (1971) Electric coupling properties of acoustic and electric surface waves, *Phys. Rep. (NDL)*, **IC**(5), 235–268.

Groslambert, J., Marianneau, G. and Olivier, M. (1975) Méthode expérimentale de caractérisation des oscillateurs, *Onde Electrique*, **55**(2), 74–81.

Grudkowski, T. W., Montress, G. K., Gilden, M. and Black, J. F. (1980) GaAs monolithic SAW devices for signal processing and frequency control, *Proc. IEEE Ultrason. Symp.*, cat. 80CH1602-2SU, 88–97.

Guediri, F., Martin, R. L., Hunsinger, B. and Fliegel, F. M. (1987) Performance of acoustic charge transport programmable tapped delay line, *Proc. IEEE Ultrason. Symp.*, cat. 87CH2492-7SU, 11–14.

Guerard, A., Glowinski, R. and Feldmann, M. (1977) Synthèse par optimisation de filtres à ondes élastiques de surface, *Ann. Télécommun.*, **32**(1–2) 37–48.

Gulyaev, Yu. V. (1969) Electroacoustic surface waves in solids, *Soviet Phys. JETP Lett.*, **9**, 37–38.

Gulyaev, Yu. V. and Pustovoit, V. I. (1965) Amplification of surface waves in semiconductors, *Sov. Phys. J.*, **20**, 1508–1509.

Hartemann, P. (1971) Narrow-bandwidth Rayleigh-wave filters, *Electron. Lett.*, **7**(22), 674–675.

Hartemann, P. (1978) Influence of annealing on the surface-acoustic wave velocity increase induced by ion implantation in quartz, *J. Appl. Phys.*, **49**(10), 5334–5335.

Hartemann, P. and Arnodo, C. (1972) Rayleigh wave delay line using two grating-array transducers at 2.55 GHz, *Electron. Lett.*, **8**(10), 265–267.

Hartemann, P. and Dieulesaint, E. (1969) Intrinsic compensation of sidelobes in a dispersive acoustic delay line, *Electron. Lett.*, **5**(10), 219–220.

Hartemann, P. and Dieulesaint, E. (1971) Pondération des lobes secondaires d'une impulsion comprimée par une ligne dispersive à ondes élastiques de Rayleigh, *Onde Electrique*, **51**(6), 523–524.

Hartemann, P. and Morizot, M. (1974) Variation of surface acoustic wave velocity produced by ion implantation, *Proc. IEEE Ultrason. Symp.*, cat. 74CH0896-1SU, 307–310.

Hartemann, P., Cauvard, P. and Desbois, D. (1978) Ion-implanted surface acoustic-wave guides on lithium niobate, *Appl. Phys. Lett.*, **32**(5), 266–268.

Hartmann, C. S. (1973) Weighting interdigital surface wave transducers by selective withdrawal of electrodes, *Proc. IEEE Ultrasonics Symp.*, cat. 73CH0807-8SU, 423–426.

Hartmann, C. S., Jones, W. S. and Vollers, H. G. (1972) Wideband unidirectional surface wave transducers, *IEEE Trans. Son. Ultrason.*, **SU-19**, 378–381.

Hartmann, C. S., Bell, D. L. T. and Rosenfeld, R. C. (1973) Impulse model design of acoustic surface wave filters, *IEEE Trans. Microwave Theory and Techniques*, **MTT-21**(4), 162–175.

Hartmann, C. S., Kansy, R. J., Daniels, W. D. and Potter, B. R. (1982) SAW devices for military communications, radar and EW systems, *Microwave Journal*, **25**(7), 73–86.

Hartmann, C. S., Andle, J. C. and King, M. B. (1987) Saw notch filters, *Proc. IEEE Ultrason. Symp.*, cat. 87CH2492-7SU, 131–138.

Hays, R. M. and Hartmann, C. S. (1976) Surface-acoustic-wave devices for communications, *Proc. IEEE*, **64**(5), 652–671.

Helms, H. D. (1968) Nonrecursive digital filters: design methods for achieving specification on frequency response, *IEEE Trans. AU*, **AU-16**(3), 336–342.

Hénaff, J. (1973) Image processing using acoustic surface waves, *Electron. Lett.*, **9**(5), 102–104.

Hénaff, J. (1976) Oscillateurs à ondes élastiques de surface, *Onde Electrique*, **56**(4), 189–196.

Hénaff, J. (1979a) Application des oscillateurs à ondes élastiques de surface en télécommunications, *Onde Electrique*, **59**(8–9), 95–101.

Hénaff, J. (1979b) Application of SAW oscillators to digital communications, *Proc. IEEE Ultrason. Symp.*, cat. 79CH1482-9SU, 855–860.

Hénaff, J. and Brossard, P. C. (1981) Implementation of satellite communication systems using surface acoustic waves, *IEEE Trans. Microwave Theory and Techniques*, **MTT-29**(5), 439–450.

Hénaff, J. and Feldmann, M. (1974) Acoustoelectric amplification of pseudo-surface waves, *Proc. IEEE Ultrason. Symp.*, cat. 74CH0896-1SU, 240–244.

Hénaff, J. and Feldmann, M. (1977a) New acoustic-surface-wave zero temperature cuts in Tl_3VS_4, *Electron. Lett.*, **13**(10), 300–302.

Hénaff, J. and Feldmann, M. (1977b) New acoustic-surface-wave zero temperature cuts in Tl_3TaSe_4, *Electron. Lett.*, **13**(22) 661–662.

Hénaff, J. and Feldmann, M. (1978) A SAW temperature compensated oscillator using the difference between metallized and free delay temperature coefficients on LiTaO$_3$, *Proc. IEEE Ultrason. Symp.*, cat. 78CH1344-1SU, 448–451.

Hénaff, J. and Feldmann, M. (1979) Design and capabilities of SAW filters: synthesis and technologies, *Proc. IEEE ISCAS*, cat. 79CH1421-7CAS, 617–620.

Hénaff, J. and Feldmann, M. (1980) Electrically tunable narrow-bandwidth SAW filter, *Proc. IEEE Ultrason. Symp.*, cat. 80CH1602-2SU, 332–335.

Hénaff, J. and Feldmann, M. (1982) SAW propagation in BANANA, *Proc. IEEE Ultrason. Symp.*, cat. 82CH1823-4SU, 394–398.

Hénaff, J. and Feldmann, M. (1983) Surface acoustic wave quasi-zero temperature cuts in Ba$_2$NaNb$_5$O$_{15}$, *Appl. Phys. Lett.*, **42**(11), 940–942.

Hénaff, J. and Le Contellec, M. (1974) Improvement of semiconducting films for acoustoelectric amplification, *Electron. Lett.*, **10**(5), 49–50.

Hénaff, J., Feldmann, M. and Le Contellec, M. (1974a) Monolithic acoustoelectric amplifier using pseudosurface waves, *Appl. Phys. Lett.*, **24**(9), 447–449.

Hénaff, J., Le Contellec, M. and Rudelle, C. (1974b) Amplification des ondes élastiques de surface, *Echo des Recherches*, no. 75, 12–33.

Hénaff, J., Pirio, F., Sinou, M. and Feldmann, M. (1974c) Wraparound ASW delay line with lens guidance and monolithic amplification, *Appl. Phys. Lett.*, **25**(5), 256–258.

Hénaff, J., Carel, M., Lainey, S. and Labasse, M. (1977) 4-phase PSK differential demodulation using ASW delay lines, *Electron. Lett.*, **13**(19), 586–588.

Hénaff, J., Carel, M., Lemen, P. and Monti, O. (1978) UHF hybrid SAW voltage-controlled-LiTaO$_3$ oscillator, *Proc. 4th European Solid State Circuits Conf.*, 181–184.

Hénaff, J., Feldmann, M. and Carel, M. (1981a) Voltage-controlled SAW filter on berlinite, *Electron, Lett.*, **17**(2), 86–87.

Hénaff, J., Feldmann, M., Carel, M. and Dubois, R. (1981b) New SSBW mode in GaAs, *Electron. Lett.*, **17**(12), 427–429.

Hénaff, J., Feldmann, M., Carel, M. and Dubois, R. (1982a) Acoustic wave propagation on indium phosphide surfaces, *Appl. Phys. Lett.*, **41**(1), 22–24.

Hénaff, J., Feldmann, M. and Kirov, M. A. (1982b) Piezoelectric crystals for surface acoustic waves, *Ferroelectrics*, **42**, 161–185.

Hikita, M., Kinoshita, Y., Kojima, H. and Tabuchi, T. (1980) Phase weighting for low loss SAW filters, *Proc. IEEE Ultrason. Symp.*, cat. 80CH 602-2SU, 308–312.

Hikita, M., Tabuchi, T., Kojima, H., Sumioka, A., Nakagoshi, A. and Kinoshita, Y. (1984) High performance SAW filters with several new technologies for cellular radio, *Proc. IEEE Ultrason. Symp.*, cat. 84CH2112-1SU, 82–92.

Hladik, J. (1969) *La Transformation de Laplace*, Masson, Paris.

Holland, M. G. and Claiborne, L. T. (1974) Practical surface acoustic wave devices, *Proc. IEEE*, **62**(5), 582–611.

IEEE (1969) Special issue on microwave acoustics, *IEEE Trans. Microwave Theory and Techniques*, **MTT 17**(11).

Ingebrigtsen, K. A. (1969) Surface waves in piezoelectrics, *J. Appl. Phys.*, **40**(7), 2681–2686.

Ingebrigtsen, K. A. (1970) Linear and non-linear attenuation of acoustic surface waves in a piezoelectric coated with a semi-conducting film, *J. Appl. Phys.*, **41**, 454–459.

Ingebrigtsen, K. A. (1972) Analysis of interdigital transducers, *Proc. IEEE Ultrason. Symp.*, cat. 72CH0708-8SU, 403–407.

Jack, M. A., Grant, P. M. and Collins, J. H. (1980) Theory, design and application of SAW Fourier transform processors, *Proc. IEEE*, **68**(4), 450–468.

Jhunjhunwala, A., Vetelino, J. F. and Field, J. C. (1976) Berlinite, a temperature compensated material for surface acoustic wave applications, *Proc. IEEE Ultrason. Symp.*, cat. 76CH1120-5SU, 523–527.

Kaiser, J. F. (1966) Digital filters, *Systems Analysis by Digital Computer*, pp. 218–277, ed. by F. F. Kuo and J. F. Kaiser, Wiley, New York.

Kaminow, I. P. and Carruthers, J. R. (1973) Optical waveguiding layers in $LiNbO_3$ and $LiTaO_3$, *Appl. Phys. Lett.*, **22**(7), 326–328.

Kato, T. (1949) On the convergence of the perturbation method, *Progr. Theor. Phys.*, **4**, 514–523.

Kittel, C. (1958) *Introduction à la Physique de l'Etat Solide*, Dunod, Paris.

Kogelnik, H. (1965) Imaging of optical modes—resonators with internal lenses, *Bell Syst. Tech. Jour.*, **44**(3), 455–494.

Kuhn, L., Dakss, M. L., Heidrich, P. F. and Scott, B. A. (1970) Deflection of an optical guided wave by a surface acoustic wave, *Appl. Phys. Lett.*, **17**(6), 265–267.

Lakin, K. M., Joseph, T. and Penunuri, D. (1974) A surface acoustic wave planar resonator employing an interdigital electrode transducer, *Appl. Phys. Lett.*, **25**, 363–365.

Landau, L. and Lifchitz, E. (1967) *Théorie de l'Elasticité*, Mir, Moscow.

Lardat, C., Maerfeld, C. and Tournois, P. (1971) Theory and performance of acoustical dispersive surface wave delay lines, *Proc. IEEE*, **59**(3), 355–368.

Latham, S. I. and Saunders, D. R. (1978) Aging and mounting developments for SAW resonators, *Proc. IEEE Ultrasonics Symp.*, cat. 78CH1344-1SU, 513–517.

Lau, K. F., Yen, K. H., Kagiwada, K. S. and Kong, A. M. (1980) High frequency temperature stable SBAW oscillators, *Proc. IEEE Ultrason. Symp.*, cat. 80CH1602-2SU, 240–244.

Lavoine, J. (1963) *Transformation de Fourier des Pseudo-fonctions*, CNRS, Paris.

Leeson, D. B. (1966) A simple model of feedback oscillator noise spectrum, *Proc. IEEE*, **54**(2), 329–330.

Lewis, M. (1977) Surface skimming bulk waves, *Proc. IEEE Ultrason. Symp.*, cat. 77CH1264-1SU, 744–752.

Lewis, M. (1979) Temperature compensation techniques for SAW devices, *Proc. IEEE Ultrason. Symp.*, cat. 79CH1482-9SU, 612–622.

Lewis, M. (1983). Low loss SAW devices employing single stage fabrication. *Proc. IEEE Ultrason. Symp.*, cat. 83CH1947-1, 104–108.

Lewis, M. F. and Patterson, E. (1971) Novel helical path surface wave delay-line, *Appl. Phys. Lett.*, **18**(7) 143–145.

Li, R. C. M., Williamson, R. C., Flanders, D. C. and Alusow, J. A. (1974) On the performance and limitations of the surface wave resonator using grooved reflectors, *Proc. IEEE Ultrason. Symp.*, cat. 74CH0896-1SU, 257–262.

Lim, T. C., Kraut, E. A. and Thompson, R. B. (1972) Nonlinear materials for acoustic-surface wave convolver, *Appl. Phys. Lett.*, **20**(3), 127–129.

Ludvik, S. and Quate, C. F. (1972) Amplification of surface shearwave mode in GaAs, *J. Appl. Phys.*, **43**(9), 3619–3622.

Luukkala, M. and Kino, G. S. (1971) Convolution and time inversion using parametric interactions of acoustic surface waves, *Appl. Phys. Lett.*, **18**(9), 393–394.

Luukkala, M. and Surakka, J. (1972) Acoustic convolution and correlation and the associated nonlinearity parameters in $LiNbO_3$, *J. Appl. Phys.*, **43**(6), 2510–2518.

McClellan, J. H., Parks, T. W. and Rabiner, L. R. (1973) A computer program for designing optimum FIR linear phase digital filters, *IEEE Trans. AU*, **AU-21**(6), 506–526.

MacFall, D., Collins, J., Schiarretta, W. and Cappon, A. (1977) The chirp-Z transform with CCD and SAW technology, *AGARD Conference proceedings*, no. 230, 5.2.1–5.2.13.

Maerfeld, C. and Farnell, G. W. (1973) Non-symmetrical multistrip coupler as a surface-wave beam compressor of large bandwidth, *Electron. Lett.*, **9**(18), 432–434.

Maerfeld, C. and Tournois, P. (1973) Perturbation theory for multistrip acousto-electric surface-wave amplifier, *Electron. Lett.*, **9**(5), 113–115.

Maerfeld, C., Gires, F. and Tournois, P. (1971) Bleustein–Gulyaev surface wave amplification in CdS, *Appl. Phys. Lett.*, **18**(7), 269–272.

Maines, J. D. and Paige, E. G. S. (1976) Surface acoustic wave devices for signal processing applications, *Proc. IEEE*, **64**(3), 639–676.

Maines, J. D., Paige, E. G. S., Saunders, A. F. and Young, A. S. (1969) Simple technique for the accurate determination of delay-time variations in acoustic surface wave structures, *Electron. Lett.*, **5**, 678–679.

Malocha, D. C. (1981) Surface wave devices using low loss filter technologies, *Proc. IEEE Ultrason. Symp.*, cat. 81CH1629-9SU, 83–88.

Malocha, D. C. and Hunsinger, B. J. (1977) Capacitive tap weighted SAW transducers with reduced losses, *Proc. IEEE Ultrason. Symp.*, cat. 77CH1264-1SU, 763–766.

Marschall, F. G. (1972) New technique for the suppression of triple transit signals in surface-acoustic-wave delay lines, *Electron. Lett.*, **8**, 311–312.

Marschall, F. G., Paige, E. G. S. and Young, A. S. (1971) New unidirectional transducer and broadband reflector of acoustic surface waves, *Electron. Lett.*, **7**, 638–640.

Marschall, F. G., Newton, C. O. and Paige, E. G. S. (1973a) Theory and design of the surface acoustic multistrip coupler, *IEEE Trans. Microwave Theory and Techniques*, **MTT-21**(4), 206–215.

Marschall, F. G., Newton, C. O. and Paige, E. G. S. (1973b) Surface acoustic wave multistrip components and their applications, *IEEE Trans. Microwave Theory and Techniques*, **MTT-21**(4), 216–225.

Mason, W. P. and Thurston, R. N., (1964–1984) (eds) *Physical Acoustics, Principles and Methods*, Academic Press, New York.

Matthews, H. (1977) (ed) *Surface Wave Filters; Design Instruction and Use*, Wiley and Sons, New York.

Mattiocco, F., Dieulesaint, E. and Royer, D. (1980) PVF$_2$ transducers for Rayleigh waves, *Electron. Lett.*, **16**(7), 250–251.

Melngailis, J., Smith, H. I. and Efremow, N. (1975) Instrumentation for conformable photomask lithography, *IEEE Trans. Electron. Devices*, **ED-22**, 496–498.

Messiah, A. (1964) *Mécanique Quantique*, vol. II, Dunod, Paris.

Mitsuyu, T., Yamazaki, O. and Wasa, K. (1981) A 4.4 GHz SAW filter using a single crystal ZnO film on sapphire, *Proc. IEEE Ultrason. Symp.*, cat. 81CH1689-9SU, 74–77.

Morgan, D. P. (1985) *Surface-wave Devices for Signal Processing*, Elsevier, Amsterdam.

Nye, J. F. (1961) *Propriétés Physiques des Cristaux*, Dunod, Paris.

Oliner, A. A. (1978) Waveguides for surface waves, Ch. 5 in *Acoustic Surface Waves*, Springer-Verlag, Berlin, Heidelberg, New York.

Onsager, L. (1931) Reciprocal relations in irreversible processes, *Phys. Rev.*, **37**, 405–426 and **38**, 2265–2279.

Parker, T. E. (1977) Current developments in SAW oscillator stability, *Proc. 31st Frequency Control Symp.*, 359–364.

Parker, T. E. (1982) Precision surface acoustic wave oscillators, *Proc. IEEE Ultrason. Symp.*, cat. 82CH1823-4SU, 268–274.

Parker, T. E. and Schulz, M. B. (1975) SiO_2 film overlays for temperature-stable surface acoustic wave devices, *Appl. Phys. Lett.*, **26**(3), 75–77.

Peled, A. and Liu, B. (1976) *Digital Signal Processing*, pp. 117–130, John Wiley and Sons, New York.

Penavaire, L., Seguignes, D., Lardat, C., Bonnier, J. J., Chevalier, J. Y. and Besson, Y. (1980) A 120 MHz SAW resonator stabilizied oscillator with high spectral purity, *Proc. IEEE Ultrason. Symp.*, cat.. 80CH1602-2SU, 256–259.

Planat, M., Theobald, G. and Gagnepain, J. J. (1980) Propagation non linéaire d'ondes élastiques dans un solide anisotrope, II. Ondes de surface, *Onde Electrique*, **60**(11), 61–67.

Potter, B. R. and MacDonald, D. B. (1981) SAW filter technology and applications, *Proc. 35th Ann. Freq. Control Symp.*, 352–357.

Proklov, V. V. (1986) Acousto-optic interactions in a planar waveguide, *Proc. ISSWAS 86*, **1**, 148–163, Novosibirsk.

Rabiner, L. R., Shaffer, R. W. and Rader, C. M. (1969) The chirp-Z transform algorithm, *IEEE Trans. AU*, **AU 17**(2), 86–92.

Rayleigh, Lord (1885) On waves propagated along the plane surface of an elastic solid, *Proc. London Math. Soc.*, **17**.

Renard, A., Hénaff, J. and Auld, B. A. (1981) SH surface wave propagation on corrugated surfaces of rotated Y-cut quartz and berlinite crystals, *Proc. IEEE Ultrason. Symp.*, cat 81CH1689-9SU, 123–128.

Ronnekleiv, A., Skeie, H. and Hanebrekke, H. (1973) Design problems in surface wave filters, *Proc. Conf. on Component Performance and System Application of SAW Devices*, IEE, Stevenage, England, 141–151.

Rosenberg, R. L. and Coldren, L. A. (1976) Reflection-dependent coupling between grating resonators, *Proc. IEEE Ultrason. Symp.*, cat. 76CH1120-5SU, 281–286.

Rosenfeld, R. C., Brown, R. B. and Hartmann, C. S. (1974) Unidirectional acoustic surface wave filters with 2 dB insertion loss, *Proc. IEEE Ultrason. Symp.*, cat. 74CH0896-1SU, 425–428.

Rossi, C. (1967) Window functions for non recursive digital filters, *Electron. Lett.*, **3**(12), 559–561.

Royer, D. and Dieulesaint, E. (1979) Elastic and piezoelectric constants of trigonal selenium and tellurium crystals, *J. Appl. Phys.*, **50**(6), 4042–4045.

Royer, D., Dieulesaint, E., Henaff, J. and Feldmann, M. (1979) SAW propagation on Y-cut and X-axis boule of selenium, *Proc. IEEE Ultrason. Symp.*, cat. 79CH1482-9SU, 574–576.

Rutman, J. (1972) Instabilité de fréquence des oscillateurs, *Onde Electrique*, **52**(11), 480–486.

Rutman, J. (1974) Relations between spectral purity and frequency stability, *Proc. 28th Frequency Control Symp.*, 160–165.

Savelli, M., Lecoy, G. and Nougier, J. P. (1983) *Noise in Physical Systems and 1/f Noise*, North Holland, Amsterdam.

Schmidt, R. V. (1975) Acoustic surface wave velocity perturbation in $LiNbO_3$ by diffusion of metals, *Appl. Phys. Lett.*, **27**(1), 8–10.

Schmidt, R. V. and Kaminow, I. P. (1974) Metal diffused optical waveguides in $LiNbO_3$, *Appl. Phys. Lett.*, **25**(8), 458–460.

Schulz, M. B., Matsinger, B. J. and Holland, M. G. (1970) Temperature dependance of surface acoustic wave velocity on alpha-quartz, *J. Appl. Phys.*, **41**, 2755–2765.

Seguin, M., Knapp-Ziller, M. and Foure, J. L. (1979) Filtres à ondes élastiques de surface pour équipements téléphoniques à courants porteurs, *Onde Electrique*, **59**(8–9), 81–88.

Shank, C. V. and Schmidt, R. V. (1973) Optical technique for producing 0.1 m periodic surface structures, *Appl. Phys. Lett.*, **23**(3), 154–155.

Shibayama, K., Yamanouchi, K. and Sato, H. (1979) Recent trends in SAW filters, *Proc. ISCAS*, cat. 79CH1421-7CAS, 600–603.

Shreve, W. R. (1975) Surface-wave two-port resonator equivalent circuit, *Proc. IEEE Ultrason. Symp.*, cat. 75CH0994-4SU, 295–298.

Shreve, W. R., Kusters, J. A. and Adams, Ch. A. (1978) Fabrication of SAW resonators for improved long term aging, *Proc. IEEE Ultrason. Symp.*, cat. 78CH1344-1SU, 573–579.

Slobodnik, A. J. Jr. (1970) Nonlinear effects in microwave acoustic LiNbO$_3$ surface-wave delay lines, *J. Acoust. Soc. Amer.*, **48**(1), 203–210.

Slobodnik, A. J. Jr. and Conway, E. D. (1970) New high-frequency high-coupling low-beam steering cut for acoustic surface waves on LiNbO$_3$, *Electron. Lett.*, **6**, 171–173.

Slobodnik, A. J. Jr., Conway, E. D. and Delmonico, R. T. (1973) *Microwave Acoustics Handbook*, vol. 1, *Surface Wave Velocities*, NTIS, Springfield, VA, USA.

Smith, H. I. (1974) Fabrication techniques for surface-acoustic-wave and thin film optical devices, *Proc. IEEE*, **62**(10), 1361–1387.

Smith, H. I. (1977) *Surface Wave Devices*, ed. by H. Matthews, Ch. 4, pp. 165–217, John Wiley and Sons, New York.

Smith, H. I., Bachner, F. J. and Efremow, N. (1971) A high-yield photolithographic technique for surface wave devices, *J. Electrochem. Soc.*, **118**, 821–825.

Smith, H. I., Efremow, N. and Kelley, P. L. (1974) Photolithographic contact printing of 4000 A linewidth patterns, *J. Electrochem. Soc.*, **121**, 1503–1506.

Smith, W. R., Gerard, H. M. and Collins, H. H. (1969a) Analysis of interdigital surface wave transducers by use of equivalent circuit model, *IEEE Trans. Microwave Theory and Techniques*, **MTT-17**(11), 856–864.

Smith, W. R., Gerard, H. M., Collins, H. H., Reeder, T. M. and Shaw, H. J. (1969b) Design of surface wave delay lines with interdigital transducers, *IEEE Trans. Microwave Theory and Techniques*, **MTT-17**(11), 865–873.

Solie, L. P. (1974) A surface acoustic wave multiplexer using offset multistrip couplers, *Proc. IEEE Ultrason. Symp.*, cat. 74CH0896-1SU, 153–156.

Solie, L. P. (1977) A SAW band pass filter technique using a fanned multistrip coupler, *Appl. Phys. Lett.*, **30**(8), 374–376.

Spears, D. L. and Smith, H. I. (1972) High-resolution pattern replication using soft X-rays, *Electron. Lett.*, **8**(4), 102–104.

Staples, E. J. (1974) UHF surface acoustics wave resonators, *Proc. 28th Symp. on Frequency Control*, 280–285.

Swierkowski, S., Van Duzer, T. and Turner, C. W. (1973) Amplification of acoustic surface waves in piezoelectric semiconductors, *IEEE Trans. Son. Ultrason.*, **SU-20**, 260–267.

Szabo, T. L. and Slobodnik, A. J. Jr. (1973) The effect of diffraction on the design of acoustic surface wave devices, *IEEE Trans. Son. Ultrason.*, **SU-20**(3), 240–251.

Takayanagi, A., Yamanouchi, K. and Shibayama, K. (1970) Piezoelectric leaky surface wave in LiNbO$_3$, *Appl. Phys. Lett.*, **17**, 225–227.

Tancrell, R. H. and Holland, M. G. (1971) Acoustic surface wave filters, *Proc. IEEE*, **59**(3), 393–409.

Taylor, T. T. (1960) Design of circular apertures for narrow beamwidth and low sidelobes, *IRE Trans.*, **AP-8**, 17–22.

Temes, C. L. (1962) Sidelobe suppression in a range-channel pulse compression radar, *IRE Trans.*, **MIL-6**, 162–169.

Thompson, R. B. and Quate, C. F. Nonlinear interaction of microwave electric fields and sound in $LiNbO_3$, *J. Appl. Phys.*, **42**(3), 907–918.

Thomson-CSF/DASM (1982) Compte rendu d'état d'avancement des travaux, contrat CNET, no. 81 35 213.

Tiersten, H. F. (1969) *Linear Piezoelectric Plate Vibrations*, Plenum, New York.

Tortoli, P. and Andreucceti, F. (1986) Chirp Fourier transform based on a single SAW filter, *Electron. Lett.*, **22**(19), 1017–1019.

Tournois, P. and Lardat, C. (1969) Love wave-dispersive delay lines for wide-band pulse compression, *IEEE Trans. Son. Ultrason.*, **SU-16**(3), 107–117.

Van Dalen, P. A. (1973) Electric interaction between transverse electroacoustic waves in piezoelectrics of the Bleustein–Gulyaev geometry and a semiconductor, *Philips Res. Rep.*, **28**, 185–209.

Van de Vaart, H. and Solie, L. (1976) Surface-acoustic-wave multiplexing techniques, *Proc. IEEE*, **64**, 688–691.

Viktorov, I. A. (1967) *Rayleigh and Lamb Waves*, Plenum, New York.

Warner, A. W., Coquin, G. A. and Fink, J. L. (1969) Elastic and piezoelectric constants of $Ba_2NaNb_5O_{15}$, *J. Appl. Phys.*, **40**, 4353–4356.

Weinert, R. W. and Isaacs, T. J. (1975) New piezoelectric materials which exhibit temperature stability for surface waves, *Proc. 29th Frequency Control Symp.*, 139–142.

White, R. M. (1970) Surface elastic waves, *Proc. IEEE*, **58**(8), 1238–1276.

White, R. M. and Voltmer, F. W. (1965) Direct piezoelectric coupling to surface elastic waves, *Appl. Phys. Lett.*, **7**, 314–316.

Whittaker, E. T. and Watson, G. N. (1952) *A Course of Modern Analysis*, University Press, Cambridge, 1st edn 1902, 4th edn 1952.

Williamson, R. C. (1977) Case studies of successful surface-acoustic-wave devices, *Proc. IEEE Ultrason. Symp.*, cat. 77CH1264-1SU, 460–468.

Wolf, E. D., Ozdemir, F. S. and Weglein, R. D. (1973) Precision electron beam microfabrication of acoustic surface wave devices, *Proc. IEEE Ultrasonics Symp.*, cat. 73CH0807-8SU, 510–516.

Wright, P. V. and Wilkus, S. A. (1983) A prototype low-loss filter employing single-phase unidirectional transducers, *Proc. IEEE Ultrason. Symp.*, cat. 83CH1947-1SU, 72–76.

Yamada, Y., Iwasaki, H. and Niizeki, N. (1970) Elastic anomaly of $Ba_2NaNb_5O_{15}$, *J. Appl. Phys.*, **41**, 4141–4147.

Yamada, J. I., Temmyo, J., Yoshikawa, S. and Kimura, T. (1980) 1.6 Gbit/s optical receiver at 1.3 μm with SAW timing retrieval circuit, *Electron. Lett.*, **16**(2), 57–58.

Yamanouchi, K. and Shibayama, K. (1972) Propagation and amplification of Rayleigh waves and piezoelectric leaky surface waves in $LiNbO_3$, *J. Appl. Phys.*, **43**, 856–862.

Yamanouchi, K., Nyffeler, F. M. and Shibayama, K. (1975) Low insertion loss acoustic surface wave filter using group-type unidirectional interdigital transducers, *Proc. IEEE Ultrason. Symp.*, cat. 75CH0994-4SU, 317–321.

Yamanouchi, K., Meguro, T. and Shibayama, K. (1980) Acoustic surface wave filters using new distance weighting techniques, *Proc. IEEE Ultrason. Symp.*, cat. 80CH1602-2SU, 313–316.

Zibis, P. (1986) UHF low loss SAW filters for front end applications, *Proc. IEEE Ultrason. Symp.*, cat. 86CH2375-4SU, 293–297.

Appendices

Programs

The following programs are written in FORTRAN IV for the CII-HB 6000 GECOS machine. For any other machine, nonportable commands would have to be modified.

The McClellan program for algorithmic synthesis is given in its primitive version in completely portable FORTRAN IV.

Appendix A

GROK

Program to compute the "exact" driving point impedance of a regular SAW transducer with large coupling.

```
*#RUN *;/LIBRARY/COURBE,R
*Impedance of regular transducer with large N * k2 values
*This program needs one routine : COURBE to plot
* diagrams
      REAL RA(100),T(100)
      REAL XA(100)
      CHARACTER REP
      COMPLEX R,Z,CMPLX,IMPED
      COMPLEX X
      COMPLEX ZZ
      COMMON X
    5 PRINT:"   ---    Exact impedance of SAW transducers"
     &,"   ---"
      PRINT:
      PRINT:"Frequency (MHZ) ?"
      READ:F0
      IF(F0.LE.0.)STOP
      PI=3.141592653
    6  PRINT:"Number of capacitance pairs ?"
      READ:N
      IF(N .LE. 0)GOTO 5
      PRINT:"Coupling coefficient k2 (%) ?"
      READ:BK2
      AK2=0.01*BK2
      IF(AK2 .LE. 0)GOTO 6
      DT=PI/N/25
      T(1)=0.
      RA(1)=0.
```

```
      K=0
      DO 10 I=1,99
      K=K+1
      TETA=(I-49)*DT
      TETA=TETA+1.E-7
      F=F0*(1.+TETA/PI)
      Z=IMPED(AK2,N,TETA)
      IF(A.LT.1.E-7)A=0.
      T(K)=F
      RA(K)=REAL(Z)
      XA(K)=AIMAG(Z)
   10 CONTINUE
      PRINT:"---    TABLE OF RESULTS   ---"
* The "step" parameter is used to sample the actual table
      PRINT:"Step (1,2,...) ?";READ:ISTEP
      ISTEP=MAX0(ISTEP,1)
      PRINT:"    F              R              X"
      PRINT 1,(T(I),RA(I),XA(I),I=2,99,ISTEP)
      PRINT:"*** Graphic display ***"
      PRINT:"Radiation resistance (yes/no) ?"
      READ:REP
      IF(REP.EQ."yes".OR.REP.EQ."YES")CALL COURBE(T,RA,K)
      PRINT:"Radiation reactive impedance (yes/no)  ?"
      READ:REP
      IF(REP.EQ."yes".OR.REP.EQ."YES" )
     & CALL COURBE(T,XA,K)
      GO TO 5
    1 FORMAT(F8.3,2F12.6)
      END
      COMPLEX FUNCTION IMPED(K2,N,TETA)
*Computation of radiation impedance
      COMPLEX P,Q, R,A,BETA,Z,X,S,CSQRT,CEXP,CMPLX
      REAL K2
      COMMON X
      PI=3.1415927
      AK2=0.718*K2
      R=CEXP(-CMPLX(0.,TETA))
      AN=FLOAT(N)
      Y=AK2
      Y=AK2*PI*COS(TETA/2.)**2/(PI+TETA+K2*SIN(TETA))
      BETA=CMPLX(0.,1.)*Y
      Z=R*(1.-BETA)+(1.+BETA)/R
      X=(Z+CSQRT(Z**2-4.))/2.
      A=1.-R+BETA*(1.+R)
      Z=X**2
      P=1.
      IMAX=2*N-2
      DO 20 I=1,IMAX
   20 P=-P*X+1.
      Q=1.
      IMAX=N-1
      DO 10 I=1,IMAX
   10 Q=Q*Z+1.
      S=0.
      KMAX=N-1
      DO 30 K=1,KMAX
   30 S=S*Z+X*FLOAT(K*(N-K))+FLOAT(K*(N-K-1))
      IMPED=(A*Q+R*P)/2./((AN-(AN-1.)*R)*Q+(1.-R)**2*S)
      IMPED=IMPED-1./2./AN
      IMPED=IMPED/BETA
      RETURN
      END
      COMPLEX FUNCTION ZZ(X,A)
*Conventional impedance for comparison not displayed here
      COMPLEX CMPLX,CEXP,II,B
      II=CMPLX(0.,1.)
      ZZ=(SIN(X)/X)**2+II*(SIN(2.*X)-2.*X)/2./X**2
      B=CEXP(-II*X)
      ZZ=ZZ+II*A/2.*B
```

```
      PHI=(X*COS(X)-SIN(X))/X**3
      B=B*((A-2.*X)*PHI-II*SIN(X)/X)
      ZZ=ZZ/(1.+B*A)
      RETURN
      END
      FUNCTION PHASE(Z)
      COMPLEX Z
      DATA PI/3.1415926/
      X=REAL(Z);Y=AIMAG(Z)
      IF(X) 10,30,20
  10  PHASE=ATAN(Y/X)+PI*SIGN(1.,Y)
      GO TO 100
  20  PHASE=ATAN(Y/X)
      GO TO 100
  30  IF(Y)40,60,50
  40  PHASE=-PI/2.
      GO TO 100
  50  PHASE=PI/2.
      GO TO 100
  60  PHASE=0.
 100  RETURN
      END
```

Appendix B

CAREFLEX

Computation of arbitrary multistrip array.

```
*#RUN *=(ULIB)LIBRARY/APPLIB,R
*Design of multistrip arrays
*This program generates a main routine REFLEX to be run
*for computing the frequency response
      CHARACTER REP
      CHARACTER FIC*8
      CHARACTER FICHE*21
      CHARACTER FICHIER*20
      FIC="REFLEX"
      PRINT:"   *** DESIGN OF MULTISTRIP ARRAYS ***"
      PRINT:" "
      PRINT:"---  SPACING OF THE ARRAY    ---"
      PRINT:"Regular spacing (0) or law given by a file"
     &," (1) ?"
      READ:IFICH
      IF(IFICH.EQ.1)IFICH=19
      IF(IFICH.EQ.0)GO TO 10
   5  CONTINUE
      PRINT:"---   COUPLING COEFFICIENTS   ---"
      PRINT:"K2 MIN (%) ?"
      READ:AK2
      AK2=AK2*0.01
      PRINT:"K2 MAX (%) ?"
      READ:AK2MAX;AK2MAX=0.01*AK2MAX
      IF(ABS(AK2-AK2MAX).LE.0.)GO TO 20
      PRINT:"NUMBER OF SAMPLES ?"
      READ:NBK2
      GO TO 20
  10  PRINT:"---   NUMBER OF STRIPS    ---"
      PRINT:"NUMBER OF CAPACITANCES = NUMBER OF STRIPS -"
     &," 1"
      PRINT:"MINIMUM NUMBER OF CAPACITANCES ?"
      READ:NCAPA
```

```
      PRINT:"MAXIMUM NUMBER ?"
      READ:NCAPAMAX
      IF(NCAPA.EQ.NCAPAMAX)GO TO 5
      PRINT:"STEP (1,2,...) ?"
      READ:NPAS
      GO TO 5
   20 PRINT:" "
      PRINT:" "
      PRINT:"---    DESCRIBING THE MULTISTRIP ARRAY    ---"
      KDIM=1
      IF(IFICH.EQ.0)GO TO 25
      PRINT:"File name ?"
      PRINT:"(EXAMPLE: /SAW/FFX)"
      READ:FICHIER
      ENCODE(FICHE,9041)FICHIER
      CALL DETACH(IFICH,ISTAT,)
      CALL ATTACH(IFICH,FICHE,1,0,ISTAT)
      READ(IFICH)KDIM
      CALL DETACH(IFICH,ISTAT,)
      PRINT:"NUMBER OF CAPACITANCES =",KDIM
      GO TO 35
   25 CONTINUE
      PRINT:"-- TRACK A --"
      PRINT:"Unit length = LAMBDA"
      PRINT:"DA (MIN) ?"
      READ:PAS1
      PRINT:"DA (MAX) ?"
      READ:PAS1MAX
      IF(ABS(PAS1MAX-PAS1).LE.0.)GO TO 30
      PRINT:"TOTAL NUMBER OF SAMPLES ?"
      READ:NBDA
   30 PRINT:" "
      PRINT:"-- TRACK B --"
   35 CONTINUE
      PRINT:"REFLECTIVE (1),TRANSMISSIVE (2) OR COUPLING"
     &," (3) DEVICE ?"
      READ:IDISPO
      PRINT:"ONE DEVICE (1) OR TWO CASCADED DEVICES (2)"
     &," ?"
      READ:IDOUBLE
      K1=2;K2=2
      IREF=-1;IF(IDISPO.EQ.1)IREF=1
      NB=2
      IF(IFICH.NE.0)GO TO 40
      IF(IDISPO.EQ.1)CALL MRA(NB,NCAPAMAX,FB,FH,DECAMI,
     & DECAMA,NBDECA,IREF,K1,K2)
      IF(IDISPO.EQ.2)CALL MTA(NB,NCAPAMAX,FB,FH,DECAMI,
     & DECAMA,NBDECA,IREF,K1,K2)
      IF(IDISPO.EQ.3)CALL MSC(NB,NCAPAMAX,FB,FH,DECAMI,
     & DECAMA,NBDECA,IREF,K1,K2)
   40 PRINT:" "
      PRINT:"-- FULL TRACK WIDTHS --"
      PRINT:"Unit length = WA"
      PRINT:"Track A : WA=1."
      W1=1.
      PRINT:"Track B :"
      PRINT:"WB (MIN) ?"
      READ:W2
      PRINT:"WB (MAX) ?"
      READ:W2MAX
      IF(ABS(W2MAX-W2).LE.0.)GO TO 50
      PRINT:"TOTAL NUMBER OF SAMPLES ?"
      READ:NBW2
   50 PRINT:" "
      IF(IDISPO.EQ.3)CALL ACCORD( W2,AK2,PAS1)
      PRINT:"----------------------------"
      PRINT:"---   FREQUENCY RESPONSE   ---"
      PRINT:"NOMINAL FREQUENCY: F=1"
      PRINT:"NUMBER OF FREQUENCIES TO BE COMPUTED?"
```

```
        READ:NBF
        IF(NBF.EQ.0)NBF=1
        IF(NBF.GT.1)PRINT:"F1 ?"
        IF(NBF.EQ.1)PRINT:"F ?"
        READ:F1
        F2=F1
        IF(NBF.EQ.1)GO TO 95
        PRINT:"F2 ?"
        READ:F2
     95 CONTINUE
        PRINT:" "
        ISOR=0
        PRINT:"---    EXECUTION    ---"
        PRINT:"TSS (1) OR BATCH (2) ?"
        READ:IEXE
        IF(IEXE.EQ.2)GO TO 100
        PRINT:"--- DISPLAY OF RESULTS ---"
        PRINT:"PLOT OF THE RESULTS (YES/NO) ?"
        READ:REP;IF(REP.EQ."yes")REP="YES"
        IF(REP.NE."YES")GO TO 100
        PRINT:"ALPHANUMERIC (1) OR GRAPHIC (2) ?"
        READ:ISOR
    100 CONTINUE
*ATTACH TEMPORARY FILE
        CALL DEFIL(FIC,1,0,ISTAT)
        CALL ATTACH(23,"REFLEX;",2,0,ISTAT)
        WRITE(23,9010)NR(1),NR(2)
        IF(IEXE.EQ.1)WRITE(23,9034)NR(1)
        WRITE(23,9001)NR(1),NB
        WRITE(23,9036)NR(1),KDIM
        WRITE(23,9013)NR(1),NCAPA
        WRITE(23,9014)NR(1),NCAPAMAX
        WRITE(23,9015)NR(1),NPAS
        WRITE(23,9002)NR(1),AK2
        WRITE(23,9011)NR(1),AK2MAX
        WRITE(23,9012)NR(1),NBK2
        WRITE(23,9003)NR(1),W2
        WRITE(23,9021)NR(1),W2MAX
        WRITE(23,9022)NR(1),NBW2
        WRITE(23,9004)NR(1),W1
        WRITE(23,9005)NR(1),PAS1
        WRITE(23,9016)NR(1),PAS1MAX
        WRITE(23,9017)NR(1),NBDA
        WRITE(23,9007)NR(1),F2
        WRITE(23,9008)NR(1),F1
        WRITE(23,9009)NR(1),NBF
        WRITE(23,9023)NR(1),ISOR
        WRITE(23,9024)NR(1),IREF
        WRITE(23,9025)NR(1),FB
        WRITE(23,9026)NR(1),FH
        WRITE(23,9027)NR(1),DECAMI
        WRITE(23,9030)NR(1),DECAMA
        WRITE(23,9031)NR(1),NBDECA
        WRITE(23,9035)NR(1),IDOUBLE
        WRITE(23,9028)NR(1),K1
        WRITE(23,9029)NR(1),K2
        WRITE(23,9037)NR(1),KDIM
        WRITE(23,9038)NR(1),IFICH
        IF(IFICH.GT.0)WRITE(23,9039)NR(1),IFICH,FICHIER
        IF(IFICH.GT.0)WRITE(23,9040)NR(1)
        PRINT:"********************"
        PRINT:"EXECUTION:"
        IF(IEXE.EQ.2)GO TO 200
        PRINT:"type : OLD REFLEX"
        GO TO 300
    200 CONTINUE
        PRINT:"type SYST CARD"
        PRINT:"then : OLD OR NEW-OLD /LIBRARY/CARDRFLX,R"
        PRINT:"adjust the LIMITS card"
```

```
  300 CONTINUE
      PRINT:"then type: RUN"
      PRINT:"**********************"
      STOP "Bye"
 9001 FORMAT(I4," PARAMETER  NB=",I4)
 9002 FORMAT(I4," AK2MIN=",E14.6)
 9003 FORMAT(I4," W2MIN=",E14.6)
 9004 FORMAT(I4," W1=",E14.6)
 9005 FORMAT(I4," DAMIN=",E14.6)
 9006 FORMAT(I4," PAS2=",E14.6)
 9007 FORMAT(I4," F2=",E14.6)
 9008 FORMAT(I4," F1=",E14.6)
 9009 FORMAT(I4," NBF=",I3)
 9010 FORMAT(I4,"*#RUN *;/LIBRARY/EXEREFLX,R;"
     &,"/LIBRARY/TEMPS,R;/LIBRARY/COURBE,R;",/,I4,
     & "*#/LIBRARY/COUVIS,R=(ULIB)SERVICE/YT4010,R;"
     &," SERVICE/HEMP,R")
 9011 FORMAT(I4," AK2MAX=",E14.6)
 9012 FORMAT(I4," NBK2=",I4)
 9013 FORMAT(I4," NCAPMI=",I4)
 9014 FORMAT(I4," NCAPMA=",I4)
 9015 FORMAT(I4," NPAS=",I4)
 9016 FORMAT(I4," DAMAX=",E14.6)
 9017 FORMAT(I4," NBDA=",I4)
 9018 FORMAT(I4," FMIN=",E14.6)
 9019 FORMAT(I4," FMAX=",E14.6)
 9020 FORMAT(I4," NBFACC=",I4)
 9021 FORMAT(I4," W2MAX=",E14.6)
 9022 FORMAT(I4," NBW2=",I4)
 9023 FORMAT(I4," ISOR=",I4)
 9024 FORMAT(I4," IREF=",I4)
 9025 FORMAT(I4," FB=",E14.6)
 9026 FORMAT(I4," FH=",E14.6)
 9027 FORMAT(I4," DECAMIN=",E14.6)
 9028 FORMAT(I4," KCAL1=",I6)
 9029 FORMAT(I4," KCAL2=",I6)
 9030 FORMAT(I4," DECAMAX=",E14.6)
 9031 FORMAT(I4," NBDECA=",I4)
 9032 FORMAT(I4," FH=",E14.6)
 9033 FORMAT(I4," FB=",E14.6)
 9034 FORMAT(I4," CALL FPARAM(1,130)")
 9035 FORMAT(I4," IDOUBLE=",I4)
 9036 FORMAT(I4," PARAMETER KDIM=",I4)
 9037 FORMAT(I4," NPAC=",I8)
 9038 FORMAT(I4," IFICH=",I3)
 9039 FORMAT(I4,' CALL ATTACH(',I2,',"',A20,';",')
 9040 FORMAT(I4,"& 1,0,ISTAT)")
 9041 FORMAT(A20,1H;)
      END
      FUNCTION NR(I)
      DATA J/0/
      J=J+1
      NR=1000+10*J
      RETURN
      END
      SUBROUTINE MRA(NB,N,FB,FH,DECAMI,
     & DECAMA,NBDECA,IREF,K1,K2)
      IREF=1
      CALL QUID(NB,N,FB,FH,DECAMI,DECAMA,NBDECA,K1,K2)
      RETURN
      END
      SUBROUTINE MTA(NB,N,FB,FH,DECAMI,
     & DECAMA,NBDECA,IREF,K1,K2)
*Multistrip transmissive array
      IREF=-1
      CALL QUID(NB,N,FB,FH,DECAMI,DECAMA,NBDECA,K1,K2)
      RETURN
      END
      SUBROUTINE MSC(NB,N,FB,FH,DECAMI,
```

```
       & DECAMA,NBDECA,IREF,K1,K2)
*Multistrip coupler
       IREF=-1
       DECAMI=0.;DECAMA=0.;NBDECA=0
       K1=2;K2=2;NB=2
       RETURN
       ENTRY ACCORD( W2,AK2,DA)
       IF(ABS(W2-1.).GT.1.E-12)GO TO 10
       FH=1.E20;GO TO 100
   10  DB=DA-0.095*AK2*(1.-W2)/(1.+W2)
       PRINT:"OPTIMUM SPACING :  DB = ",DB," LAMBDA"
       PRINT:"NEW SPACING : DB "
       READ:DDB;IF(DDB.LE.0.)GO TO 20
       DB=DDB
   20  FH=1./(DB-DA)
  100  FB=FH;RETURN
       END
       SUBROUTINE QUID(NB,N,FB,FH,DECAMI,
     & DECAMA,NBDECA,IREF,K1,K2)
       PRINT:"MULTICHANNEL (1) OR FAN (2) ?"
       READ:ITYP
       IF(ITYP.EQ.1)CALL NCOUP(NB,N,FB,FH,DECAMI,
     & DECAMA,NBDECA,IREF,K1,K2)
       IF(ITYP.EQ.2)CALL RLB(NB,N,FB,FH,DECAMI,
     & DECAMA,NBDECA,IREF,K1,K2)
       RETURN
       END
       SUBROUTINE NCOUP(NB,N,FB,FH,DECAMI,
     & DECAMA,NBDECA,K1,K2)
*Multichannel
       PRINT:"Incident wave travelling from left to right"
     &," on track A"
       PRINT:"Reflected beams on track B"
       PRINT:"NUMBER OF DISCRETE OUTPUT CHANNELS ON TRACK"
     &," B ?" ;READ:NB
       IF(NB.GT.1)GO TO 10
       NB=2;K1=2;K2=2
       PRINT:"CENTER FREQUENCY ?"
       READ:FH;FB=FH;DECAMI=0.;DECAMA=0.;NBDECA=0
       RETURN
   10  PRINT:"CENTER FREQUENCY OF THE FIRST CHANNEL"
     &,"  (TRACK B) ?"
       READ:FH
       PRINT 9001,NB
 9001  FORMAT(1X,"CENTER FREQUENCY OF THE LAST"
     &," CHANNEL NR",I3," (TRACK B) ?")
       READ:FB
       PRINT:"--- GEOMETRY OF THE ARRAY ---"
       PRINT:"ORIGINE OF COORDINATES : CENTER OF FIRST"
     &," CHANNEL"
       EXU=0.
       PRINT:"CENTER OF LAST CHANNEL :"
       PRINT:"MINIMUM SHIFT ?";READ:DECAMI
       PRINT:"Unit length = LAMBDA"
       PRINT:"MAXIMUM SHIFT ?";READ:DECAMA
       IF(ABS(DECAMA-DECAMI).LE.0.)GO TO 20
       PRINT:"NUMBER OF SAMPLES ?";READ:NBDECA
   20  CONTINUE
       PRINT:"---   OUTPUT   ---"
       PRINT:"SUM OF CHANNELS  K1 TO K2:"
       PRINT:"K1 ?";READ:K1
       PRINT:"K2 ?";READ:K2
       K1=K1+1;K2=K2+1;NB=NB+1
       IF(K1.LE.K2)RETURN
       K=K1;K1=K2;K2=K
       RETURN
       END
       SUBROUTINE RLB(NB,N,FB,FH,DECAMI,
     & DECAMA,NBDECA,K1,K2)
```

```
*Broadband fan device
      PRINT:"Incident wave travelling from left to"
      &," right on track A"
      PRINT:"Reflected wave on broad band fan track"
      &," B device"
      PRINT:"CENTER FREQUENCY ON THE TOP OF THE FAN ?"
      READ:F1
      PRINT:"CENTER FREQUENCY ON THE BOTTOM OF THE FAN ?"
      READ:F2
      PRINT:"ORIGINE OF COORDINATES : CENTER OF THE"
      &," TOP OF THE FAN"
      PRINT:"CENTER OF THE BOTTOM OF THE FAN :"
      PRINT:"Unit length = LAMBDA"
      PRINT:"MINIMUM SHIFT ?";READ:DECAMI
      PRINT:"MAXIMUM SHIFT ?";READ:DECAMA
      IF(ABS(DECAMI-DECAMA).LE.0.)GO TO 20
      PRINT:"NUMBER OF SAMPLES ?";READ:NBDECA
   20 CONTINUE
      PRINT:"---    COMPUTATION    ---"
      PN=N*(F1-F2)
      PN=(1.+PN**4)**0.25
      PRINT 9001,PN
 9001 FORMAT(1X,"NUMBER OF CHANNELS=",F6.1)
      PRINT:"NUMBER OF SUBCHANNELS IN EACH CHANNEL ?"
      READ:NPT
      NB=PN*NPT
      NB=MAX0(NB,1)
      FB=F2+(F1-F2)/NB/2.
      FH=F1+(F2-F1)/NB/2.
      PRINT:"---    OUTPUT    ---"
      PRINT:"VERSUS THE LOCATION ALONG THE FAN"
      &," (1) ... OR"
      PRINT:"SUMMED OVER A PART THE FAN (2) ?"
      READ:ISOR
      IF(ISOR.EQ.2)GO TO 10
      K1=0;K2=0;NB=NB+1;RETURN
   10 PRINT:"SUMMATION OVER CENTRAL FREQUENCIES F1 TO F2"
      PRINT:"F1 ?";READ:F
      K=1.+(F-F1)*(NB-1)/(F2-F1)
      K1=MAX0(K,1)
      PRINT:"F2 ?";READ:F
      K=1.+(F-F1)*(NB-1)/(F2-F1)
      K2=MAX0(K,1)
      K1=K1+1;K2=K2+1;NB=NB+1
      IF(K1.LE.K2)RETURN
      K=K1;K1=K2;K2=K
      RETURN
      END
```

EXEREFLX

Library overlay for concatenation with self-generated temporary file REFLEX.

```
      REAL DAK(KDIM),DBK(KDIM)
      PARAMETER NDIM=2*NB
      COMPLEX SIJ1(NB)
      COMPLEX SIJ2(NB)
      COMPLEX AIJ
      COMPLEX A(NDIM,NDIM),B(NDIM,NDIM),C(NDIM,NDIM),D
      CALL TEMPS
      IF(IFICH.EQ.0)GO TO 5
      READ(IFICH)NPAC
      READ(IFICH)(DAK(K),K=1,NPAC)
      READ(IFICH)(DBK(K),K=1,NPAC)
```

```
5 CONTINUE
  NDIM1=NDIM
  NB1=NB
  CALL INIPUI(A,B,C,NDIM1)
  CALL SETDIM(SIJ1,NB1,1)
  CALL SETDIM(SIJ2,NB1,1)
  REAL X(121),FF(121)
  REAL PHA(121)
  COMPLEX S11,S21,S31,S41,D
  CHARACTER REP
  DATA INEUF/0071040040040/
  PI=3.141592653
  NRPT=0
  EPS=1.E-3
  IF(NPAS.LE.0)NPAS=1
  CALL LIMITE(AK2MAX,AK2MIN,NBK2,AK20,DAK2)
  CALL LIMITE(W2MAX,W2MIN,NBW2,W20,DW2)
  CALL LIMITE(DAMAX,DAMIN,NBDA,DA0,DDA)
  CALL LIMITE (DECAMAX,DECAMIN,NBDECA,DECA1,DDECA)
  DO 1000 NN=NCAPMI,NCAPMA,NPAS
  N=NN
  DO 1000 KK2=1,NBK2
  AK2=AK20+KK2*DAK2
  DO 1000 KW2=1,NBW2
  W2=W20+KW2*DW2
  DO 1000 KDA=1,NBDA
  IF(IFICH.GT.0)GO TO 6
  DA=DA0+KDA*DDA
  DBH=1./FH-IREF*DA
  DBB=1./FB-IREF*DA
6 CONTINUE
  DO 1000 IDECA=1,NBDECA
  DECA=DECA1+IDECA*DDECA
  DO 1000 IF=1,NBF
  F=F1+(IF-1)*(F2-F1)/MAX0(1,NBF-1)
  OMEGA=2.*PI*F
  CA=0.5*W1;CB=0.5*W2/(NB-1)
  RA=1.19*AK2/W1/OMEGA
  RB=1.19*AK2*(NB-1)/W2/OMEGA
  SIGC=0.5*(W1+W2)
  YA=RA*CA*OMEGA
  YB=RB*CB*OMEGA
  CA=CA/SIGC ; CB=CB/SIGC
  SQA=SQRT(RA)
  SQB=SQRT(RB)
  DAT=0.;DBTH=0.;DBTB=0.;NT=0
  DO 250 KPAC=1,NPAC
  N1=N;K1P=KPAC;N1P=NPAC
  IF(IFICH.EQ.0)GO TO 20
  DA=DAK(KPAC)
  DBH=DBK(KPAC)
  DBB=DBH
  N1=1
20 CONTINUE
  DO 10 I=1,NDIM
  DO 10 J=1,NDIM
10 A(I,J)=0.
  DO 100 I=1,NB
  YI=YA; IF(I.GT.1)YI=YB
  SQI=SQA;IF(I.GT.1)SQI=SQB
  A(I,I)=CMPLX(1.,YI);A(I+NB,I+NB)=CMPLX(1.,-YI)
  A(I+NB,I)=-CMPLX(0.,YI);A(I,I+NB)=CMPLX(0.,YI)
  DO 100 J=1,NB
  CJ=CA;IF(J.GT.1)CJ=CB
  SQJ=SQA;IF(J.GT.1)SQJ=SQB
  AIJ=CMPLX(0.,CJ*YI*SQJ/SQI)
  A(I,J)=A(I,J)-AIJ
  A(I+NB,J)=A(I+NB,J)+AIJ
  A(I,J+NB)=A(I,J+NB)-AIJ
```

```
      A(I+NB,J+NB)=A(I+NB,J+NB)+AIJ
100 CONTINUE
      TETA=DA*OMEGA
      COA=COS(TETA);SIA=SIN(TETA)
      DO 200 I=1,NB
      COI=COA;SII=SIA
      IF(I.EQ.1)GO TO 110
      TI=DBH+(DBB-DBH)*(I-2)/MAX0(1,NB-2)
      TETI=OMEGA*TI
      COI=COS(TETI);SII=SIN(TETI)
110 DO 200 J=1,NDIM
      A(I,J)=A(I,J)*CMPLX(COI,SII)
      A(I+NB,J)=A(I+NB,J)*CMPLX(COI,-SII)
200 CONTINUE
      CALL PUISSA(N1)
      NT=NT+N1
      DAT=DAT+DA*N1
      DBTH=DBTH+DBH*N1
      DBTB=DBTB+DBB*N1
250 CALL MULT(K1P,N1P)
      DA=DAT/NT
      DBH=DBTH/NT
      DBB=DBTB/NT
      N=NT
      TETA=DA*OMEGA*N/2.
      COA=COS(TETA);SIA=SIN(TETA)
      SIJ1(1)=CMPLX(COA,SIA)
      DO 260 I=2,NB
      SIJ1(I)=0.
260 CONTINUE
      DO 270 I=1,NB
      DO 270 J=1,NB
270 C(I,J)=A(I+NB,J)
*Use system routine of complex linear equations
      CALL HECSEQ(A,NB,SIJ1,1,$1000)
*Use system routine of complex matrix product
      CALL CCCFMP(C,NB1,NB1,SIJ1,1,SIJ2)
      DO 290 I=1,NB
      IF(I.NE.1)GO TO 280
      TETA1=DA*OMEGA*N/2.
      TETA2=DA*OMEGA*N/2.
      GO TO 285
280 TI=DBH+(DBB-DBH)*(I-2)/MAX0(1,NB-2)
      TETA1=N/2.*TI+DECA*(I-2)/MAX0(1,NB-2)
      TETA1=TETA1*OMEGA
      TETA2=N/2.*TI-DECA*(I-2.)/MAX0(1,NB-2)
      TETA2=TETA2*OMEGA
285 CO1=COS(TETA);SI1=SIN(TETA)
      CO2=COS(TETA2);SI2=SIN(TETA2)
      SIJ1(I)=SIJ1(I)*CMPLX(CO1,SI1)
      SIJ2(I)=SIJ2(I)*CMPLX(CO2,SI2)
290 CONTINUE
      IF(KCAL2.EQ.0)GO TO 400
      S11=0.;S21=0.;S31=0.;S41=0.
      DO 350 K=KCAL1,KCAL2
      S21=S21+SIJ2(K)**IDOUBLE
350 S41=S41+SIJ1(K)**IDOUBLE
      S11=SIJ2(1)
      S31=SIJ1(1)
      IF(IDOUBLE.NE.1)GO TO 300
      S21=S21/SQRT(NB-1.)
      S41=S41/SQRT(NB-1.)
300 CONTINUE
      A11=20.*ALOG10(CABS(S11))
      A21=20.*ALOG10(CABS(S21))
      A31=20.*ALOG10(CABS(S31))
      A41=20.*ALOG10(CABS(S41))
      CALL ARCTA(S21,PHI21)
      CALL ARCTA(S41,PHI41)
```

```
      NRPT=NRPT+1
      FF(NRPT)=NRPT
      IF(IREF.GT.0)X(NRPT)=A21
      IF(IREF.GT.0)PHA(NRPT)=PHI21
      IF(IREF.LT.0)PHA(NRPT)=PHI41
      IF(IREF.LT.0)X(NRPT)=A41
      CALL OUTPUT(N,AK2,W2,DA,DBH,DBB,DECA,F,A11,A21
     &,A31,A41,PHI21,PHI41)
      GO TO 1000
  400 NRPT=0
      DO 450 K=2,NB
      NRPT=NRPT+1
      A21=CABS(SIJ2(K));CALL ARCTA(SIJ2(K),PHI21)
      A41=CABS(SIJ1(K));CALL ARCTA(SIJ1(K),PHI41)
      FF(NRPT)=K
      X(NRPT)=A21;IF(IREF.LT.0)X(NRPT)=A41
      PHA(NRPT)=PHI21;IF(IREF.LT.0)PHA(NRPT)=PHI41
  450 CONTINUE
      IF(ISOR.NE.2)GO TO 460
      PRINT:"Plotting ?";IF(ISOR.EQ.2)READ:REP
      CALL COUVIS(FF,X,NRPT)
      PRINT:"F=",F
      PRINT:"SHIFT=",DECA
      PRINT:"PHASE ?";IF(ISOR.EQ.2)READ:REP
      CALL COUVIS(FF,PHA,NRPT)
      PRINT:"F=",F
      PRINT:"SHIFT=",DECA
      PRINT:"TABLE (YES/NO) ?"
      IF(ISOR.EQ.2)READ:REP;IF(REP.EQ."yes")REP="YES"
      IF(REP.NE."YES")GO TO 1000
      PRINT 9004, (FF(I),X(I),PHA(I),I=1,NRPT)
      GO TO 1000
  460 PRINT 9005,
      CALL COURBE(FF,X,NRPT)
      PRINT:"AMPLITUDE"
      PRINT:" "
      PRINT 9005,
      CALL COURBE(FF,PHA,NRPT)
      PRINT:"PHASE"
      PRINT:" "
      PRINT 9005,
      PRINT:"SHIFT=",DECA
      PRINT:"F=",F
      PRINT 9004,(FF(I),X(I),PHA(I),I=1,NRPT)
 1000 CONTINUE
      IF(ISOR.LE.0)STOP
      IF(ISOR.EQ.2)
     &PRINT:"Plotting ?";IF(ISOR.EQ.2)READ:REP
      IF(ISOR.EQ.1)CALL COURBE(FF,X,NRPT)
      IF(ISOR.EQ.2)CALL COUVIS(FF,X,NRPT)
      IF(IREF.GT.0)PRINT:"AMPLITUDE OF S21"
      IF(IREF.LT.0)PRINT:"AMPLITUDE OF S41"
      PRINT:" "
      PRINT:" "
      IF(ISOR.EQ.2)PRINT:"PHASE ?";IF(ISOR.EQ.2)READ:REP
      IF(ISOR.EQ.1)CALL COURBE(FF,PHA,NRPT)
      IF(ISOR.EQ.2)CALL COUVIS(FF,PHA,NRPT)
      IF(IREF.GT.0)PRINT:"PHASE OF S21"
      IF(IREF.LT.0)PRINT:"PHASE OF S41"
      PRINT:" "
 2000 CONTINUE
      CALL TEMPS
      STOP
 9001 FORMAT(I5,F7.3,F7.3,5F8.5,4F9.3,2F7.2)
 9004 FORMAT(3F12.4)
 9005 FORMAT(1H1)
      END
      SUBROUTINE ARCTA(Z,ANGLE)
      COMPLEX Z
```

```
      X=REAL(Z)
      Y=AIMAG(Z)
      PI=3.14159265
      IF(X) 10,30,20
   10 ANGLE=ATAN(Y/X)+PI*SIGN(1.,Y)
      RETURN
   20 ANGLE=ATAN(Y/X)
      RETURN
   30 IF(Y)40,60,50
   40 ANGLE=-PI/2.
      RETURN
   50 ANGLE=PI/2.
      RETURN
   60 ANGLE=0.
      RETURN
      END
      SUBROUTINE LIMITE(XMAX,XMIN,NBPT,X1,DX)
      N=NBPT
      IF(NBPT.LT.1)NBPT=1
      DX=(XMAX-XMIN)/MAX0(1,NBPT-1)
      X1=XMIN-DX
      RETURN
      END
      SUBROUTINE INIPUI(A,B,C,NDIM)
      LOGICAL OK
      COMPLEX A(NDIM,NDIM),B(NDIM,NDIM),C(NDIM,NDIM)
      NDIM1=NDIM
*Use system routine SETDIM to set dimension of arrays
      CALL SETDIM(A,NDIM1,NDIM1,B,NDIM1,NDIM1,
     & C,NDIM1,NDIM1)
      CALL INIPRO(A,B,C,NDIM1)
      RETURN
      ENTRY PUISSA(N)
      IF(N.EQ.1)RETURN
      IF(N.LT.1)STOP"ERROR PUISSA"
      OK=.FALSE.
      IF(N.EQ.2)OK=.TRUE.
      N2=N
    5 CONTINUE
   10 DO 600 IGENE=1,33
   20 IGC=IGENE-1
      N1=N;ICAS=4
      DO 500 ITER=1,20
      IBIT=MOD(N1,2)
      N1=N1/2
      IF(IBIT.EQ.0)GO TO 200
      IF(ICAS.LT.4)GO TO 1000
      IVA=ICAS-3
      IF(ICAS.GT.6)GO TO 100
      ICAS=IVA;GO TO 200
  100 IVA=ICAS-6
      IF(OK)CALL PROD(ICAS)
      GO TO (110,120,130,140,150,160),IVA
  110 ICAS=8;GO TO 200
  120 ICAS=7;GO TO 200
  130 ICAS=10;GO TO 200
  140 ICAS=9;GO TO 200
  150 ICAS=12;GO TO 200
  160 ICAS=11
  200 IF(N1.EQ.0)GO TO 400
      IF(ICAS.GT.6)GO TO 300
      ICHOIX=MOD(IGC,2);IGC=IGC/2
      IVA=2*ICAS-ICHOIX
      ICALCUL=MOD(IVA-1,6)+1
      IF(OK)CALL PROD(ICALCUL)
      GO TO (201,202,203,204,205,206,207,208,
     & 209,210,211,212),IVA
  201 ICAS=9 ; GO TO 500
  202 ICAS=11 ; GO TO 500
```

```
 203 ICAS=7 ; GO TO 500
 204 ICAS=12 ; GO TO 500
 205 ICAS=8 ; GO TO 500
 206 ICAS=10 ; GO TO 500
 207 ICAS=5 ; GO TO 500
 208 ICAS=6 ; GO TO 500
 209 ICAS=4 ; GO TO 500
 210 ICAS=6 ; GO TO 500
 211 ICAS=4 ; GO TO 500
 212 ICAS=5 ; GO TO 500
 300 IVA=ICAS-6
     GO TO (301,302,303,304,305,306),IVA
 301 ICAS=12;ICALCUL=2;GO TO 350
 302 ICAS=10;ICALCUL=1;GO TO 350
 303 ICAS=11;ICALCUL=4;GO TO 350
 304 ICAS=8;ICALCUL=3;GO TO 350
 305 ICAS=9;ICALCUL=6;GO TO 350
 306 ICAS=7;ICALCUL=5;GO TO 350
 350 IF(OK)CALL PROD(ICALCUL)
     GO TO 500
 400 IF(N2.EQ.2)GO TO 700
     IF(OK)RETURN
     GO TO 550
 500 CONTINUE
 550 IF(ICAS.EQ.1)OK=.TRUE.
     IF(ICAS.EQ.9)OK=.TRUE.
     IF(ICAS.EQ.11)OK=.TRUE.
     IF(OK)GO TO 20
 600 CONTINUE
     OK=.TRUE.;N2=2
     GO TO 5
 700 GO TO (1000,710,720,1000,1000,1000
    &,710,720,1000,720,
    & 1000,710),ICAS
 710 CALL TRANS(1);RETURN
 720 CALL TRANS(2);RETURN
1000 STOP"ERROR"
     END
     SUBROUTINE INIPRO(A,B,C,N1)
     COMPLEX A(N1,N1),B(N1,N1),C(N1,N1)
     N=N1
     RETURN
     ENTRY PROD(K)
     GO TO (1,2,3,4,5,6,7,8,9,10,11,12),K
*Matrix product
   1 CALL CCCFMP(A,N,N,A,N,B);RETURN
   2 CALL CCCFMP(A,N,N,A,N,C);RETURN
   3 CALL CCCFMP(B,N,N,B,N,A);RETURN
   4 CALL CCCFMP(B,N,N,B,N,C);RETURN
   5 CALL CCCFMP(C,N,N,C,N,A);RETURN
   6 CALL CCCFMP(C,N,N,C,N,B);RETURN
   7 CALL CCCFMP(B,N,N,A,N,C);RETURN
   8 CALL CCCFMP(C,N,N,A,N,B);RETURN
   9 CALL CCCFMP(A,N,N,B,N,C);RETURN
  10 CALL CCCFMP(C,N,N,B,N,A);RETURN
  11 CALL CCCFMP(A,N,N,C,N,B);RETURN
  12 CALL CCCFMP(B,N,N,C,N,A);RETURN
     ENTRY TRANS(L)
     GO TO (100,200,300),L
 100 DO 110 I=1,N
     DO 110 J=1,N
 110 A(I,J)=B(I,J)
     RETURN
 200 DO 210 I=1,N
     DO 210 J=1,N
 210 A(I,J)=C(I,J)
     RETURN
 300 DO 310 I=1,N
     DO 310 J=1,N
```

```
  310 B(I,J)=A(I,J)
      RETURN
      END
      SUBROUTINE MULT(K,N)
      IF(N.EQ.1)RETURN
      IF(K.NE.1)GO TO 5
      CALL TRANS(3);J=1;RETURN
    5 M=J+6
      J=3-J
      CALL PROD(M)
      IF(K.LT.N)RETURN
      CALL TRANS(J)
      RETURN
      END
      SUBROUTINE OUTPUT(N,AK2,W2,DA,DBH,DBB,DECA
     &,F,A11,A21,A31,A41,PHI21,PHI41)
      REAL P(7),P1(7)
      CHARACTER TEXTE
      DATA ICOU/0/
      P(1)=AK2;P(2)=W2;P(3)=DA;P(4)=DBH
      P(5)=DBB;P(6)=DECA;P(7)=F
      IF(ICOU.EQ.0)GO TO 200
      IF(N.EQ.N1)GOTO 10
      TEXTE="N=     ";IPARA=N;N1=N;GOTO 100
   10 DO 20 I=1,7
      IF(ABS(P(I)-P1(I)).LT.1.E-20)GO TO 20
      IF(I.EQ.1)TEXTE="K2 =   "
      IF(I.EQ.2)TEXTE="WB =   "
      IF(I.EQ.3)TEXTE="DA =   "
      IF (I.EQ.4)TEXTE="DBT =  "
      IF (I.EQ.5)TEXTE="DBB =  "
      IF(I.EQ.6)TEXTE="SHIFT="
      IF(I.EQ.7)TEXTE="F =    "
      GO TO 110
   20 CONTINUE
  100 PRINT 9001,TEXTE,N,A11,A21,A31,A41,PHI21,PHI41
      GO TO 300
  110 PRINT 9002,TEXTE,P(I),A11,A21,A31,A41,PHI21,PHI41
      GO TO 300
  200 PRINT:"N=",N
      PRINT:"K2=",100*AK2," %"
      PRINT:"WB=",W2," WA"
      PRINT:"DA=",DA
      PRINT:"DBT(top)=",DBH," LAMBDA"
      PRINT:"DBB(bottom)=",DBB," LAMBDA"
      PRINT:"SHIFT=",DECA," LAMBDA"
      PRINT:"F=",F
      PRINT:" "
      PRINT:"                   S11        S21        S31"
     &,"        S41        PHI21      PHI41"
      PRINT:"                  (dB)       (dB)       (dB)"
     &        (dB)       (rad)      (rad)"
      PRINT 9003,A11,A21,A31,A41,PHI21,PHI41
  300 ICOU=ICOU+1
      DO 310 I=1,7
  310 P1(I)=P(I)
      N1=N
      RETURN
 9001 FORMAT(1X,1A6,I5,6F10.2)
 9002 FORMAT(1X,1A6,F5.2,6F10.2)
 9003 FORMAT(12X,6F10.2)
      END
```

Appendix C

ABAC1

Feasible Dolph-Chebyshev windows.

```
*    ABACUS : LIST DOLPH-CHEBYSHEV WINDOWS
********************************************************
*
     DOUBLE PRECISION PAS,W0,OME,PHI,PI,AX1,AN,X1,ALF,
   & AAA,PK,X0,P,ALF2,UALF,X,Y,REJ
   &,X3,BETA,TETA,RN,RNM1
   &,ANM1(300),AN(300),ANP1(300),AT1,AT2
     REAL AK(300),TAU(300)
     REAL BB(300)
     LOGICAL PAIR
     DATA PI/3.14159265359/
     PRINT: "                        TABLE OF DOLPH-"
   &,"CHEBYSHEV WINDOWS"
     PRINT: "2*N = Number of filter coefficients (FIR)"
     PRINT: "Amax/Amin = ratio of max/min value of"
   &," coefficients"
     PRINT:"Transition bandwidth = 1st lobe bandwidth"
     PRINT:"3db-bandwidth = 3dB-banwidth of 1st lobe"
 500 CONTINUE
     PRINT:"                          ***"
     PRINT:"Number of half-wavelengths between adjacent"
   &," fingers ?"
     READ:M
     IF(M.EQ.0)STOP
     PM=M
     PAS=PM*0.25
     PRINT:" Transition bandwith (%) ?"
     READ:UA
     UA=UA*0.01
     UALF=COS(UA*PAS*PI)
     ALF=1./UALF
     ALF2=ALF*ALF
     N=300
     BN=N
     AX1=PI/(2.D0*(2.D0*BN-1.D0))
     X1=DCOS(AX1)
     X0=X1*UALF
     AT1=3.D0*ALF2-2.D0
     AT2=2.D0*(ALF2-1.D0)
     ANM1(1)=3.D0*ALF*(ALF2-1.D0)
     ANM1(2)=ALF2*ALF
     T2NM3=ALF*(4.D0*ALF2-3.D0)
     DO 530 K=1,2
 530 ANM1(K)=ANM1(K)/T2NM3
     AN(1)=5.D0*ALF*(1.D0-3.D0*ALF2+2.D0*ALF2*ALF2)
     AN(2)=5.D0*ALF*(-ALF2+ALF2*ALF2)
     AN(3)=ALF2*ALF2*ALF
     T2NM1=ALF*(5.D0-20.D0*ALF2+16.D0*ALF2*ALF2)
     DO 510 K=1,3
 510 AN(K)=AN(K)/T2NM1
     RNM1=T2NM3/T2NM1
     PRINT:"   N        Amax/Amin      IL (dB)      3 DB-BDW"
   &," (%)"
     DO 200 NN=3,N-1
     RN=1.D0/(4.D0*ALF2-2.D0-RNM1)
     ANP1(1)=(AT1*AN(1)+ALF2*AN(2))*RN- ANM1(1)*RNM1*RN
     DO 220 K=2,NN-1
     ANP1(K)=(AT2*AN(K)+ALF2*AN(K+1)+ALF2*AN(K-1))*RN-
   &ANM1(K)*RNM1*RN
```

```
220 CONTINUE
210 ANP1(NN)=(AT2*AN(NN)+ALF2*AN(NN-1))*RN
    ANP1(NN+1)=ALF2*AN(NN)*RN
    DO 250 K=1,NN+1
    BB(K)=ANP1(K)
250 CONTINUE
 22 FORMAT(E18.7)
    SS=BB(1)
    AMIN=1.E30
    AMAX=0.
    DO 302 K=1,NN+1
    AK(K)=BB(K)/SS
    IF(AMIN.GT.AK(K))AMIN=AK(K)
    IF(AMAX.LT.AK(K))AMAX=AK(K)
    TAU(K)=(2*K-1)*PAS
  1 FORMAT(I5,2F12.3)
302 CONTINUE
    RAP=AMAX/AMIN
  3 FORMAT(" AMAX/AMIN" F10.2)
    DO 240 K=1,NN+1
    ANM1(K)=AN(K)
    AN(K)=ANP1(K)
240 CONTINUE
    RNM1=RN
    IF(RAP.LT.0.OR.RAP.GT.1000.)GO TO 200
    Y=ALF+DSQRT(ALF2-1.D0)
    X=DLOG(Y)
    Y=DEXP((2*NN-1)*X)
    REJ=0.5D0*(Y+1.D0/Y)
    FALF=REJ
    REJ=20.*ALOG10(REJ)
  2 FORMAT("   Insertion Loss"  F10.2," DB")
    BETA=10.**(3./20.)
    BETA=FALF/BETA
    IF(BETA.LT.1)GO TO 400
    Z=BETA+DSQRT(BETA*BETA-1.)
    Y=DLOG(Z)
    Y3=EXP(Y/(2*NN-1))
    X3=0.5*UALF*(Y3+1./Y3)
    GO TO 410
400 SB=SQRT(1.-BETA*BETA)
    Y=ATAN2(SB,BETA)
    X3=Y*UALF/(2*NN-1)
410 TETA=DSQRT(2.*(1.-X3))
    B3DB=4.*TETA/(PI*PM)
    B3DB=B3DB*100.
  4 FORMAT(" 3 dB-bandwidth",F10.3)
    IF(B3DB.GT.100.)GO TO 200
    PRINT 5,NN+1,RAP,REJ,B3DB
  5 FORMAT(I5,3F12.2)
200 CONTINUE
    GO TO 500
    END
```

GENERE1

Program to generate a Dolph-Chebyshev window.

```
*#RUN *;/SAW/ATAFIC,R
 DOUBLE PRECISION PAS,WO,OME,PHI,PI,AX1,AN,X1,
& ALF,AAA,PK,XO,PM,ALF2,UALF,X,Y,REJ
& ,X3,BETA,TETA,RN,RNM1,T2NM3,T2NM1
& ,ANM1(300),AN(300),ANP1(300),AT1,AT2
 REAL AK(300),TAU(300)
 REAL AA(600),TT(600)
```

```
      REAL BB(300)
      LOGICAL PAIR
      DATA PI/3.14159265359/
500   CONTINUE
      PRINT:" Number of half wavelengths between"
     &," adjacent fingers?"
      READ:M
      IF(M.EQ.0)STOP
      PM=M
      PAS=PM*0.25
      PRINT:" Transition bandwidth (%) ?"
      READ:UAPC
      UA=0.01*UAPC
      UALF=COS(UA*PAS*PI)
      ALF=1./UALF
      ALF2=ALF*ALF
      PRINT:" Number of fingers /2 (<300)"
      READ:N
      BN=N
      AX1=PI/(2.D0*(2.D0*BN-1.D0))
      X1=DCOS(AX1)
      X0=X1*UALF
      AT1=3.D0*ALF2-2.D0
      AT2=2.D0*(ALF2-1.D0)
      ANM1(1)=3.D0*ALF*(ALF2-1.D0)
      ANM1(2)=ALF2*ALF
      T2NM3=ALF*(4.D0*ALF2-3.D0)
      DO 530 K=1,2
530   ANM1(K)=ANM1(K)/T2NM3
      AN(1)=5.D0*ALF*(1.D0-3.D0*ALF2+2.D0*ALF2*ALF2)
      AN(2)=5.D0*ALF*(-ALF2+ALF2*ALF2)
      AN(3)=ALF2*ALF2*ALF
      T2NM1=ALF*(5.D0-20.D0*ALF2+16.D0*ALF2*ALF2)
      DO 510 K=1,3
510   AN(K)=AN(K)/T2NM1
      RNM1=T2NM3/T2NM1
      DO 200 NN=3,N-1
      RN=1.D0/(4.D0*ALF2-2.D0-RNM1)
      ANP1(1)=(AT1*AN(1)+ALF2*AN(2))*RN- ANM1(1)*RNM1*RN
      DO 220 K=2,NN-1
      ANP1(K)=(AT2*AN(K)+ALF2*AN(K+1)+ALF2*AN(K-1))*RN-
     &ANM1(K)*RNM1*RN
220   CONTINUE
210   ANP1(NN)=(AT2*AN(NN)+ALF2*AN(NN-1))*RN
      ANP1(NN+1)=ALF2*AN(NN)*RN
      DO 250 K=1,NN+1
      BB(K)=ANP1(K)
250   CONTINUE
 22   FORMAT(E18.7)
      SS=BB(1)
      AMIN=1.E30
      AMAX=0.
      DO 302 K=1,NN+1
      AK(K)=BB(K)/SS
      IF(AMIN.GT.AK(K))AMIN=AK(K)
      IF(AMAX.LT.AK(K))AMAX=AK(K)
      TAU(K)=(2*K-1)*PAS
  1   FORMAT(I5,2F12.3)
302   CONTINUE
      RAP=AMAX/AMIN
  3   FORMAT(" AMAX/AMIN" F10.2)
      DO 240 K=1,NN+1
      ANM1(K)=AN(K)
      AN(K)=ANP1(K)
240   CONTINUE
      RNM1=RN
      Y=ALF+DSQRT(ALF2-1.D0)
      X=DLOG(Y)
      Y=DEXP((2*NN-1)*X)
```

```
      REJ=0.5D0*(Y+1.D0/Y)
      FALF=REJ
      REJ=20.*ALOG10(REJ)
    2 FORMAT("    REJECTION"  F10.2," DB")
      BETA=10.**(3./20.)
      BETA=FALF/BETA
      IF(BETA.LT.1)GO TO 400
      Z=BETA+DSQRT(BETA*BETA-1.)
      Y=DLOG(Z)
      Y3=EXP(Y/(2*NN-1))
      X3=0.5*UALF*(Y3+1./Y3)
      GO TO 410
  400 SB=SQRT(1.-BETA*BETA)
      Y=ATAN2(SB,BETA)
      X3=Y*UALF/(2*NN-1)
  410 TETA=DSQRT(2.*(1.-X3))
      B3DB=4.*TETA/(PI*PM)
    4 FORMAT(" 3 dB-bandwidth",F10.3)
  200 CONTINUE
      PRINT 3,RAP
      PRINT 2,REJ
      PRINT 4,B3DB
      PRINT:" 0 = do not list"
      PRINT :" 1 = list TAU(K) and A(K)"
      READ:IP
      IF(IP.EQ.0)GO TO 570
      PRINT:"    K     TAU(K)      A(K)"
      DO 520 K=1,N
      PRINT 1,K,TAU(K),AK(K)
  520 CONTINUE
  570 CONTINUE
      PRINT:" Save : 0=NO, 1=YES"
      READ:IP
      IF(IP.EQ.0)GO TO 500
      CALL ATAFIC(01,2)
      N2=2*N
      DO 580 K=1,N
      KK=N+1-K
      TT(K)=-TAU(KK)
      AA(K)=AK(KK)
  580 CONTINUE
      DO 540 K=1,N
      KK=N+K
      TT(KK)=TAU(K)
      AA(KK)=AK(K)
  540 CONTINUE
      WRITE(01)N2
      WRITE(01)(TT(K),K=1,N2)
      WRITE(01)(AA(K),K=1,N2)
      STOP
      END
```

Appendix D

Program for designing optimum FIR linear phase digital filters (McClellan *et al.* 1973)[†]

```
C     PROGRAM FOR THE DESIGN OF LINEAR PHASE FINITE IMPULSE
C     RESPONSE (FIR) FILTERS USING THE REMEZ EXCHANGE ALGORITHM
C     JIM MCCLELLAN, RICE UNIVERSITY, APRIL 13, 1973
C     THREE TYPES OF FILTERS ARE INCLUDED--BANDPASS FILTERS
C     DIFFERENTIATORS, AND HILBERT TRANSFORM FILTERS
C
C     THE INPUT DATA CONSISTS OF 5 CARDS
C
C     CARD 1--FILTER LENGTH, TYPE OF FILTER.  1-MULTIPLE
C     PASSBAND/STOPBAND, 2-DIFFERENTIATOR, 3-HILBERT TRANSFORM
C     FILTER.  NUMBER OF BANDS, CARD PUNCH DESIRED, AND GRID
C     DENSITY.
C
C     CARD 2--BANDEDGES, LOWER AND UPPER EDGES FOR EACH BAND
C     WITH A MAXIMUM OF 10 BANDS.
C
C     CARD 3--DESIRED FUNCTION (OR DESIRED SLOPE IF A
C     DIFFERENTIATOR) FOR EACH BAND
C
C     CARD 4--WEIGHT FUNCTION IN EACH BAND.  FOR A
C     DIFFERENTIATOR, THE WEIGHT FUNCTION IS INVERSELY
C     PROPORTIONAL TO F.
C
C     CARD 5--RIPPLE AND ATTENUATION IN PASSBAND AND STOPBAND.
C     THIS CARD IS OPTIONAL AND CAN BE USED TO SPECIFY LOWPASS
C     FILTERS DIRECTLY IN TERMS OF PASSBAND RIPPLE AND STOPBAND
C     ATTENUATION IN DB. THE FILTER LENGTH IS DETERMINED FROM
C     THE APPROXIMATION RELATIONSHIPS GIVEN IN :
C     L. R. RABINER, APPROXIMATE DESIGN RELATIONSHIPS FOR
C     LOWPASS DIGITAL FILTERS, IEEE TRANS. ON AUDIO AND
C     ELECTROACUSTICS, VOL. AU-21, NO. 5, OCTOBER 73.

C     **** WHEN THIS OPTION IS USED THE FILTER LENGTH ON
C     CARD 1 SHOULD BE SET TO 0. ******
C
C     THE FOLLOWING INPUT DATA SPECIFIES A LENGTH 32 BANDPASS
C     FILTER WITH STOPBANDS 0 TO 0.1 AND 0.425 TO 0.5, AND
C     PASSBAND FROM 0.2 TO 0.35 WITH WEIGHTING OF 10 IN THE
C     STOPBANDS AND 1 IN THE PASSBAND.  THE IMPULSE RESPONSE
C     WILL BE PUNCHED AND THE GRID DENSITY IS 32.
C     SAMPLE INPUT DATA SETUP
C     32,1,3,1,32
C     0,0.1,0.2,0.35,0.425,0.5
C     0,1,0
C     10,1,10
C
C     THE FOLLOWING INPUT DATA SPECIFIES A LENGTH 32 WIDEBAND
C     DIFFERENTIATOR WITH SLOPE 1 AND WEIGHTING OF 1/H.  THE
C     IMPULSE RESPONSE WILL NOT BE PUNCHED AND THE GRID
C     DENSITY IS ASSUMED TO BE 16.
C     32,2,1,0,0
C     0,0.5
C     1.0
C     1.0
C
```

```
C     THE FOLLOWING INPUT DATA SPECIFIES A LOWPASS FILTER
C     BY GIVING DIRECTLY THE RIPPLE AND ATTENUATION.
C     0,1,2,0,32
C     0,0.2,0.3,0.5
C     1,0
C     1,1
C     0.2,40
C
      COMMON DES,WT,ALPHA,IEXT,NFCNS,NGRID,PI2,AD,DEV,X,Y,GRID
      DIMENSION IEXT(66),AD(66),ALPHA(66),X(66),Y(66)
      DIMENSION H(66)
      DIMENSION DES(1045),GRID(1045),WT(1045)
      DIMENSION EDGE(20),FX(10),WTX(10),DEVIAT(10)
      DIMENSION OMEGA(50),RESPA(50)
      DOUBLE PRECISION OMEGA,SUMAR,SUMAC,RESPA,ATTN,RIPPLE,SVRIP,DELTAF
      DOUBLE PRECISION PI2,PI
      DOUBLE PRECISION AD,DEV,X,Y
      PI2=6.283185307179586
      PI=3.1415926535899793
C
C     THE PROGRAM IS SET UP FOR A MAXIMUM LENGTH OF 128, BUT
C     THIS UPPER LIMIT CAN BE CHANGED BY REDIMENSIONING THE
C     ARRAYS IEXT, AD, ALPHA, X, Y, H TO BE NFMAX/2 + 2.
C     THE ARRAYS DES, GRID, AND WT MUST DIMENSIONED
C     16(NFMAX/2 + 2).
C
      NFMAX=128
  100 CONTINUE
      JTYPE=0
C
C     PROGRAM INPUT SECTION
C
      READ *,NFILT,JTYPE,NBANDS,JPUNCH,LGRID
      IF(NFILT.GT.NFMAX.OR.NFILT.EQ.3) CALL ERROR
      IF(NBANDS.LE.0) NBANDS=1
C
C     GRID DENSITY IS ASSUMED TO BE 16 UNLESS SPECIFIED
C     OTHERWISE
C
      IF(LGRID.LE.0) LGRID=16
      JB=2*NBANDS
      READ*,(EDGE(J),J=1,JB)
      READ*,(FX(J),J=1,NBANDS)
      READ *,(WTX(J),J=1,NBANDS)
      IF(JTYPE.EQ.0) CALL ERROR
      IF(NFILT.EQ.0) GO TO 10
      NROX = 0
      GO TO 11
   10 READ *,RIPPLE,ATTN
      RIPPLE=10**(RIPPLE/20)
      ATTN=10**(-ATTN/20)
      RIPPLE=(RIPPLE-1)/(RIPPLE+1)
      RIPPLE=DLOG10(RIPPLE)
      ATTN=DLOG10(ATTN)
      SVRIP=RIPPLE
      RIPPLE=(0.005309*(RIPPLE**2)+0.07114*RIPPLE-0.4761)*ATTN
     1+(-0.00266*(RIPPLE**2)-0.5941*RIPPLE-0.4278)
      ATTN=11.01217+0.51244*SVRIP-0.51244*ATTN
      DELTAF=EDGE(3)-EDGE(2)
      NFILT=RIPPLE/DELTAF-ATTN*(DELTAF**2)+1
      NROX=1
   11 NEG=1
      IF(JTYPE.EQ.1) NEG=0
      NODD=NFILT/2
      NODD=NFILT-2*NODD
      NFCNS=NFILT/2
      IF(NODD.EQ.1.AND.NEG.EQ.0) NFCNS=NFCNS+1
C
C     SET UP THE DENSE GRID.  THE NUMBER OF POINTS IN THE GRID
C     IS (FILTER LENGTH + 1)*GRID DENSITY/2
C
```

```
      GRID(1)=EDGE(1)
      DELF=LGRID*NFCNS
      DELF=0.5/DELF
      IF(NEG.EQ.0) GO TO 135
      IF(EDGE(1).LT.DELF) GRID(1)=DELF
  135 CONTINUE
      J=1
      L=1
      LBAND=1
  140 FUP=EDGE(L+1)
  145 TEMP=GRID(J)
C
C     CALCULATE THE DESIRED MAGNITUDE RESPONSE AND THE WEIGHT
C     FUNCTION ON THE GRID
C
      DES(J)=EFF(TEMP,FX,WTX,LBAND,JTYPE)
      WT(J)=WATE(TEMP,FX,WTX,LBAND,JTYPE)
      J=J+1
      GRID(J)=TEMP+DELF
      IF(GRID(J).GT.FUP) GO TO 150
      GO TO 145
  150 GRID(J-1)=FUP
      DES(J-1)=EFF(FUP,FX,WTX,LBAND,JTYPE)
      WT(J-1)=WATE(FUP,FX,WTX,LBAND,JTYPE)
      LBAND=LBAND+1
      L=L+2
      IF(LBAND.GT.NBANDS) GO TO 160
      GRID(J)=EDGE(L)
      GO TO 140
  160 NGRID=J-1
      IF(NEG.NE.NODD) GO TO 165
      IF(GRID(NGRID).GT.(0.5-DELF)) NGRID=NGRID-1
  165 CONTINUE
C
C     SET UP A NEW APPROXIMATION PROBLEM WHICH IS EQUIVALENT
C     TO THE ORIGINAL PROBLEM
C
      IF(NEG) 170,170,180
  170 IF(NODD.EQ.1) GO TO 200
      DO 175 J=1,NGRID
      CHANGE=DCOS(PI*GRID(J))
      DES(J)=DES(J)/CHANGE
  175 WT(J)=WT(J)*CHANGE
      GO TO 200
  180 IF(NODD.EQ.1) GO TO 190
      DO 185 J=1,NGRID
      CHANGE=DSIN(PI*GRID(J))
      DES(J)=DES(J)/CHANGE
  185 WT(J)=WT(J)*CHANGE
      GO TO 200
  190 DO 195 J=1,NGRID
      CHANGE=DSIN(PI2*GRID(J))
      DES(J)=DES(J)/CHANGE
  195 WT(J)=WT(J)*CHANGE
C
C     INITIAL GUESS FOR THE EXTREMAL FREQUENCIES--EQUALLY
C     SPACED ALONG THE GRID
C
  200 TEMP=FLOAT(NGRID-1)/FLOAT(NFCNS)
      DO 210 J=1,NFCNS
  210 IEXT(J)=(J-1)*TEMP+1
      IEXT(NFCNS+1)=NGRID
      NM1=NFCNS-1
      NZ=NFCNS+1
C
C     CALL THE REMEZ EXCHANGE ALGORITHM TO DO THE APPROXIMATION
C     PROBLEM
C
      CALL REMEZ(EDGE,NBANDS)
C
```

```
C     CALCULATE THE IMPULSE RESPONSE.
C
      IF(NEG) 300,300,320
  300 IF(NODD.EQ.0) GO TO 310
      DO 305 J=1,NM1
  305 H(J)=0.5*ALPHA(NZ-J)
      H(NFCNS)=ALPHA(1)
      GO TO 350
  310 H(1)=0.25*ALPHA(NFCNS)
      DO 315 J=2,NM1
  315 H(J)=0.25*(ALPHA(NZ-J)+ALPHA(NFCNS+2-J))
      H(NFCNS)=0.5*ALPHA(1)+0.25*ALPHA(2)
      GO TO 350
  320 IF(NODD.EQ.0) GO TO 330
      H(1)=0.25*ALPHA(NFCNS)
      H(2)=0.25*ALPHA(NM1)
      DO 325 J=3,NM1
  325 H(J)=0.25*(ALPHA(NZ-J)-ALPHA(NFCNS+3-J))
      H(NFCNS)=0.5*ALPHA(1)-0.25*ALPHA(3)
      H(NZ)=0.0
      GO TO 350
  330 H(1)=0.25*ALPHA(NFCNS)
      DO 335 J=2,NM1
  335 H(J)=0.25*(ALPHA(NZ-J)-ALPHA(NFCNS+2-J))
      H(NFCNS)=0.5*ALPHA(1)-0.25*ALPHA(2)
C
C     PROGRAM OUTPUT SECTION.
C
  350 PRINT 360
  360 FORMAT(1H1, 70(1H*)//25X,'FINITE IMPULSE RESPONSE (FIR)'
     125X,'LINEAR PHASE DIGITAL FILTER DESIGN'/
     225X,'REMEZ EXCHANGE ALGORITHM'/)
      IF(JTYPE.EQ.1) PRINT 365
  365 FORMAT(25X,'BANDPASS FILTER'/)
      IF(JTYPE.EQ.2) PRINT 370
  370 FORMAT(25X,'DIFFERENTIATOR'/)
      IF(JTYPE.EQ.3) PRINT 375
  375 FORMAT(25X,'HILBERT TRANSFORMER'/)
      PRINT 378,NFILT
  378 FORMAT(15X,'FILTER LENGTH = ',I3/)
      IF(NROX.EQ.1) PRINT 379
  379 FORMAT(15X,'FILTER LENGTH DETERMINED BY APPROXIMATION'/)
      PRINT 380
  380 FORMAT(15X,'***** IMPULSE RESPONSE *****')
      DO 381 J=1,NFCNS
      K=NFILT+1-J
      IF(NEG.EQ.0) PRINT 382,J,H(J),K
      IF(NEG.EQ.1) PRINT 383,J,H(J),K
  381 CONTINUE
  382 FORMAT(20X,'H(',I3,') = ',E15.8,' = H(',I4,')')
  383 FORMAT(20X,'H(',I3,') = ',E15.8,' = -H(',I4,')')
      IF(NEG.EQ.1.AND.NODD.EQ.1) PRINT 384,NZ
  384 FORMAT(20X,'H(',I3,') =  0.0')
      DO 450 K=1,NBANDS,4
      KUP=K+3
      IF(KUP.GT.NBANDS) KUP=NBANDS
      PRINT 385,(J,J=K,KUP)
  385 FORMAT(/24X,4('BAND',I3,8X))
      PRINT 390,(EDGE(2*J-1),J=K,KUP)
  390 FORMAT(2X,'LOWER BAND EDGE',5F15.9)
      PRINT 395,(EDGE(2*J),J=K,KUP)
  395 FORMAT(2X,'UPPER BAND EDGE',5F15.9)
      IF(JTYPE.NE.2) PRINT 400,(FX(J),J=K,KUP)
  400 FORMAT(2X,'DESIRED VALUE',2X,5F15.9)
      IF(JTYPE.EQ.2) PRINT 405,(FX(J),J=K,KUP)
  405 FORMAT(2X,'DESIRED SLOPE',2X,5F15.9)
      PRINT 410,(WTX(J),J=K,KUP)
  410 FORMAT(2X,'WEIGHTING',6X,5F15.9)
      DO 420 J=K,KUP
  420 DEVIAT(J)=DEV/WTX(J)
      PRINT 425,(DEVIAT(J),J=K,KUP)
```

```
  425 FORMAT(2X,'DEVIATION',6X,5F15.9)
      IF(JTYPE.NE.1) GO TO 450
      DO 430 J=K,KUP
      IF (FX(J).EQ.1.0) DEVIAT(J)=(1.0+DEVIAT(J))/(1.0-DEVIAT(J))
  430 DEVIAT(J)=20.0*ALOG10(DEVIAT(J))
      PRINT 435,(DEVIAT(J),J=K,KUP)
  435 FORMAT(2X,'DEVIATION IN DB',5F15.9)
  450 CONTINUE
      PRINT 455,(GRID(IEXT(J)),J=1,NZ)
  455 FORMAT( 2X,'EXTREMAL FREQUENCIES'/(2X,5F12.7))
      PRINT 460
  460 FORMAT( 1X,70(1H*)/1H1)
C     CALCULATE FREQUENCY RESPONSE
      PRINT 710
  710 FORMAT(15X,'**********  FREQUENCY  RESPONSE  **********')
      DO 610 IKA = 1,50
      OMEGA(IKA) = 0.010000000*(IKA - 1)
      SUMAR = 0.0
      SUMAC = 0.0
      DO 620 NIK = 1,NFCNS
      SUMAR=SUMAR+H(NIK)*(DCOS(PI2*OMEGA(IKA)*(NIK-1)) +
     1DCOS(PI2*OMEGA(IKA)*(NFILT-NIK)))
      SUMAC = SUMAC + H(NIK)*(DSIN(PI2*OMEGA(IKA)*(NIK-1)) +
     1DSIN(PI2*OMEGA(IKA)*(NFILT-NIK)))
  620 CONTINUE
      IF (NODD.EQ.1) SUMAR=SUMAR-H(NFCNS)*DCOS(PI2*OMEGA(IKA)*(NFCNS
     1-1))
      IF (NODD.EQ.1) SUMAC=SUMAC-H(NFCNS)*DSIN(PI2*OMEGA(IKA)*(NFCNS
     1-1))
      RESPA(IKA) = DSQRT(SUMAR**2 + SUMAC**2)
      RESPA(IKA) = 20.0*DLOG10(RESPA(IKA))
      PRINT 630, OMEGA(IKA),RESPA(IKA)
  610 CONTINUE
  630 FORMAT(15X,F5.3,8X,F9.3)
      IF(JPUNCH.NE.0) WRITE(10,730) (H(J),J=1,NFCNS)
      IF(NFILT.NE.0) GO TO 100
  730 FORMAT(5E15.8)
      RETURN
      END
      FUNCTION EFF(TEMP,FX,WTX,LBAND,JTYPE)
C
C     FUNCTION TO CALCULATE THE DESIRED MAGNITUDE RESPONSE
C     AS A FUNCTION OF FREQUENCY.
C
      DIMENSION FX(5),WTX(5)
      IF(JTYPE.EQ.2) GO TO 1
      EFF=FX(LBAND)
      RETURN
    1 EFF=FX(LBAND)*TEMP
      RETURN
      END
      FUNCTION WATE(TEMP,FX,WTX,LBAND,JTYPE)
C
C     FUNCTION TO CALCULATE THE WEIGHT FUNCTION AS A FUNCTION
C     OF FREQUENCY.
      DIMENSION FX(5),WTX(5)
      IF(JTYPE.EQ.2) GO TO 1
      WATE=WTX(LBAND)
      RETURN
    1 IF(FX(LBAND).LT.0.0001) GO TO 2
      WATE=WTX(LBAND)/TEMP
      RETURN
    2 WATE=WTX(LBAND)
      RETURN
      END
      SUBROUTINE ERROR
      PRINT 1
    1 FORMAT(' **********  ERROR IN INPUT DATA  **********')
      STOP
      END
      SUBROUTINE REMEZ(EDGE,NBANDS)
```

```
C
C     THIS SUBROUTINE IMPLEMENTS THE REMEZ EXCHANGE ALGORITHM
C     FOR THE WEIGHTED CHEBYCHEV APPROXIMATION OF A CONTINUOUS
C     FUNCTION WITH A SUM OF COSINES.  INPUTS TO THE SUBROUTINE
C     ARE A DENSE GRID WHICH REPLACES THE FREQUENCY AXIS, THE
C     DESIRED FUNCTION ON THIS GRID, THE WEIGHT FUNCTION ON THE
C     GRID, THE NUMBER OF COSINES, AND AN INITIAL GUESS OF THE
C     EXTREMAL FREQUENCIES.   THE PROGRAM MINIMIZES THE CHEBYCHEV
C     ERROR BY DETERMINING THE BEST LOCATION OF THE EXTREMAL
C     FREQUENCIES (POINTS OF MAXIMUM ERROR) AND THEN CALCULATES
C     THE COEFFICIENTS OF THE BEST APPROXIMATION.
C
      COMMON DES,WT,ALPHA,IEXT,NFCNS,NGRID,PI2,AD,DEV,X,Y,GRID
      DIMENSION EDGE(20)
      DIMENSION IEXT(66),AD(66),ALPHA(66),X(66),Y(66)
      DIMENSION DES(1045),GRID(1045),WT(1045)
      DIMENSION A(66),P(65),Q(65)
      DOUBLE PRECISION PI2,DNUM,DDEN,DTEMP,A,P,Q
      DOUBLE PRECISION AD,DEV,X,Y
C
C     THE PROGRAM ALLOWS A MAXIMUM NUMBER OF ITERATIONS OF 25
C
      ITRMAX=25
      DEVL=-1.0
      NZ=NFCNS+1
      NZZ=NFCNS+2
      NITER=0
  100 CONTINUE
      IEXT(NZZ)=NGRID+1
      NITER=NITER+1
      IF(NITER.GT.ITRMAX) GO TO 400
      DO 110 J=1,NZ
      DTEMP=GRID(IEXT(J))
      DTEMP=DCOS(DTEMP*PI2)
  110 X(J)=DTEMP
      JET=(NFCNS-1)/15+1
      DO 120 J=1,NZ
  120 AD(J)=D(J,NZ,JET)
      DNUM=0.0
      DDEN=0.0
      K=1
      DO 130 J=1,NZ
      L=IEXT(J)
      DTEMP=AD(J)*DES(L)
      DNUM=DNUM+DTEMP
      DTEMP=K*AD(J)/WT(L)
      DDEN=DDEN+DTEMP
  130 K=-K
      DEV=DNUM/DDEN
      NU=1
      IF(DEV.GT.0.0) NU=-1
      DEV=-NU*DEV
      K=NU
      DO 140 J=1,NZ
      L=IEXT(J)
      DTEMP=K*DEV/WT(L)
      Y(J)=DES(L)+DTEMP
  140 K=-K
      IF(DEV.GE.DEVL) GO TO 150
      CALL OUCH
      GO TO 400
  150 DEVL=DEV
      JCHNGE=0
      K1=IEXT(1)
      KNZ=IEXT(NZ)
      KLOW=0
      NUT=-NU
      J=1
C
C     SEARCH FOR THE EXTREMAL FREQUENCIES OF THE BEST
C     APPROXIMATION
```

```
C
200 IF(J.EQ.NZZ) YNZ=COMP
    IF(J.GE.NZZ) GO TO 300
    KUP=IEXT(J+1)
    L=IEXT(J)+1
    NUT=-NUT
    IF(J.EQ.2) Y1=COMP
    COMP=DEV
    IF(L.GE.KUP) GO TO 220
    ERR=GEE(L,NZ)
    ERR=(ERR-DES(L))*WT(L)
    DTEMP=NUT*ERR-COMP
    IF(DTEMP.LE.0.0) GO TO 220
    COMP=NUT*ERR
210 L=L+1
    IF(L.GE.KUP) GO TO 215
    ERR=GEE(L,NZ)
    ERR=(ERR-DES(L))*WT(L)
    DTEMP=NUT*ERR-COMP
    IF(DTEMP.LE.0.0) GO TO 215
    COMP=NUT*ERR
    GO TO 210
215 IEXT(J)=L-1
    J=J+1
    KLOW=L-1
    JCHNGE=JCHNGE+1
    GO TO 200
220 L=L-1
225 L=L-1
    IF(L.LE.KLOW) GO TO 250
    ERR=GEE(L,NZ)
    ERR=(ERR-DES(L))*WT(L)
    DTEMP=NUT*ERR-COMP
    IF(DTEMP.GT.0.0) GO TO 230
    IF(JCHNGE.LE.0) GO TO 225
    GO TO 260
230 COMP=NUT*ERR
235 L=L-1
    IF(L.LE.KLOW) GO TO 240
    ERR=GEE(L,NZ)
    ERR=(ERR-DES(L))*WT(L)
    DTEMP=NUT*ERR-COMP
    IF(DTEMP.LE.0.0) GO TO 240
    COMP=NUT*ERR
    GO TO 235
240 KLOW=IEXT(J)
    IEXT(J)=L+1
    J=J+1
    JCHNGE=JCHNGE+1
    GO TO 200
250 L=IEXT(J)+1
    IF(JCHNGE.GT.0) GO TO 215
255 L=L+1
    IF(L.GE.KUP) GO TO 260
    ERR=GEE(L,NZ)
    ERR=(ERR-DES(L))*WT(L)
    DTEMP=NUT*ERR-COMP
    IF(DTEMP.LE.0.0) GO TO 255
    COMP=NUT*ERR
    GO TO 210
260 KLOW=IEXT(J)
    J=J+1
    GO TO 200
300 IF(J.GT.NZZ) GO TO 320
    IF(K1.GT.IEXT(1)) K1=IEXT(1)
    IF(KNZ.LT.IEXT(NZ)) KNZ=IEXT(NZ)
    NUT1=NUT
    NUT=-NU
    L=0
    KUP=K1
    COMP=YNZ*(1.00001)
```

```
      LUCK=1
  310 L=L+1
      IF(L.GE.KUP) GO TO 315
      ERR=GEE(L,NZ)
      ERR=(ERR-DES(L))*WT(L)
      DTEMP=NUT*ERR-COMP
      IF(DTEMP.LE.0.0) GO TO 310
      COMP=NUT*ERR
      J=NZZ
      GO TO 210
  315 LUCK=6
      GO TO 325
  320 IF(LUCK.GT.9) GO TO 350
      IF(COMP.GT.Y1) Y1=COMP
      K1=IEXT(NZZ)
  325 L=NGRID+1
      KLOW=KNZ
      NUT=-NUT1
      COMP=Y1*(1.00001)
  330 L=L-1
      IF(L.LE.KLOW) GO TO 340
      ERR=GEE(L,NZ)
      ERR=(ERR-DES(L))*WT(L)
      DTEMP=NUT*ERR-COMP
      IF(DTEMP.LE.0.0) GO TO 330
      J=NZZ
      COMP=NUT*ERR
      LUCK=LUCK+10
      GO TO 235
  340 IF(LUCK.EQ.6) GO TO 370
      DO 345 J=1,NFCNS
  345 IEXT(NZZ-J)=IEXT(NZ-J)
      IEXT(1)=K1
      GO TO 100
  350 KN=IEXT(NZZ)
      DO 360 J=1,NFCNS
  360 IEXT(J)=IEXT(J+1)
      IEXT(NZ)=KN
      GO TO 100
  370 IF(JCHNGE.GT.0) GO TO 100
C     CALCULATION OF THE COEFFICIENTS OF THE BEST APPROXIMATION
C     USING THE INVERSE DISCRETE FOURIER TRANSFORM
  400 CONTINUE
      NM1=NFCNS-1
      FSH=1.0E-06
      GTEMP=GRID(1)
      X(NZZ)=-2.0
      CN=2*NFCNS-1
      DELF=1.0/CN
      L=1
      KKK=0
      IF(EDGE(1).EQ.0.0.AND.EDGE(2*NBANDS).EQ.0.5) KKK=1
      IF(NFCNS.LE.3) KKK=1
      IF(KKK.EQ.1) GO TO 405
      DTEMP=DCOS(PI2*GRID(1))
      DNUM=DCOS(PI2*GRID(NGRID))
      AA=2.0/(DTEMP-DNUM)
      BB=-(DTEMP+DNUM)/(DTEMP-DNUM)
  405 CONTINUE
      DO 430 J=1,NFCNS
      FT=(J-1)*DELF
      XT=DCOS(PI2*FT)
      IF(KKK.EQ.1) GO TO 410
      XT=(XT-BB)/AA
      FT=ARCOS(XT)/PI2
  410 XE=X(L)
      IF(XT.GT.XE) GO TO 420
      IF((XE-XT).LT.FSH) GO TO 415
      L=L+1
      GO TO 410
  415 A(J)=Y(L)
```

```
      GO TO 425
  420 IF((XT-XE).LT.FSH) GO TO 415
      GRID(1)=FT
      A(J)=GEE(1,NZ)
  425 CONTINUE
      IF(L.GT.1) L=L-1
  430 CONTINUE
      GRID(1)=GTEMP
      DDEN=PI2/CN
      DO 510 J=1,NFCNS
      DTEMP=0.0
      DNUM=(J-1)*DDEN
      IF(NM1.LT.1) GO TO 505
      DO 500 K=1,NM1
  500 DTEMP=DTEMP+A(K+1)*DCOS(DNUM*K)
  505 DTEMP=2.0*DTEMP+A(1)
  510 ALPHA(J)=DTEMP
      DO 550 J=2,NFCNS
  550 ALPHA(J)=2*ALPHA(J)/CN
      ALPHA(1)=ALPHA(1)/CN
      IF(KKK.EQ.1) GO TO 545
      P(1)=2.0*ALPHA(NFCNS)*BB+ALPHA(NM1)
      P(2)=2.0*AA*ALPHA(NFCNS)
      Q(1)=ALPHA(NFCNS-2)-ALPHA(NFCNS)
      DO 540 J=2,NM1
      IF(J.LT.NM1) GO TO 515
      AA=0.5*AA
      BB=0.5*BB
  515 CONTINUE
      P(J+1)=0.0
      DO 520 K=1,J
      A(K)=P(K)
  520 P(K)=2.0*BB*A(K)
      P(2)=P(2)+A(1)*2.0*AA
      JM1=J-1
      DO 525 K=1,JM1
  525 P(K)=P(K)+Q(K)+AA*A(K+1)
      JP1=J+1
      DO 530 K=3,JP1
  530 P(K)=P(K)+AA*A(K-1)
      IF(J.EQ.NM1) GO TO 540
      DO 535 K=1,J
  535 Q(K)=-A(K)
      Q(1)=Q(1)+ALPHA(NFCNS-1-J)
  540 CONTINUE
      DO 543 J=1,NFCNS
  543 ALPHA(J)=P(J) .
  545 CONTINUE
      IF(NFCNS.GT.3) RETURN
      ALPHA(NFCNS+1)=0.0
      ALPHA(NFCNS+2)=0.0
      RETURN
      END
      DOUBLE PRECISION FUNCTION D(K,N,M)
C     FUNCTION TO CALCULATE THE LAGRANGE INTERPOLATION
C     COEFFICIENTS FOR USE IN THE FUNCTION GEE.
      COMMON DES,WT,ALPHA,IEXT,NFCNS,NGRID,PI2,AD,DEV,X,Y,GRID
      DIMENSION IEXT(66),AD(66),ALPHA(66),X(66),Y(66)
      DIMENSION DES(1045),GRID(1045),WT(1045)
      DOUBLE PRECISION AD,DEV,X,Y
      DOUBLE PRECISION Q
      DOUBLE PRECISION PI2
      D=1.0
      Q=X(K)
      DO 3 L=1,M
      DO 2 J=L,N,M
      IF(J-K)1,2,1
    1 D=2.0*D*(Q-X(J))
    2 CONTINUE
    3 CONTINUE
      D=1.0/D
```

```
      RETURN
      END
      DOUBLE PRECISION FUNCTION GEE(K,N)
C     FUNCTION TO EVALUATE THE FREQUENCY RESPONSE USING THE
C     LAGRANGE INTERPOLATION FORMULA IN THE BARYCENTRIC FORM
      COMMON DES,WT,ALPHA,IEXT,NFCNS,NGRID,PI2,AD,DEV,X,Y,GRID
      DIMENSION IEXT(66),AD(66),ALPHA(66),X(66),Y(66)
      DIMENSION DES(1045),GRID(1045),WT(1045)
      DOUBLE PRECISION P,C,D,XF
      DOUBLE PRECISION PI2
      DOUBLE PRECISION AD,DEV,X,Y
      P=0.0
      XF=GRID(K)
      XF=DCOS(PI2*XF)
      D=0.0
      DO 1 J=1,N
      C=XF-X(J)
      C=AD(J)/C
      D=D+C
    1 P=P+C*Y(J)
      GEE=P/D
      RETURN
      END
      SUBROUTINE OUCH
      PRINT 1
    1 FORMAT(' *********** FAILURE TO CONVERGE **********'/
     1'OPROBABLE CAUSE IS MACHINE ROUNDING ERROR';
     2'OTHE IMPULSE RESPONSE MAY BE CORRECT'/
     3'OCHECK WITH A FREQUENCY RESPONSE')
      RETURN
      END
```

Appendix E

GENEFOS

Program of synthesis of SAW filters using a window and a conventional prototype.

```
*#RUN *;/LIBRARY/COUVIS,R;/LIBRARY/COURBE,R;
*# /LIBRARY/ATAFIC,R;/LIBRARY/TEMPS,R=
*#(ULIB)LIBRARY/APPLIB,R;SERVICE/YT4010,R
      CHARACTER FICHE*20,FICHIER*21
      REAL TAU(2101),A(2101),X(103),Y(103)
      REAL DB(103),AMOY(103),SIGMA(103)
      REAL PHASE(103)
      REAL BB(2101)
      CHARACTER REP
      COMMON/CFSFR/N,FSFR
      COMMON/PHANGLE/ANGLE
      COMMON /CPHASE/NPHASE
      CALL TEMPS
      PI=3.141592653
      LITER=0
    1 IF (LITER.GT.0)CALL TEMPS
      PRINT:"FIRST ORDER SYNTHESIS OF SAW FILTERS"
      PRINT:"-------------------------------------------"
      PRINT:"DISPLAY ? (1=GRAPHIC ;2=ALPHABETIC ;0=STOP)"
      READ:MINAL;IF(MINAL.EQ.0)STOP
      LITER=LITER+1
      PRINT:"NUMBER OF PHASES (2,3) ?"
      READ:NPHASE
```

```
      PRINT:"***   WINDOW   ***"
      PRINT:"TYPE ?";PRINT:" 0=STOP"
      PRINT:" 1=RECTANGULAR"
      PRINT:" 2=HAMMING"
      PRINT:" 3=EXTERNAL FILE"
      READ:IFENET;IF(IFENET.EQ.0)STOP
      IF(IFENET.GT.2)GO TO 2
      PRINT:"NUMBER OF COEFFICIENTS(<1901) ?"
      READ:N
      PRINT:"SAMPLING M (1,3,...) ?"
      READ:M ;IF(M.EQ.0)M=1
      AM=(M-1.)+2./NPHASE
      DO 101 K=1,N
      TAU(K)=0.5*(K-1.-(N-1.)/2.)
      TETA=4.*PI*TAU(K)/(N-1.)
      TAU(K)=AM*TAU(K)
      POI=1.
      IF(IFENET.EQ.2)POI=0.54+0.46*COS(TETA)
      A(K)=POI
 101  CONTINUE
      GO TO 4
   2  CALL ATAFIC(1,1)
      READ(01)N
      PRINT:"N=",N
      READ(01)(TAU(K),K=1,N)
      READ(01)(A(K),K=1,N)
      REWIND(01)
   4  CONTINUE
      SB=0.
      DO 3 K=1,N
      BB(K)=A(K);SB=SB+A(K)
   3  CONTINUE
   5  CONTINUE
      PRINT:"Frequency F ? (STOP if F<0) "
      READ:FSFR
      IF(FSFR.LT.0.)STOP
      CALL INI(B)
      NBPT=101
      IREP=0
   6  CONTINUE
      OMEGA0=2.*PI*FSFR
      AMAX=0. ; AMIN=1.E37
      DO 10 K=1,N
      TT=TAU(K)
      TETA=OMEGA0*TT-(K-1)*2.*PI/NPHASE
      TETA=TETA+PI/2.*MOD(N-1,2)
      AA=A(K)*H(TT)*COS(TETA)
      TETA=0.
      AMIN=AMIN1(AMIN,ABS(AA))
      AMAX=AMAX1(AMAX,ABS(AA))
  10  A(K)=AA
      PRINT:"AMAX/AMIN=",AMAX/AMIN
      PRINT:"THRESHOLD ?"
      READ:SEUIL
      SA=0.
      DO 15 K=1,N
      A(K)=A(K)/AMAX
      AA=A(K)
      SA=SA+AA
      AA=ABS(AA)
  15  IF(AA.LT.SEUIL)A(K)=0.
      PRINT:"SUM OF A(K)=",SA
      PRINT:"AVERAGE=",SA/N
      IF(B.GT.0.)DF=B/50.
      IF(B.LE.0.)DF=0.1/TAU(N)
  25  CONTINUE
      PRINT:"DISCRETISATION (YES/NO/STOP) ?"
      READ:REP;IF(REP.EQ."STOP")STOP
      IF(REP.NE."YES")GO TO 27
```

```
         PRINT:"NUMBER OF SEPARATED STEPS ?"
         READ:NBPAS;DAK=1./NBPAS
         DO 26 K=1,N
  26 A(K)=IFIX(A(K)/DAK)*DAK
  27 IF(IREP.GT.0)GO TO 31
         IF(FSFR.GT.0.)GO TO 31
         PRINT:"CANCELLATION OF DC COMPONENT :"
         PRINT:"    0=NO"
         PRINT:"    1=SAME SHIFT FOR ALL A(K)"
         PRINT:"    2=OPTIMUM COMPUTED SHIFT"
         PRINT:"    3=USE EXTERNAL MATCHED FILTER"
         READ:IREP
         IF(IREP.LE.0)GO TO 31
         IF(IREP.GT.1)GO TO 29
         DAMAX=-SA/N
         DO 28  K=1,N
  28 A(K)=A(K)+DAMAX
         GO TO 6
  29 IF(IREP.GT.2)GO TO 33
         ST=SA/SB
         DO 32 K=1,N
  32 A(K)=A(K)-BB(K)*ST
         GO TO 31
  33 IREP=2
         PRINT:"FILE 02"
         READ(02) N1
         IF(N1.NE.N)PRINT:"<<< N NON CONSISTENT >>>"
         READ(02)(BTAU,I=1,N)
         READ(02)(BB(K),K=1,N)
         SB=0.
         DO 34 K=1,N
  34 SB=SB+BB(K)
         GO TO 29
  31 PRINT:
         PRINT:"FREQUENCY RESPONSE (YES/NO) ?";READ:REP
         IF(REP.NE."YES")GO TO 100
  37 CONTINUE
         F=FSFR-(NBPT+1)*0.5*DF
         DO 30 I=1,NBPT
         F=F+DF
         IF(I.EQ.1)FMIN=F
         IF(I.EQ.NBPT)FMAX=F
         Y(I)=DBPHI(A,TAU,N,F)
         PHASE(I)=-ANGLE
  30 X(I)=F
         YMAX=-1.E30
         DO 40 I=1,NBPT
  40 YMAX=AMAX1(YMAX,Y(I))
         YT=0.
         DO 50 I=1,NBPT
         Y(I)=Y(I)-YMAX
         YT=AMAX1(YT,-Y(I))
  50 CONTINUE
         PRINT:"TABLE OF RESULTS (YES/NO/STOP) ?"
         READ:REP;IF(REP.EQ."STOP")STOP
         IF(REP.NE."YES")GO TO 55
         PRINT:"SAMPLING (1,2,...) ?"
         READ:J
         IF(J.LE.0)J=1
         I1=1; IF(FSFR.LE.0.)I1=(NBPT+1)/2
         PRINT:"       F            dB           DEGREES"
         PRINT 9001,(X(I),Y(I),PHASE(I),I=I1,NBPT,J)
9003 FORMAT(A20,";")
  55 CONTINUE
         PRINT:"PLOTTING RESULTS (YES/NO/STOP) ?"
         READ:REP;IF(REP.EQ."STOP")STOP
         IF(REP.NE."YES")GO TO 60
         PRINT:"FULL SCALE INSERTION LOSS (dB) ?"
         READ:DBMAX
```

```
      DO 51 I=1,NBPT
   51 Y(I)=AMAX1(Y(I),-DBMAX)
      X(NBPT+1)=X(NBPT);Y(NBPT+1)=-DBMAX
      IF(MINAL.EQ.1)CALL COUVIS(X,Y,NBPT+1)
      IF(MINAL.EQ.2)CALL COURBE(X,Y,NBPT+1)
      PRINT:"FMIN=",FMIN," FMAX=",FMAX
      PRINT:"MAXIMUM INSERTION LOSS=",YT," DB"
      PRINT:"FULL SCALE =",DBMAX," DB"
      PRINT:"PLOTTING PHASE (YES/NO/STOP) ?";READ:REP
      IF(REP.EQ."YES".AND.MINAL.EQ.1)CALL
     & COUVIS(X,PHASE,NBPT+1)
      TMIN=1.E30;TMAX=-1.E30
      DO 56 I=1,NBPT-1
      PHASE(I)=PHASE(I+1)-PHASE(I)
      IF(PHASE(I).LT.0.)PHASE(I)=PHASE(I)+360.
      TMIN=AMIN1(TMIN,PHASE(I));TMAX=AMAX1(TMAX,PHASE(I))
   56 CONTINUE
      TMIN=TMIN/360./DF
      TMAX=TMAX/360./DF
      PRINT:"PLOTTING GROUPE DELAY (YES/NO/STOP) ?"
      READ:REP
      IF(REP.EQ."YES".AND.MINAL.EQ.1)CALL
     & COUVIS(X,PHASE,NBPT-1)
      IF(REP.EQ."YES")PRINT:"FMIN=",FMIN,"  FMAX=",FMAX
      IF(REP.EQ."YES")PRINT:"TMIN=",TMIN,"  TMAX=",TMAX
   60 PRINT:"NEW FREQUENCY SCALE (YES/NO/STOP) ?"
      READ:REP;IF(REP.EQ."STOP")STOP
      IF(REP.NE."YES")GO TO 100
      PRINT:"MAGNIFICATION FACTOR ?"
      READ:G
      DF=DF*G
      GO TO 37
 9001 FORMAT(F12.4,F12.2,F12.2)
  100 CONTINUE
      PRINT:"PLOTTING COMB PROFILE (YES/NO/STOP) ?"
      READ:REP;IF(REP.EQ."STOP")STOP
      IF(REP.EQ."YES".AND.MINAL.EQ.1)CALL COUVIS(TAU,A,N)
      IF(REP.EQ."YES".AND.MINAL.EQ.2)CALL COURBE(TAU,A,N)
      PRINT:"TO BE SAVED (YES/NO/STOP) ?"
      READ:REP;IF(REP.EQ."STOP")STOP
      IF(REP.EQ."STOP")STOP
      IF(REP.NE."YES")GO TO 115
      CALL ATAFIC(12,2)
      IS=1
      K=0
      DO 110 I=1,N
      AA=A(I)*IS;TT=TAU(I)
      IF(ABS(AA).LT.SEUIL)GO TO 110
      K=K+1 ; A(K)=AA ; TAU(K)=TT
      BB(K)=2.*MOD(I-1,NPHASE)/NPHASE
  110 CONTINUE
      N=K
      WRITE(12)N
      IF(REP.EQ."STOP")STOP
      WRITE(12)(TAU(K),K=1,N)
      WRITE(12)(A(K),K=1,N)
      WRITE(12)(BB(K),K=1,N)
      REWIND(12)
      PRINT:"DATA SAVED"
  115 CONTINUE
      PRINT:"PRINTING COEFFICIENTS A(K) ? (YES/NO/STOP)"
      READ:REP;IF(REP.EQ."STOP")STOP
      IF(REP.EQ."YES")PRINT:"    *** A ***"
      IF(REP.EQ."YES")PRINT:(A(K),K=1,N)
      PRINT:"PRINTING TIME DELAYS TAU(K) ?(YES/NO/STOP)"
      READ:REP;IF(REP.EQ."STOP")STOP
      IF(REP.NE."YES")GO TO 116
      PRINT:"    *** TAU ***";PRINT:(TAU(K),K=1,N)
  116 IF(SEUIL.LE.0.)GO TO 200
```

```
      PRINT:"SAVE ONLY NON ZERO COEFFICIENTS AND TIME"
    &," DELAYS"
      READ:REP;IF(REP.EQ."STOP")STOP
      IF(REP.EQ."STOP")STOP
      IF(REP.NE."YES")GO TO 1
      READ(1)N
      READ(01)(TAU(K),K=1,N)
      READ(01)(BB(K),K=1,N)
      REWIND(01)
      K=0.;N1=1+N/2
      DO 120 I=N1,N
      AA=ABS(A(I))
      IF(AA.LE.0.)GO TO 120
      K=K+1
      TAU(K)=TAU(I)
      A(K)=BB(I)
  120 CONTINUE
      PRINT:K," SAMPLES"
      WRITE(11)K
      WRITE(11)(TAU(I),I=1,K)
      WRITE(11)(A(I),I=1,K)
      PRINT:"DATA SAVED IN FILE  11"
  200 PRINT:"MONTE-CARLO SIMULATION (YES/NO/STOP) ?"
      READ:REP;IF(REP.EQ."STOP")STOP
      IF(REP.NE."YES")GO TO 1
      PRINT:"     ***    MONTE-CARLO SIMULATION   ***"
  210 PRINT:"NUMBER OF TRIALS?"
      READ:NBTIR;IF(NBTIR.EQ.0)GO TO200
  220 PRINT:"INTERVALLE OF FREQUENCY : F1,F2 ?"
      READ:F1,F2
      PRINT:"DF ?"
      READ:DF
      NBF=1
      IF(DF.LE.0)GO TO 222
      NBF=1+(F2-F1)/DF
      NBF=AMIN1(103,NBF)
  222 CONTINUE
      CALL INSTAT(NBF)
      DBMAX=-1.E37
      DO 230 I=1,NBF
      F=F1+(I-1)*DF
      X(I)=F;Y(I)=DBPHI(A,TAU,N,F)
      DBMAX=AMAX1(DBMAX,Y(I))
  230 CONTINUE
      DO 232 I=1,NBF
      Y(I)=Y(I)-DBMAX
  232 CONTINUE
      PRINT:"UNIFORM ERROR ON 3*SIGMA INTERVALLE"
  225 CONTINUE
      PRINT:"SIGMA/AMAX (%) ?"
      READ:SIG;SIG=SIG*0.01*SIG
      IF(SIG.LE.0.)GO TO 210
      CALL INSTAT(NBF)
      DO 300 ITIR=1,NBTIR
      DO 250 K=1,N
  250 BB(K)=ALEA(A(K),SIG)
      DBMAX=-1.E37
      DO 260 I=1,NBF
      F=X(I)
      DB(I)=DBPHI(BB,TAU,N,F)
  260 DBMAX=AMAX1(DBMAX,DB(I))
      DO 265 I=1,NBF
      DB(I)=DB(I)-DBMAX
  265 CONTINUE
  300 CALL STAT(DB)
      CALL RESTAT(AMOY,SIGMA)
      PRINT:"     F              RESPONSES IN DB"
      PRINT:"             NOMINAL     AVERAGE"
    &,"      SIGMA"
```

```
      PRINT 9002,(X(I),Y(I),AMOY(I),SIGMA(I),I=1,NBF)
9002  FORMAT(4F12.4)
      PRINT:" ";PRINT:"--------------------------------"
      GO TO 225
      END
      FUNCTION H(T)
      REAL SIG(300),OME(300)
      REAL ZERO(300)
      ARGSH(X)=ALOG(X+SQRT(X**2+1.))
      CH(X)=(1.+EXP(-2.*X))/2./EXP(-X)
      SH(X)=(1.-EXP(-2.*X))/2./EXP(-X)
      IF(ICLEF.EQ.5)GO TO 30
      IF(ICLEF.EQ.4)GO TO 25
      H=1.;X=PI*B*T
      IF(ICLEF.EQ.0)RETURN
      IF(ICLEF.EQ.9)H=ELLIPT(X)
      IF(ICLEF.EQ.9)RETURN
      IF(JCLEF.GT.0)GO TO 40
      IF(ICLEF.GT.1)GO TO 10
      IF(ABS(X).LT.1.E-6)RETURN
      H=SIN(X)/X ; RETURN
10    H=0.
      X=ABS(X)
      DO 20 I=1,NCELL
      TETA=OME(I)*X
20    H=H+EXP(-SIG(I)*X)*(SHA*SIG(I)*COS(TETA)+
     & CHA*OME(I)*SIN(TETA))
      RETURN
25    H=XSINX(T);RETURN
30    H=TRAPEZ(T);RETURN
40    H=CAUSAL(X);RETURN
      ENTRY INI(B)
      PI=3.141592653
      ICLEF=0
      B=0.
      PRINT:"***  NOMINAL  SPECIFICATIONS  ***"
      PRINT:" 0=SINGLE FREQUENCY"
      PRINT:" 1=RECTANGULAR"
      PRINT:" 2=SYMMETRICAL MAXIMALLY FLAT"
      PRINT:" 3=SYMMETRICA1 EQUIRIPPLED"
      PRINT:" 4=X/SIN(X)"
      PRINT:" 5=TRAPEZE"
      PRINT:" 6=BUTTERWORTH"
      PRINT:" 7=CHEBYSHEV"
      PRINT:" 8=CAUER"
      PRINT:" 9=SYMMETRICAL ELLIPTIC"
      READ:ICLEF
      IF(ICLEF.EQ.5)B=1.
      JCLEF=0;IF(ICLEF.EQ.6)JCLEF=1
      IF(ICLEF.EQ.0)RETURN
      IF(ICLEF.NE.5)PRINT:"Bandwidth ?"
      IF(ICLEF.NE.5)READ:B
      IF(ICLEF.EQ.9)NCELL=0
      IF(ICLEF.EQ.9)CALL INIELL(B,ICLEF,NCELL,SIG,
     & OME,ZERO)
      IF(ICLEF.EQ.9)RETURN
      IF(ICLEF.EQ.6)ICLEF=2
      IF(ICLEF.EQ.7)JCLEF=1
      IF(ICLEF.EQ.7)ICLEF=3
      IF(ICLEF.EQ.8)JCLEF=1
      IF(ICLEF.EQ.4)GO TO 120
      IF(ICLEF.EQ.5)GO TO 130
      IF(ICLEF.LT.2)RETURN
      IF(ICLEF.EQ.8)CALL INIRES(B,ICLEF,NCELL,SIG,OME)
      IF(ICLEF.EQ.8)RETURN
      PRINT:"Number of cells (<300) ?"
      READ:NCELL
      SHA=1.;CHA=1.
      BB=1.
```

```
       IF(JCLEF.EQ.0)BB=2.*NCELL
       ACLEF=4.;IF(JCLEF.EQ.1)ACLEF=2.
       IF(ICLEF.LT.3)GO TO 100
       PRINT:"RIPPLES (dB) ?"
       READ:ONDUL
       EPS=SQRT(10.**(ONDUL/10.)-1.)
       A=ARGSH(1./EPS)/BB
       SHA=SH(A);CHA=CH(A)
100 DO 110 K=1,NCELL
       TETA=(2.*K-1.)*PI/ACLEF/NCELL
       SIG(K)=SHA*SIN(TETA)
       OME(K)=CHA*COS(TETA)
110 CONTINUE
       SC=SHA;SHA=CHA*CHA;CHA=SC*SC
       IF(JCLEF.EQ.1)CALL INIRES(B,ICLEF,NCELL,SIG,OME)
       RETURN
120 CALL INXS(B,1.E-6)
       RETURN
130 CALL INTRZ(B)
       RETURN
       END
       FUNCTION XSINX(T)
       XSINX=0.
       DO 10 I=1,1200
       T1=T-(2*I-1)*TAU
       T2=T+(2*I-1)*TAU
       X1=OMEGA*T1;X2=OMEGA*T2
       DXSINX=DSINC(X1)-DSINC(X2)
       XSINX=XSINX+DXSINX
10 IF(ABS(DXSINX).LT.EPS)GO TO 20
20 RETURN
       ENTRY INXS(B,EPS)
       NBAPPEL=0
       PI=3.141592653
       PRINT:"PULSE DURATION ?"
       READ:TAU;TAU=TAU/2.
       OMEGA=B*PI
       RETURN
       END
       FUNCTION DSINC(X)
       DSINC=-X*(1.-(1.-X**2/28)*X**2/10.)/3.
       IF(ABS(X).LT.3.E-2)RETURN
       DSINC=(X*COS(X)-SIN(X))/X**2
       RETURN
       END
       SUBROUTINE STAT(X)
       REAL X(1),TOT1(103),TOT2(103),SIGMA(1),AMOY(1)
       N=N+1
       DO 10 K=1,JJ
       TOT1(K)=TOT1(K)+X(K)
       TOT2(K)=TOT2(K)+X(K)*X(K)
10 CONTINUE
       RETURN
       ENTRY RESTAT(AMOY,SIGMA)
       DO 20 K=1,JJ
       AMOY(K)=TOT1(K)/N
       SIGMA(K)=0.
       IF(N.EQ.1)GO TO 20
       SIGMA(K)=SQRT(ABS(TOT2(K)-N*AMOY(K)**2)/(N-1))
20 CONTINUE
       RETURN
       ENTRY INSTAT(JJ)
       DO 30 K=1,JJ
       N=0;TOT1(K)=0.;TOT2(K)=0.
30 CONTINUE
       RETURN
       END
       FUNCTION DBPHI(A,TAU,N,F)
       COMPLEX PSI1,PSI,PHI
```

```
      COMMON/PHANGLE/ANGLE
      COMMON/CPHASE/NPHASE
      REAL A(1),TAU(1)
      PI=3.141592653
      OMEGA=2.*PI*F
      PHI=0.
      DO 20 K=1,N
      TETA=-OMEGA*TAU(K)
      DTETA=2.*PI/NPHASE*(K-1)
      TETA=TETA+DTETA
      CO=COS(TETA)
      SI=SIN(TETA)
      PSI1=CMPLX(CO,SI)
      PSI=PSI1*A(K)
      PHI=PHI+PSI
   20 CONTINUE
      CALL ARCTA(PHI,ANGLE)
      ABPHI=CABS(PHI)
      DBPHI=20.*ALOG10(ABPHI)
      RETURN
      END
      FUNCTION  ALEA(X,DX)
*System random function FRAN(X)
      DATA IRO/123456/
      ALEA=X+DX/SQRT(12.)*(FRAN(IRO)-0.5)
      RETURN
      END
      FUNCTION TRAPEZ(T)
      COMMON/CFSFR/N,FSFR
      IF(ABS(T).LT.1.E-12)GO TO 100
      TRAPEZ=(1./T**2)*((COS(OMEGA1*T+TT)-
     & COS(OMEGA2*T+TT))/(F2-
     & F1)-(COS(OMEGA3*T+TT)-COS(OMEGA4*T+TT))/(F4-F3))
      TETA=OMEGA0*T+TT
      TRAPEZ=TRAPEZ/COS(TETA)
      RETURN
  100 TRAPEZ=(OMEGA2**2/2.-OMEGA1**2/2.)/(F2-F1)-
     & (OMEGA4**2-OMEGA3**2)/2./(F4-F3)
      TETA=PI/2.*MOD(N-1,2)
      TRAPEZ=TRAPEZ/COS(TETA)
      RETURN
      ENTRY INTRZ(B)
      PI=3.141592653
      PRINT:"CHARACTERISTIC FREQUENCIES :F1<F2<F3<F4 ?"
      READ:F1,F2,F3,F4
      OMEGA1=F1*2.*PI
      OMEGA2=F2*2.*PI
      OMEGA3=F3*2.*PI
      OMEGA4=F4*2.*PI
      OMEGA0=FSFR*2.*PI
      TT=PI/2.*MOD(N-1,2)
      RETURN
      END
      FUNCTION CAUSALE(XX)
      CHARACTER REP
      REAL OME(300),SIG(300),RX(300),RY(300)
      REAL ZERO(300)
      COMPLEX PI,PK,RESIDU
      COMPLEX ZI
      CAUSALE=0.
      T=XX+HP0/H0
      IF(T.LT.0.)RETURN
      DO 10 K=1,KMAX
      CAUSALE=CAUSALE+(RX(K)*COS(OME(K)*T)+
     & RY(K)*SIN(OME(K)*T))*EXP(-SIG(K)*T)
   10 CONTINUE
      RETURN
      ENTRY INIRES(B,ICLEF,NCELL,SIG,OME)
      IF(ICLEF.EQ.8)GO TO 100
```

```
 15 CONTINUE
    KMAX=(NCELL+1)/2
    H0=0.;HP0=0.
    DO 30 K=1,KMAX
    RESIDU=1.
    PK=CMPLX(-SIG(K),OME(K))
    DO 20 I=1,NCELL
    ZI=CMPLX(0.,ZERO(I))
    IF(ICLEF.LE.7)GO TO 17
    IF(MOD(NCELL,2).EQ.1.AND.I.EQ.NCELL/2+1)GO TO 17
    RESIDU=RESIDU*(PK-ZI)
 17 CONTINUE
    IF(I.EQ.K)GO TO 20
    PI=CMPLX(-SIG(I),OME(I))
    RESIDU=RESIDU/(PK-PI)
 20 CONTINUE
    IF(K.NE.NCELL/2+1)RESIDU=2.*RESIDU
    H0=H0-REAL(RESIDU/PK)
    HP0=HP0+REAL(RESIDU/PK**2)
    RX(K)=REAL(RESIDU)
    RY(K)=-AIMAG(RESIDU)
 30 CONTINUE
    PRINT:"H0=",H0
    PRINT:"HP0=",HP0
    RETURN
100 CONTINUE
115 PRINT:"Number of cells ?";READ:NCELL
    M=NCELL;IF(MOD(M,2).EQ.0)GO TO 500
    N=(M-1)/2
    PRINT:"Transition interval frequency ?"
    READ:RAIDE
    FR=(B+RAIDE)/B
    FC=SQRT(FR)
    G=FC+FC
    DO 155 K=1,2
    A=FR+1.E00
    DO 135 J=1,6
    H=SQRT(A*G)
    A=(A+G)/2
    IF(1.E08*(A-H).LT.A)GO TO 45
135 G=H
 45 IF(K.GE.2)GO TO 65
    Q=M/A
155 G=FR-1.E00
 65 H=Q*A
    G=3.141592654
    Y=EXP(-G/H)
    PRINT:"NOMINAL INSERTION LOSS (dB) ?"
    READ:A
    IF(A.LE.0)GO TO 15
    Q=.2302585093
    A=EXP(A*Q/2)
    R=EXP(G*H)
    Q=(ALOG(1+(A*A-1)/(R/4+1/R)**2))/Q
    PRINT:"RIPPLES (dB)",Q
    PRINT:"CORRECTION (YES/NO) ?"
    READ:REP;IF(REP.EQ."YES")GO TO 100
    Q=R/(2*(A+SQRT(A*A-1)))
    A=ALOG(Q+SQRT(Q*Q+1))/(2*H)
    X=SIN(A)/COS(A)
    Z=Y
    A=X
    X=X*X
    DO 75 J=1,M-1
 75 ZERO(J)=1
    K=1
    DO 95 J=1,1024
    ZERO(K)=ZERO(K)*(1-Z)/(1+Z)
    IF(K.LT.M-1)GO TO 85
```

```
         Z=Z*Y
         W=((1-Z)/(1+Z))**2
         A=A*(W+X)/(1.E00+W*X)
         K=0
  85     Z=Z*Y
         IF(Z.LT..25E-08)GO TO 105
  95     K=K+1
 105     DO 215 J=1,N
         ZERO(J)=ZERO(J)*ZERO(M-J)
 215     ZERO(M-J)=ZERO(J)
         X=FC*A
         SIG(N+1)=X;OME(N+1)=0.
         X=X/2
         Y=SQRT((1.E00+FR*A**2)*(FR+A**2))
         DO 125 J=1,N
         Z=1.E00+(A*ZERO(J))**2
         G=X*ZERO(2*J)*(1.E00-ZERO(J)**4)/(ZERO(J)*Z)
         H=Y*ZERO(J)/Z
         SIG(J)=G;OME(J)=H
         SIG(N+J+1)=G;OME(N+J+1)=-H
 125     CONTINUE
         DO 300 J=1,N
         ZERO(J)=FC/ZERO(J)
         ZERO(N+J+1)=-ZERO(J)
 300     CONTINUE
         GO TO 15
 500     CALL INIELL(B,ICLEF,NCELL,SIG,OME,ZERO)
         GO TO 15
         END
         SUBROUTINE ARCTA(Z,ANGLE)
         COMPLEX Z
         DATA CONVER/57.29578/
         DATA PI/3.1415926/
         X=REAL(Z);Y=AIMAG(Z)
         IF(X) 10,30,20
  10     ANGLE=ATAN(Y/X)+PI*SIGN(1.,Y)
         GO TO 100
  20     ANGLE=ATAN(Y/X)
         GO TO 100
  30     IF(Y)40,60,50
  40     ANGLE=-PI/2.
         GO TO 100
  50     ANGLE=PI/2.
         GO TO 100
  60     ANGLE=0.
 100     ANGLE=ANGLE*CONVER
         RETURN
         END
         FUNCTION ELLIPT(X)
         PARAMETER LM=50
         PARAMETER NM=4*LM
         PARAMETER NC=2*LM
         DIMENSION F(NM)
         DIMENSION SIG(NC),OME(NC),ZERO(NC)
         COMPLEX RESIDU,PK,PI
         DIMENSION RX(NC),RY(NC)
         ELLIPT=0.
         T=ABS(X)
         DO 5 K=1,KMAX
         TETA=OME(K)*T
         CO=COS(TETA);SI=SIN(TETA)
         ELLIPT=ELLIPT+(RX(K)*CO+RY(K)*SI)*EXP(-SIG(K)*T)
   5     CONTINUE
         RETURN
         ENTRY INIELL(B,ICLEF,NCELL,SIG,OME,ZERO)
  15     CONTINUE
         PRINT:"RIPPLES (dB) ?";READ:A1
         PRINT:"INSERTION LOSS (dB) ?";READ:A2
         IF(NCELL.NE.0)GO TO 20
```

```
      A1=A1/2.; A2=A2/2.
      PRINT:"NUMBER OF CELLS ?";READ:M
      NCELL=M
   20 M=NCELL
      IF(ABS(A1).LE.0.)GO TO 15
      FN=1.
      N=2*M
      Q=.1151292547
      E1=EXP(2*Q*A1)-1
      A2=Q*A2
      E2=EXP(2*A2)-1
      P=3.141592654
      U=P*P/ALOG(16*E2/E1)
      A=U*(A2+.6931471805)/P
      A=COS(A)/SIN(A)
      DO 75 J=1,N
   75 F(J)=1
      Y=EXP(-U)
      Z=Y
      K=M-1
      DO 95 J=1,1024
      F(K)=F(K)*(1-Z)/(1+Z)
      Z=Z*Y
      IF(Z.LT..25E-08)GO TO 105
      K=K-1
   95 IF(K.EQ.0)K=N
  105 PRINT:
      F0=F(N)**2
      FN=F0
      DO 115 J=1,M-1
      F(J)=F(J)*F(N-J)
      IF(MOD(J,2).EQ.1)ZERO((J+1)/2)=1/F(J)/FN
  115 CONTINUE
      X=SQRT(A*A+1/(A*A)+F0*F0+1/(F0*F0))
      MM=LM+LM
      MN=MM+LM
      DO 125 J=1,M-1,2
      Y=A*F(J)
      Y=Y+1/Y
      Z=F0*F(J)
      K=(J+1)/2
      F(MM+K)=F(M-J)*(1/Z-Z)/Y
      F(MN+K)=X/Y
      SIG((J+1)/2)=F(MM+K)/FN
      OME((J+1)/2)=F(MN+K)/FN
  125 CONTINUE
      A=A/FN
      IF(J.EQ.M-2)SIG((J+3)/2)=A
      IF(J.EQ.M-2)OME((J+3)/2)=0.
      DO 210 K=1,M/2
      J=M+1-K
      ZERO(J)=-ZERO(K)
      SIG(J)=SIG(K)
      OME(J)=-OME(K)
  210 CONTINUE
      KMAX=(M+1)/2
      DO 230 K=1,KMAX
      RESIDU=1./CMPLX(SIG(K),OME(K))
      PK=CMPLX(SIG(K),OME(K))**2
      DO 220 I=1,M
      ZI=-ZERO(I)**2
      IF(MOD(M,2).EQ.0.OR.I.NE.M/2+1)RESIDU=
     & RESIDU*(PK-ZI)
      IF(I.EQ.K)GO TO 220
      PI=CMPLX(SIG(I),OME(I))**2
      RESIDU=RESIDU/(PK-PI)
  220 CONTINUE
      IF(MOD(M,2).EQ.0.OR.K.NE.NCELL/2+1)RESIDU=2.*RESIDU
      RESIDU=-RESIDU
```

```
      RX(K)=REAL(RESIDU)
      RY(K)=AIMAG(RESIDU)
  230 CONTINUE
      RETURN
      END
```

Appendix F

VERIFOS

Program to compute frequency response of FIR filters.

```
*#RUN*;/LIBRARY/COUVIS,R;/LIBRARY/ATAFIC,R;
*#/LIBRARY/TEMPS,R=(ULIB)SERVICE/YT4010,R
      PARAMETER NDIM=2101
      PARAMETER NBPT=101
      REAL TAU(NDIM),A(NDIM)
      COMMON/CSGN/NPHASE
      CHARACTER REP,FICHE*20,FICHIER*21
      REAL X(NBPT),Y(NBPT)
      REAL PHASE(NBPT),TPG(NBPT)
      PRINT:"FREQUENCY RESPONSE OF FIR-SAW FILTER"
      JJ=10
   10 CONTINUE
      CALL TEMPS
      PRINT:" "
      CALL ATAFIC(1,1)
      READ(01)N
      PRINT:"NUMBER OF COEFFICIENTS =",N
      IF(N.GT.NDIM)STOP"TOO MANY !!!!!"
      READ(01)(TAU(K),K=1,N)
      READ(01)(A(K),K=1,N)
      REWIND(01)
      CALL DETACH(01,ISTAT,)
      PMIN=A(1);PMAX=PMIN
      DTMIN=1.E30
      DO 3 K=1,N
      PMIN=AMIN1(PMIN,A(K))
      PMAX=AMAX1(PMAX,A(K))
      IF(K.LT.2)GO TO 3
      DTMIN=AMIN1(TAU(K)-TAU(K-1),DTMIN)
    3 CONTINUE
      IF(ABS(PMIN).GT.PMAX)PMAX=PMIN
      K1=1;K2=N
      DO 5 K=1,N
      IF(ABS(A(K)).GT.0.)GO TO 15
      K1=K
    5 CONTINUE
   15 DO 25 K=1,N
      J=N-K+1
      IF(ABS(A(J)).GT.0.)GO TO 35
      K2=J-1
   25 CONTINUE
   35 CONTINUE
      INORM=0
      PRINT:"TABLE OF COEFFICIENTS (yes/no) ?"
      READ:REP;IF(REP.EQ."yes")REP="YES"
      IF(REP.NE."OUI")GO TO 100
      PRINT:"PAS (1,2,...) ?"
      READ:IPAS;IF(IPAS.LE.0.)IPAS=1
      PRINT:"   K        TAU(K)      A(K)"
      PRINT 9002,(K,TAU(K),A(K),K=1,N,IPAS)
```

```
100 PRINT:" "
    IF(ABS(PMAX-1.).LT.1.E-3)GO TO 103
    PRINT:"NORMALIZING COEFFICIENTS (YES/NO) ?"
    READ:REP;IF(REP.EQ."yes")REP="YES"
    IF(REP.EQ."YES")INORM=1
    IF(INORM.EQ.0)GO TO 103
    DO 101 K=1,N
101 A(K)=A(K)/PMAX
103 CONTINUE
    IF(INORM.EQ.0.AND.K1.EQ.1.AND.K2.EQ.N)GO TO 105
    IF(K1.EQ.1.AND.K2.EQ.N)GO TO 109
    K1=K1+1
    PRINT:"FIRST NON-ZERO COEFFICIENT FOR K=",K1
    PRINT:"LAST NON-ZERO COEFFICIENT FOR K=",K2
    PRINT:"ERASE ALL ZERO COEFFICIENTS (YES/NO) ?"
    READ:REP;IF(REP.EQ."yes")REP="YES"
    IF(REP.NE."YES".AND.INORM.EQ.0)GO TO 105
    IF(REP.NE."YES")GO TO 109
    J=0
    DO 104 K=K1,K2
    J=J+1
    TAU(J)=TAU(K);A(J)=A(K)
104 CONTINUE
    N=K2-K1+1
109 CONTINUE
    PRINT:"RESAVE (YES/NO) ?"
    READ:REP;IF(REP.EQ."yes")REP="YES"
    IF(REP.NE."YES")GO TO 105
    JJ=JJ+1
    CALL ATAFIC(JJ,2)
    WRITE(JJ)N
    WRITE(JJ)(TAU(K),K=1,N)
    WRITE(JJ)(A(K),K=1,N)
    REWIND(JJ)
105 DTA=TAU(1)
    DO 107 K=1,N
107 TAU(K)=TAU(K)-DTA
    PRINT:"PLOTTING COEFFICIENTS (GRAPHIC DISPLAY"
    &," ONLY) (YES/NO) ?"
    READ:REP;IF(REP.EQ."yes")REP="YES"
    IF(REP.EQ."YES")CALL COUVIS(TAU,A,N)
    PRINT:"NUMBER OF PHASES (2,3) ?"
    READ:NPHASE
    IF(NPHASE.EQ.0)NPHASE=1
    M=1+2*(DTMIN-1./NPHASE)
110 CONTINUE
    PRINT:" "
    PRINT:"---   FREQUENCY RESPONSE   ---"
    PRINT:"SCALE : dB (1) or linear (2) ?"
    READ:ILINE
    IF(ILINE.EQ.0)GO TO 10
    PI=3.141592653
    PRINT:"TABLE (YES/NO) ?"
    READ:REP;IF(REP.EQ."yes")REP="YES"
    ITABLE=0
    IF(REP.EQ."YES")ITABLE=1
    IF(REP.NE."YES")GO TO 200
150 PRINT:"F1 ?";READ:F1
    PRINT:"F2 ?";READ:F2
    IPAS=1
    IF(ICOUR.EQ.1)GO TO 155
    PRINT:"SAMPLING STEP (1,2,...) ?"
    READ:IPAS;IF(IPAS.LE.0.)IPAS=1
155 CONTINUE
    DF=(F2-F1)/(NBPT-1.)
    SMAX=-1.E30
    SMIN=1.E30
    DO 160 K=1,NBPT
    F=F1+(K-1)*DF
```

```
      SF=SFDB(PHA,TAU,A,N,F)
      SMAX=AMAX1(SMAX,SF);SMIN=AMIN1(SMIN,SF)
      X(K)=F;Y(K)=SF
      PHASE(K)=PHA*180./PI
      IF(K.LT.NBPT)TPG(K+1)=(PHA1-PHA)/2./PI/DF
      TPG(K+1)=AMOD(TPG(K+1),1./DF)
      IF(TPG(K+1).LT.0.)TPG(K+1)=TPG(K+1)+1./DF
      PHA1=PHA
  160 CONTINUE
      DO 165 K=1,NBPT
  165 Y(K)=Y(K)-SMAX
      IF(ILINE.NE.2)GO TO 167
      DO 166 K=1,NBPT
  166 Y(K)=10.**(Y(K)/20.)
  167 CONTINUE
      TPG(1)=TPG(3);TPG(2)=TPG(1)
      IF(ITABLE.EQ.1)PRINT:
     & "       F            dB            DEGREES"
     &," Gr.Delay"
      IF(ITABLE.EQ.1)PRINT 9003,
     & (X(I),Y(I),PHASE(I),TPG(I),I=1,NBPT,IPAS)
      IF(ITABLE.EQ.0)GO TO 250
  200 CONTINUE
      ICOUR=0
      PRINT:"Plotting response (YES/NO)"
     &," (on graphic display) ?"
      READ:REP;IF(REP.EQ."yes")REP="YES"
      IF(REP.NE."YES")GO TO 300
      ICOUR=1
      IF(ITABLE.EQ.0)GO TO 150
  250 IF(ILINE.EQ.2)GO TO   256
      PRINT:"Maximum insertion loss =",SMAX-SMIN," dB"
      PRINT:"Full scale (dB) ?"
      READ:AMPMAX
      DO 255 K=1,NBPT
      Y(K)=AMAX1(Y(K),-AMPMAX)
  255 CONTINUE
      Y(NBPT)=-AMPMAX
  256 CONTINUE
      CALL COUVIS(X,Y,NBPT)
      ICOUR=0
      PRINT:"F1=",F1," ; F2=",F2
      IF(ILINE.EQ.2)PRINT:"LINEAR SCALE"
      IF(ILINE.EQ.2)GO TO 110
      PRINT:"MAXIMUM INSERTION LOSS =",SMAX-SMIN," dB"
      PRINT:"FULL SCALE =",AMPMAX," dB"
      PRINT:"Plotting phase (YES/NO) ?"
      READ:REP;IF(REP.eq."yes")REP="YES"
      IF(REP.EQ."YES")CALL COUVIS(X,PHASE,NBPT)
      IF(REP.EQ."YES")PRINT:"PHASE"
      PRINT:"Plotting group delay (YES/NO) ?"
      READ:REP;IF(REP.EQ."yes")REP="YES"
      IF(REP.EQ."YES")CALL COUVIS(X,TPG,NBPT)
      IF(REP.EQ."YES")PRINT:"Group delay"
      GO TO 110
  300 CONTINUE
      GO TO 10
 9001 FORMAT(A20,";")
 9002 FORMAT(I4,2E16.8)
 9003 FORMAT(4F14.6)
      END
      FUNCTION SFDB(PHA,TAU,A,N,F)
      COMMON/CSGN/NPHASE
      COMPLEX S21
      REAL A(1),TAU(1)
      PI=3.141592653
      OMEGA=2.*PI*F
      S21=0.
      DO 100 K=1,N
```

```
        DTETA=(K-1)*2.*PI/NPHASE
        TETA=-OMEGA*TAU(K)
        TETA=TETA+DTETA
        CO=COS(TETA);SI=SIN(TETA)
        S21=S21+A(K)*CMPLX(CO,SI)
100  CONTINUE
        CALL ARCTA(S21,PHA)
        S21A=CABS(S21)
        SFDB=20.*ALOG10(S21A)
        RETURN
        END
        SUBROUTINE ARCTA(Z,ANGLE)
        COMPLEX Z
        DATA CONVER/57.29578/
        DATA PI/3.1415926/
        X=REAL(Z);Y=AIMAG(Z)
        IF(X) 10,30,20
 10  ANGLE=ATAN(Y/X)+PI*SIGN(1.,Y)
        GO TO 100
 20  ANGLE=ATAN(Y/X)
        GO TO 100
 30  IF(Y)40,60,50
 40  ANGLE=-PI/2.
        GO TO 100
 50  ANGLE=PI/2.
        GO TO 100
 60  ANGLE=0.
100  RETURN
        END
```

Appendix G

MAREFOS

Program MAREFOS to compute arbitrary SAW device.
This program generates a second program QUIK for execution.

```
*#RUN *; /LIBRARY/ATAFIC,R; /LIBRARY/TEMPS=
*#(ULIB)LIBRARY/applib,R
***    DESIGN OF SAW DEVICES    ***
        COMMON /DONNEE/NU,NTOT,TAU(301),A(301),NTTOT,
       &NT(10),FADA(10),QADA(10),JADA(10),NTE,NTS,NREF
       & ,NTOTAL,NTTOTAL,RADA(10),RG(10),IMPLE(10),FZERO,
       &DF,DELTA,AK2,DB,R0,MINAL
        COMMON/CMODIF/MODIF
        COMMON/CREF/JPOSE,JCODE
        COMMON/CATAFI/FICHE
        COMMON/SONDE/ISOR,IDOI
        CHARACTER REP,FICHIER*20,FICHE*21
        CHARACTER FIC*8
        CHARACTER DATA*21,RESULT*21
 10  PRINT:" ";PRINT:" "
*Display memory size
        CALL TEMPS
        KT=0;NTOT=0
        PRINT:"    ***    DESIGN OF SAW DEVICES    ***"
        PRINT:" "
        MODIF=0;NTOT=0;NTOTAL=0;NTTOT=0;NTTOTAL=0
        PRINT:"File : OLD  or NEW ( OLD/NEW ) ?"
        READ:REP;IF(REP.EQ."OLD" .OR. REP.EQ."old")MODIF=1
        IF(REP.EQ." ")GO TO 600
```

```
      IF(MODIF.NE.1)GO TO 20
      PRINT:"File identification ?"
      PRINT:"(EXAMPLE: /DIR/FILE)"
      READ:FICHIER
      ENCODE(FICHE,9003)FICHIER
*Use specific ATTACH routine
      CALL ATTACH(01,FICHE,1,0,ISTAT)
      READ(01)NTOT,NU
      READ(01)NTOTAL,NTTOTAL
      READ(01)(TAU(K),K=1,NTOT)
      READ(01)(A(K),K=1,NTOT)
      READ(01)NTTOT
      READ(01)(NT(KT),KT=1,NTTOT)
      READ(01)(FADA(KT),KT=1,NTTOT)
      READ(01)(QADA(KT),KT=1,NTTOT)
      READ(01)(RG(KT),KT=1,NTTOT)
      READ(01)(JADA(KT),KT=1,NTTOT)
      READ(01)(IMPLE(KT),KT=1,NTTOT)
      READ(01)(RADA(KT),KT=1,NTTOT)
      READ(01)NTE,NTS,NREF,FZERO,DF,DELTA,AK2,DB,RO,MINAL
      REWIND(01)
      PRINT:"Listing of the file (yes/no) ?"
      READ:REP;IF(REP.EQ."yes")REP="YES"
      IF(REP.EQ."YES")CALL ETAT
   20 CONTINUE
      PRINT:"*** SUBSTRATE ***"
*Describe the SAW mode
      PRINT:"RAYLEIGH (1) or BLEUSTEIN/SSBW (2)"
      READ:NU ; IF(NU.LE.0)NU=1
      PRINT:"Coupling coefficient K2 (%) ?"
      READ:AK2;AK2=0.01*AK2
      IF(AK2.LE.0.)GO TO 600
      PRINT:"Decay coefficient (dB/LAMBDA) ?"
      READ:DB
      PRINT:" "
      PRINT:"*** GEOMETRICAL DESIGN ***"
      PRINT:"All combs have the same MAXIMUM aperture"
     &," width W"
      PRINT:"RO= Radiation resistance of the regular"
     &," comb"
      RO=1.
      PRINT:" "
      IF(MODIF.NE.1)GO TO 40
      PRINT:"TILT :The number of capacitances should not"
     &," change"
   30 PRINT:"Comb code to be modified ?"
      READ:ICODE;IF(ICODE.EQ.0)GO TO 300
      CALL DESCRI(ICODE)
      IF(ICODE.LT.(NTE+NTS+1))CALL ADA(ICODE)
      IF(ICODE.GT.NTE+NTS)CALL FERME(ICODE)
      GO TO 30
   40 CONTINUE
      PRINT:"*** INPUT ***"
      PRINT:"Number of transducers in parallel ?"
      READ:NTE
      IF(NTE.LE.0)STOP
      DO 100 NTR=1,NTE
      PRINT 9001,NTR,KT+1
 9001 FORMAT(1X,"--- TRANSDUCER NR ",I1," --- CODE=",I2)
      CALL DESCRI(KT)
  100 CONTINUE
      CALL ADA(1)
      PRINT:" "
      PRINT:"*** OUTPUT ***"
      PRINT:"S21 may cascade 2 independent transducers"
      PRINT:"with acoustical port"
      PRINT:"To obtain acoustical port specify a"
      PRINT:"2-finger output transducer"
      PRINT:
```

```
          PRINT:"Number of transducers in parallel   ?"
          READ:NTS
          IF(NTS.LE.0)GO TO 210
          IF(NTS.EQ.1)ISOR=1
          DO 200 NTR=1,NTS
          PRINT 9001,NTR,KT+1
          CALL DESCRI(KT)
 200  CONTINUE
          CALL ADA(NTE+1)
 210  PRINT:" "
          ISOR=0
          PRINT:"*** REFLECTORS ***"
          PRINT:"Number of combs ?"
          READ:NREF
          IF (NREF.LE.0)GO TO 300
          DO 250 IREF=1,NREF
          PRINT 9002,IREF,KT+1
9002  FORMAT(1X,"--- REFLECTOR NR ",I1," --- CODE=",I2)
          JPOSE=0
          PRINT:"Part of an unidirectionnal transducer"
          &," (yes/no) ?"
          READ:REP;IF (REP.EQ."yes")REP="YES"
          IF(REP.NE."YES")GO TO 220
          PRINT:"Relevant comb CODE ?"
          READ:JCODE
 215  PRINT:"REFLECTOR ON THE LEFT(L) OR ON THE "
          &,"RIGHT(R) ?"
          READ:REP;JPOSE=0
          IF(REP.EQ."R")JPOSE=1;IF(REP.EQ."L")JPOSE=-1
          IF(JPOSE.EQ.0)GO TO 215
 220  CONTINUE
          CALL DESCRI(KT)
          CALL FERME (KT)
 250  CONTINUE
 300  CONTINUE
          PRINT:"Gap between hot and dummy fingers :"
          PRINT:"DELTA (% of W) ?"
          PRINT:" "
          READ:DELTA;DELTA=0.01*DELTA
          IF(DELTA.LE.0.)DELTA=0.02
          PRINT:"***    FREQUENCY RESPONSE    ***"
 400  PRINT:"Center frequency FZERO ?"
          READ:FZERO
          PRINT:"Step DF ?"
          READ:DF
          PRINT:"F1=",FZERO-30.*DF
          PRINT:"F2=",FZERO+30.*DF
          PRINT:"To be modified (yes/no) ?"
          READ:REP;IF (REP.EQ."yes")REP="YES"
          IF(REP.EQ."YES")GO TO 400
          PRINT:"Number of active capacitances ",NTOT
          PRINT:"Total number = ",NTOTAL
          NTTOT=NTE+NTS+NREF
          PRINT:"Printing of data (yes/no) ?"
          READ:REP;IF (REP.EQ."yes")REP="YES"
          IF(REP.EQ."YES")CALL ETAT
          PRINT:"Saving data to run programme (yes/no) ?"
          READ:REP;IF(REP.EQ."yes")REP="YES"
          IF(REP.NE."YES")GO TO 10
*Use routine to attach file 01 and 11
          CALL ATAFIC(1,2)
          DATA=FICHE
          PRINT:"Saving results to run S21"
          CALL ATAFIC(11,2)
          RESULT=FICHE
          GO TO 410
 405  WRITE(01)NTOT,NU
          WRITE(01)NTOTAL,NTTOTAL
          WRITE(01)(TAU(K),K=1,NTOT)
```

```
      WRITE(01)(A(K),K=1,NTOT)
      WRITE(01)NTTOT
      WRITE(01)(NT(KT),KT=1,NTTOT)
      WRITE(01)(FADA(KT),KT=1,NTTOT)
      WRITE(01)(QADA(KT),KT=1,NTTOT)
      WRITE(01)(RG(KT),KT=1,NTTOT)
      WRITE(01)(JADA(KT),KT=1,NTTOT)
      WRITE(01)(IMPLE(KT),KT=1,NTTOT)
      WRITE(01)(RADA(KT),KT=1,NTTOT)
      WRITE(01)NTE,NTS,NREF,FZERO,DF,DELTA,AK2,DB,R0
     &,MINAL
      REWIND(01)
      IF(JTSS.EQ.2)GO TO 500
      STOP"Bye"
  410 FIC="QUIK"
'Create temporary file QUIK
      CALL DEFIL(FIC,1,0,ISTA)
      CALL ATTACH(02,"QUIK;",2,0,ISTA)
      WRITE (02,9004)
      WRITE(02,9005)NTOTAL,NTTOTAL
      WRITE(2,9006)DATA
      WRITE(2,9008)RESULT
      REWIND (02)
      MINAL=0
      PRINT:"   ***   EXECUTION   ***"
      PRINT:"TSS (1) or BATCH (2) ?"
      READ:JTSS
      IF(JTSS.EQ.2)GO TO 405
      PRINT:"Display : Graphic (1) or alphanumeric (0) ?"
      READ:MINAL
      PRINT:"TSS execution:"
      PRINT:"Type : OLD QUIK ,then:RUN"
      GO TO 405
  500 CALL BATCH
      GO TO 10
*Display processor time
  600 CALL TEMPS
      STOP"Bye"
*Adjust this FORMAT to your personnal directories
 9004 FORMAT("10*#RUN *;/LIBRARY/TSSFOS,R;",
     &"/LIBRARY/COURBE,R;/LIBRARY/COUVIS,R;",
     &"/LIBRARY/TEMPS,R=",/,
     &"11*#(ULIB)SERVICE/HEMP,R;SERVICE/YT4010,R")
 9005 FORMAT("20 PARAMETER  NBCAPA=",I4,", NB COMB=",I3)
 9006 FORMAT("30 PARAMETER FICHIER=",1H",A21,1H")
 9007 FORMAT("30 CHARACTER FICHIER*21,RESULT*21")
 9003 FORMAT(A20,";")
 9008 FORMAT("40 PARAMETER RESULT=",1H",A21,1H")
      END
      SUBROUTINE DESCRI(KT)
      COMMON/SONDE/ISOR,IDOI
      COMMON/DONNEE/NU,NTOT,TAU(301),A(301),NTTOT,NT(10)
     &,FADA(10),QADA(10),JADA(10),NTE,NTS,NREF
     & ,NTOTAL,NTTOTAL,RADA(10),RG(10),IMPLE(10),FZERO,DF
     &,DELTA,AK2,DB,R0,MINAL
      COMMON/CMODIF/MODIF
      COMMON/CREF/JPOSE,JCODE
      CHARACTER FICHIER*20,FICHE*21
      IF(MODIF.EQ.1)GO TO 20
      KT=KT+1
      NTT=NTOT
      GO TO 30
   20 NTT=0
      NT1=NT(KT)
      IF(KT.EQ.1)GO TO 30
      DO 25 KT1=1,KT-1
   25 NTT=NTT+NT(KT1)
   30 CONTINUE
      PRINT:"Regular (1) or described by a file (2) ?"
```

```
      READ:ID
      IF(ID.GT.1)GO TO 100
      PRINT:"Nominal frequency: F=1."
      PRINT:"Central frequency of the transducer ?"
      READ:FC;IF(FC.LE.0.)FC=1.
      PRINT:"LAMBDA=",1./FC
      PRINT:"Number of fingers ?"
      PRINT:" "
      READ:NBELEC
      IF(NBELEC.EQ.2)IDOI=1
      IF(MODIF.EQ.1.AND.NBELEC-1.NE.NT1)
    & STOP"Data non consistent"
      NT(KT)=NBELEC-1
      DO 40 K=NTT+1,NTT+NT(KT)
      A(K)=1.;TAU(K)=0.5*K/FC
  40  CONTINUE
  50  PRINT:"Dummy capacitances:"
      PRINT:"   0 = to be neglected"
      PRINT:"   1 = single electrodes"
      PRINT:"   2 = double electrodes"
      READ:IMP
      IF(JPOSE.EQ.0)GO TO 53
      KT2=JCODE-1;IF(JPOSE.EQ.1)KT2=JCODE
      KTT=1;IF(JPOSE.EQ.1)KTT=0
      IF(KT2.EQ.0)GO TO 52
      DO 51 KT1=1,KT2
  51  KTT=KTT+NT(KT1)
  52  XC=TAU(KTT)
      JD=NT(KT)+NT(JCODE)
      DECAL=1.5
      XC=XC+0.5*JPOSE*(ABS(TAU(NTT+NT(KT))-
    & TAU(NTT+1))+DECAL)
      JPOSE=0
      ISIG=0
      IF(JPOSE.EQ.(-1))KT1=NTT+NT(KT)
      NDT=NT(JCODE);IF(JPOSE.EQ.(-1))NDT=NT(KT)
      S=1.;IF(MOD(NDT,2).EQ.0)S=-1.
      GO TO 54
  53  CONTINUE
      PRINT:"Sign (1 or -1) ?"
      READ:ISIG
      PRINT:"Coordinate of the center of the comb "
    &,"(in LAMBDAs) ?"
      READ:XC
  54  CONTINUE
      DTAU=0.5*(TAU(NTT+1)+TAU(NTT+NT(KT)))-XC
      DO 60 K=NTT+1,NTT+NT(KT)
      TAU(K)=TAU(K)-DTAU
  60  CONTINUE
      IF(ISIG*A(NTT+1).GT.0.)GO TO 80
      IF(JPOSE.NE.0.AND.A(KTT)*A(KT1)*S.LT.0.)GO TO 80
      DO 70 K=NTT+1,NTT+NT(KT)
  70  A(K)=-A(K)
  80  IF(MODIF.NE.1)NTOT=NTOT+NT(KT)
      GO TO 200
 100  PRINT:"File description ?"
      PRINT:"(Example :  /FOS/1N120200)"
      READ:FICHIER
      ENCODE(FICHE,9003)FICHIER
9003  FORMAT(A20,";")
      CALL ATTACH(01,FICHE,1,0,ISTAT)
      READ(01)NT(KT)
      PRINT:"NB DE CAPAS=",NT(KT)
      IF(MODIF.EQ.1.AND.NT(KT).NE.NT1)
    & STOP"Data not consistent"
      READ(01)(TAU(K),K=NTT+1,NTT+NT(KT))
      READ(01)(A(K),K=NTT+1,NTT+NT(KT))
      REWIND(01)
      GO TO 50
```

```
200 NTOTAL=NTOTAL+NT(KT)
    NTTOTAL=NTTOTAL+1
    IF(ID.GT.1)GO TO 250
    IF(IMP.LE.1)IMP=0
    IF(IMP.EQ.0)GO TO 300
    NTTOTAL=NTTOTAL+2
    NTOTAL=NTOTAL+NT(KT)-1
    GO TO 300
250 IF(IMP.LE.0)GO TO 300
    NTTOTAL=NTTOTAL+2
    NTOTAL=NTOTAL+2*NT(KT)
    IF(IMP.LE.1)GO TO 300
    NTOTAL=NTOTAL+2*(NT(KT)-1)
300 IMPLE(KT)=IMP
    RETURN
    END
    SUBROUTINE ETAT
    COMMON /DONNEE/NU,NTOT,TAU(301),A(301),NTTOT,NT(10)
   &,FADA(10),QADA(10),JADA(10),NTE,NTS,NREF
   & ,NTOTAL,NTTOTAL,RADA(10),RG(10),IMPLE(10)
   &,FZERO,DF,DELTA,AK2,DB,RO,MINAL
    PRINT:" "
    PRINT:"****************************************"
    PRINT:"NB CAPA=",NTOTAL," NB COMBS = ",NTTOTAL
    PRINT:"****************************************"
    PRINT:" "
    PRINT:"*** SUBSTRATE ***"
    PRINT:"NU=",NU
    PRINT:"K2=",AK2
    PRINT:"DB/LAMBDA=",DB
    PRINT:" "
    PRINT:"*** INPUT ***"
    K2=0
    DO 10 KT=1,NTE
    S=1.
    PRINT:"--- CODE ",KT,"---"
    PRINT:"  TAU(K)     A(K)"
    K1=K2+1;K2=K1+NT(KT)-1
    IF(IMPLE(KT).EQ.1)PRINT:"Single fingers"
    IF(IMPLE(KT).EQ.2)PRINT:"Double fingers"
    DO 10 K=K1,K2
    PRINT 9001,TAU(K),A(K)*S
 10 S=-S
    IF(NTS.EQ.0)GO TO 30
    PRINT:" "
    PRINT:"*** OUTPUT ***"
    DO 20 KT=NTE+1,NTE+NTS
    PRINT:"--- CODE",KT,"---"
    K1=K2+1;K2=K1+NT(KT)-1
    S=1.
    IF(IMPLE(KT).EQ.1)PRINT:"Single fingers"
    IF(IMPLE(KT).EQ.2)PRINT:"Double fingers"
    DO 20 K=K1,K2
    PRINT 9001,TAU(K),A(K)*S
 20 S=-S
 30 IF(NREF.EQ.0)GO TO 50
    PRINT:" "
    PRINT:"*** REFLECTORS ***"
    DO 40 KT=NTE+NTS+1,NTE+NTS+NREF
    PRINT:"--- CODE ",KT,"---"
    K1=K2+1;K2=K1+NT(KT)-1
    S=1.
    DO 40 K=K1,K2
    IF(IMPLE(KT).EQ.1)PRINT:"Single fingers"
    IF(IMPLE(KT).EQ.2)PRINT:"Double fingers"
    PRINT 9001,TAU(K),A(K)*S
 40 S=-S
 50 PRINT:"FZERO=",FZERO
    PRINT:"DF=",DF
```

```
      PRINT:"DELTA=",DELTA
      PRINT:" "
      PRINT:"*** MATCHING ***"
      PRINT 9002,"INPUT ",FADA(1),JADA(1)
     & ,RG(1)
      IF(NTS.GT.0)PRINT9002,"OUTPUT"
     &,FADA(NTE+1),JADA(NTE+1)
     &,RG(NTE+1)
      IF(NREF.EQ.0)RETURN
      DO 60 KT=NTE+NTS+1,NTTOT
      PRINT 9003,KT,FADA(KT)
     &,JADA(KT),QADA(KT),RG(KT)
   60 CONTINUE
      RETURN
 9003 FORMAT(1X,"T",I2,"    F= ",E12.6,"    JADA="
     &,I6," 1/Q= ",E12.6,"   R  = ",E12.6)
 9002 FORMAT(1X,A6," F= ",E12.6,"    JADA=",I6
     &," R  = ",E12.6)
 9001 FORMAT(2E12.4)
      END
      SUBROUTINE FERME(KT)
      COMMON /DONNEE/NU,NTOT,TAU(301),A(301),NTTOT
     &,NT(10),FADA(10),QADA(10),JADA(10),NTE,NTS,NREF
     &,NTOTAL,NTTOTAL,RADA(10),RG(10),IMPLE(10)
     &,FZERO,DF,DELTA,AK2,D,R0,MINAL
      PRINT:"--- LOAD ---"
   10 CONTINUE
      PRINT:"JADA ?"
      PRINT:"   1=INDUCTANCE+RESISTANCE"
      PRINT:"   0=Open circuit"
      PRINT:"  -1=Short circuit"
      PRINT:"  -2=tuned INDUCTANCE only"
      READ:J;JADA(KT)=J
      IF(J.EQ.1)CALL ADA(KT)
      IF(J.EQ.(-2))GO TO 20
      IF(J*(J**2-1).NE.0)GO TO 10
      RETURN
   20 PRINT:"Tuning frequency ?"
      READ:FADA(KT)
      PRINT:"1/Q of the INDUCTANCE ?";READ:QADA(KT)
      RETURN
      END
      SUBROUTINE ADA(KT)
      COMMON/SONDE/ISOR,IDOI
      COMMON/DONNEE/NU,NTOT,TAU(301),A(301),NTTOT
     &,NT(10),FADA(10),QADA(10),JADA(10),NTE,NTS,NREF
     & ,NTOTAL,NTTOTAL,RADA(10),RG(10),IMPLE(10)
     &,FZERO,DF,DELTA,AK2,DB,R0,MINAL
      ISOR=ISOR*IDOI
      PRINT:"Load resistance RG/R0 ?"
      READ:RG(KT)
      PRINT:"--- MATCHING ---"
   10 CONTINUE
      PRINT:" JADA ?"
      PRINT:"   1=port not matched"
      PRINT:"   2=cancellation of the capacitance only"
      PRINT:"   3=independent matching of the port"
      PRINT:"   4=matched unidirectionnal port"
      IF(ISOR.EQ.1)PRINT:" 999=Acoustical port"
      READ:JADA(KT)
      IF(JADA(KT).EQ.999)GO TO 20
      IF(JADA(KT).LE.0)GO TO 10
      IF(JADA(KT).GT.4)GO TO 10
      IF(JADA(KT).LE.1)GOTO 20
      PRINT:"Frequency of exact matching ?"
      READ:FADA(KT)
      RETURN
   20 ISOR=0;IDOI=0
      FADA(KT)=1.
```

```
        RETURN
        END
        SUBROUTINE BATCH
*This routine generates the relevant batch cards
*to be fitted to your system
        CHARACTER FIC*8
        CHARACTER NOM*12
        FIC="EXE"
        PRINT:"IDENT ?";READ:NOM
        CALL DEFIL(FIC,2,0,ISTAT)
        CALL ATTACH(21,"EXE;",2,0,ISTAT)
        WRITE(21,9012)NOR(J)
 9012 FORMAT(I4,"77N(^)")
        WRITE(21,9013)NOR(J),NOM
 9013 FORMAT(I4,"$^IDENT^DTS310,43",1A12)
        WRITE(21,9009)NOR(J)
 9009 FORMAT(I4,"$^OPTION^FORTRAN")
        WRITE(21,9001)NOR(J)
 9001 FORMAT(I4,"$^LIBRARY^HE")
        WRITE(21,9010)NOR(J)
 9010 FORMAT(I4,"$^FORTRAN^NFORM,NLNO")
        WRITE(21,9017)NOR(J)
 9017 FORMAT(I4,"$^SELECTA^QUIK")
        WRITE(21,9019)NOR(J)
 9019 FORMAT(I4,"$^SELECTA^ /FOS/TSSFOS")
 9020 FORMAT(I4,"$^SELECTA^ /LIBRARY/COURBE")
        WRITE(21,9020)NOR(J)
        WRITE(21,9034)NOR(J)
        WRITE(21,9023)NOR(J)
 9023 FORMAT(I4,"$^EXECUTE")
        WRITE(21,9025)NOR(J)
        WRITE(21,9033)NOR(J)
 9025 FORMAT(I4,"$^PRMFL^HE,R,R,SERVICE/HEMP")
 9033 FORMAT(I4,"$^LIMITS^10,40K,,10000")
        WRITE(21,9024)NOR(J)
 9024 FORMAT(I4,"$^ENDJOB")
        REWIND(21)
        PRINT:" "
        PRINT:"Immediate execution (yes/no) ?"
        READ:FIC ;IF(FIC.EQ."yes")FIC="YES"
        IF(FIC.NE."YES")GO TO 100
        REWIND(21)
        PRINT:"*****************************"
*System routine for launching jobs
        CALL CALLSS("RUN EXE7","CDIN")
        PRINT:"*****************************"
        RETURN
  100 PRINT:" "
        PRINT:"*****************************"
        PRINT:"Type : CARD"
        PRINT:"Then : OLD EXE"
        PRINT:"Modify the LIMITS card"
        PRINT:"then : RUN"
        PRINT:"*****************************"
        STOP
 9034 FORMAT(I4,"$^SELECTA^ /LIBRARY/TEMPS")
        END
        FUNCTION NOR(J)
        DATA I/0/
        I=I+1
        NOR=10*I+1000
        RETURN
        END
```

TSSFOS

Library overlay TSSFOS to be used for execution of program MAREFOS.

```
*Routine segment to be concatened with temporary
*    file QUIK  automatically generated by program MAREFOS
*System library HEMP for linear matrix computations,
*      system library YT4010 for graphics and other
*      library routines COURBE, COUVIS,TEMPS are used.
*
      PARAMETER   NB POINTS=61
      PARAMETER KDIM=2*NBCOMB+1
      DIMENSION TAU(NBCAPA),A(NBCAPA),NT(NBCOMB),
     & FADA(NBCOMB),QADA(NBCOMB),JADA(NBCOMB),
     & LISTRA(NBCOMB) ,CT(NBCAPA,NBCOMB),RT(NBCAPA
     &,NBCOMB),RADA(NBCOMB), IMPLE(NBCOMB),KJK(NBCAPA)
     &, RG(NBCOMB), YTOP(NBCAPA),YBOT(NBCAPA),T(NBCAPA)
     & ,P(NBCAPA),CTAU(NBCAPA)
     & , G(NBCAPA,NBCAPA),YY(NBCOMB,NBCOMB),
     & SELF(NBCOMB),RESIST(NBCOMB)
     & , X(NBPOINTS),Y(NBPOINTS),TAMPON(KDIM)
      COMPLEX G,CT,YY,CTAU,CDELTA,CS12
      COMMON/DONNEE/NU,RZERO,NTOT,NTTOT,NTE,NTS,NREF
     &,FZERO,DF,DELTA,AK2,DB,MINAL
      PRINT:"N=",NBCAPA
*Display memory size
      CALL TEMPS
      PI=3.1415927
      NDIM=NBCAPA;MDIM=NBCOMB;NBPT=NBPOINTS
*System routine SETDIM in system library HEMP specifies
*actual dimension of arrays G,YY,CT for further use
      CALL SETDIM(G,NDIM,NDIM,YY,MDIM,MDIM,CT,NDIM,MDIM)
*Read data
      CALL ATTACH(11,RESULT,2,0,ISTAT,)
      CALL ATTACH(01,FICHIER,1,0,ISTAT,)
      IFICH=1
      CALL LECTUR(IMPLE,RADA,TAU,A,NT,FADA,QADA,RG,
     & JADA,IFICH,NDIM,MDIM)
      REWIND(01)
      WRITE(11)NBPT,FZERO,DF,RZERO,JADA(1),
     &JADA(NTE+1),NTS
*Load impedance
      SEUIL=1.E-4
      CALL LOAD(NBTRA,SELF,RESIST,LISTRA,JADA,QADA,
     &FADA,RG,A,NT,CT,RT,NDIM,MDIM,TAU,YTOP,YBOT,T
     &,P,G,CTAU,YY, RADA,IMPLE,SEUIL,KJK)
*Capacitances
      CALL SUPCAPA(TAU,A,YTOP,YBOT,P,
     & JADA,IMPLE,NT,SEUIL,T,RT,MDIM,NDIM)
      IF(NTOT.GT.NDIM)STOP"Too much capacitances"
      IF(NTTOT.GT.MDIM)STOP"Too much transducers"
      PRINT:"NTTOT=",NTTOT
*Neglegting too small ponderations
      CALL ECRETE(KJK,IMPLE,RADA,SEUIL,A,TAU,P,T,
     &YTOP,YBOT,NT)
*Compute
      F=FZERO-DF*(NBPT+1)/2
      JF=1
      IF(NTS.GT.0)PRINT:"       F        S21(dB)"
     & ,"       S21(LIN)      DEGRES  Time delay"
      IF(NTS.EQ.0)PRINT:"       F             R"
     &,"       X        R(dB)"
      DO 100 IF=1,NBPT
      F=F+DF;X(IF)=F
*Compute admittance matrix between capacitances
```

```
      CALL CALCUL (F,NBTRA,LISTRA,NTOT,NT,CT,RT,CTAU
     &,P,T,G,YTOP,YBOT,YY,NDIM,MDIM)
*Organising parallel combs
      CALL PARAL(YY,CT,G,MDIM,NDIM,NBA)
*Loading ports, matching and normalising coefficients
      CALL FERME(F,NBA,YY,RESIST,SELF,TAMPON,JADA,MDIM)
      IF(NTS.GT.0)GO TO 10
*Compute actual impedance
      R=REAL(YY(1,1));AX=AIMAG(YY(1,1))
      IF(MOD(IF,JF).EQ.1.OR.JF.EQ.1)
     &PRINT:F,R,AX,10.*ALOG10(R/2.)
      Y(IF)=R
      GO TO 90
   10 CONTINUE
*Compute S21
      CDELTA=(YY(1,1)+1.)*(YY(2,2)+1.)-YY(1,2)*YY(2,1)
      IF(JADA(NTE+1).EQ.999)CDELTA=1.+YY(1,1)
      CS12=2.*YY(1,2)/CDELTA
      CALL ARCTA(CS12,FASE)
      S12=20.*ALOG10(CABS(CS12))
      Y(IF)=S12
      IF(IF.EQ.1)FASE1=FASE
   80 IF(FASE1.LT.FASE)FASE1=FASE1+2.*PI
      IF(FASE1.LT.FASE)GO TO 80
      TPG=(FASE1-FASE)/DF/2./PI
      FASE1=FASE
      FASE=FASE*180./PI
      IF(MOD(IF,JF).EQ.1.OR.JF.EQ.1)
     &PRINT 9001,F,S12,CABS(CS12),FASE,TPG
   90 CONTINUE
  100 CONTINUE
*Plot frequency response (alphanumeric display)
      IF(MINAL.NE.1)CALL COURBE(X,Y,NBPT)
      IF(MINAL.NE.1)GO TO 200
      CHARACTER REP
      PRINT:"Plot frequency response (YES/NO) ?"
      READ:REP;IF(REP.EQ."yes")REP="YES"
      IF(REP.NE."YES")GO TO 200
*Plot frequency response (graphic display)
      CALL COUVIS(X,Y,NBPT)
  200 PRINT:"Results are saved on file ",RESULT
      PRINT:"Other matching networks are checked by"
     &," /SAW/S21"
*Evaluate time processor
      CALL TEMPS
      STOP
 9001 FORMAT(1X,F12.4,F12.2,F12.6,F12.2,F12.4)
      END
      SUBROUTINE LECTUR(IMPLE,RADA,TAU,A,NT,FADA,QADA,RG,
     & JADA, IFICH,NDIM,MDIM)
*Read data file
      DIMENSION RADA(1),IMPLE(1),KJK(1),TAU(1),A(1)
     & ,NT(1),FADA(1),QADA(1),RG(1),JADA(1)
      COMMON/DONNEE/NU,RZERO,NTOT,NTTOT,NTE,NTS,NREF,
     & FZERO,DF,DELTA,AK2,DB,MINAL
      CHARACTER TITRE*72
      COMMON/CTITRE/TITRE
      DATA PI/3.1415927/
      READ(IFICH)NTOT,NU
      READ(IFICH)NTOTAL,NTTOTAL
      IF(NTOT.GT.NDIM)STOP"DIMENSIONS NOT CONSISTENT"
      READ(IFICH)(TAU(K),K=1,NTOT)
      READ(IFICH)(A(K),K=1,NTOT)
      READ(IFICH)NTTOT
      READ(IFICH)(NT(KT),KT=1,NTTOT)
      READ(IFICH)(FADA(KT),KT=1,NTTOT)
      READ(IFICH)(QADA(KT),KT=1,NTTOT)
      READ(IFICH)(RG(KT),KT=1,NTTOT)
      READ(IFICH)(JADA(KT),KT=1,NTTOT)
```

```
      READ(IFICH)(IMPLE(KT),KT=1,NTTOT)
      READ(IFICH)(RADA(KT),KT=1,NTTOT)
      READ(IFICH)NTE,NTS,NREF,FZERO,DF,DELTA,AK2,
     &DB,RZERO,MINAL
      IF(NTTOT.GT.MDIM)STOP"Too much transducers"
      IF(NU.EQ.2)AK2=SQRT(AK2)
*Parameter 0.6 instead of 0.718 to fit with conventional
*values of K2; the value of K2 is reported as .6*K2
      AK2=0.6*AK2
      DB=DB*ALOG(10.)/40./PI
      RZERO=AK2/2./PI
      DO 5 KT=1,NTTOT
    5 RG(KT)=RG(KT)*RZERO
      IF(MINAL.NE.1)GO TO 9
      PRINT:"List input data (YES/NO) ?"
      CHARACTER REP; READ:REP;IF(REP.EQ."yes")REP="YES"
      IF (REP.EQ."YES")GO TO 9
      RETURN
    9 CONTINUE
      PRINT:" "
      PRINT:"****************************************"
      PRINT:"NB CAPA=",NDIM,"   NB COMB=",MDIM
      PRINT:"****************************************"
      PRINT:" "
      PRINT:"*** Substrate ***"
      PRINT:"NU=",NU
      PRINT:"K2=",AK2
      PRINT:"DB/LAMBDA=",DB
      PRINT:" "
      PRINT:"*** Input transducers ***"
      K2=0
      DO 10 KT=1,NTE
      S=1.
      PRINT:"--- CODE ",KT,"---"
      K1=K2+1;K2=K1+NT(KT)-1
      IF(IMPLE(KT).EQ.1)PRINT:"Single fingers"
      IF(IMPLE(KT).EQ.2)PRINT:"Double fingers"
      PRINT:"   TAU(K)      A(K)"
      DO 10 K=K1,K2
      PRINT 9001,TAU(K),A(K)*S
   10 S=-S
      IF(NTS.EQ.0)GO TO 30
      PRINT:" "
      PRINT:"*** Output transducers ***"
      DO 20 KT=NTE+1,NTE+NTS
      PRINT:"--- CODE",KT,"---"
      K1=K2+1;K2=K1+NT(KT)-1
      S=1.
      IF(IMPLE(KT).EQ.1)PRINT:"Single fingers"
      IF(IMPLE(KT).EQ.2)PRINT:"Double Fingers"
      DO 20 K=K1,K2
      PRINT 9001,TAU(K),A(K)*S
   20 S=-S
   30 IF(NREF.EQ.0)GO TO 50
      PRINT:" "
      PRINT:"*** REFLECTORS ***"
      DO 40 KT=NTE+NTS+1,NTE+NTS+NREF
      PRINT:"--- CODE ",KT,"---"
      K1=K2+1;K2=K1+NT(KT)-1
      S=1.
      DO 40 K=K1,K2
      IF(IMPLE(KT).EQ.1)PRINT:"Single fingers"
      IF(IMPLE(KT).EQ.2)PRINT:"Double fingers"
      PRINT 9001,TAU(K),A(K)*S
   40 S=-S
   50 PRINT:"FZERO=",FZERO
      PRINT:"DF=",DF
      PRINT:"DELTA=",DELTA
      PRINT:" "
```

```
      PRINT:"*** MATCHING NETWORK ***"
      PRINT 9002,"INPUT ",FADA(1),JADA(1),RG(1)
      IF(NTS.GT.0)PRINT9002,"OUTPUT"
     &,FADA(NTE+1),JADA(NTE+1),RG(NTE+1)
      IF(NREF.EQ.0)RETURN
      DO 60 KT=NTE+NTS+1,NTTOT
      PRINT 9003,KT,FADA(KT),JADA(KT),QADA(KT),RG(KT)
   60 CONTINUE
      RETURN
 9001 FORMAT(2E12.4)
 9002 FORMAT(1X,A6," F= ",E12.6,"    JADA=",I6,
     &" R  = ",E12.6)
 9003 FORMAT(1X,"T",I2,"    F= ",E12.6,"    JADA="
     &,I6," 1/Q= ",E12.6," R  = ",E12.6)
      END
      SUBROUTINE SELECT(KJK,IMPLE,NBTRA,LISTRA,JTOT,A,NT,
     & CT,RT,NDIM,MDIM,TAU,YTOP,YBOT,T,P)
      DIMENSION RADA(1),IMPLE(1),KJK(1),NT(1),LISTRA(1),
     & A(1),CT(NDIM,MDIM),RT(NDIM,MDIM)
      COMPLEX CT
      REAL TAU(1),YTOP(1),YBOT(1),T(1),P(1)
      COMMON/DONNEE/NU,RZERO,NTOT,NTTOT,NTE,NTS,NREF
     & ,FZERO ,DF,DELTA,AK2,DB,MINAL
      JTOT=0;W=1.
      DO 10 JT=1,NBTRA
   10 JTOT=JTOT+NT(LISTRA(JT))
      DO 20 JT=1,MDIM
      DO 20 J=1,NDIM
   20 RT(J,JT)=0.
      JT=1;J=0;K1=1
      DO 40 KT=1,NTTOT
      IF(KT.NE.LISTRA(JT))GO TO 40
      LT=KT;SIG=1.
      CALL CALPEI(LT,KJK,IMPLE,K1,TAU,A,NT(KT),YTOP,YBOT
     & ,SIG,ITYPE,W,DELTA)
      DO 30 K=K1,K1+NT(KT)-1
      J=J+1
      T(J)=TAU(K);P(J)=ABS(A(K))
      YTOP(J)=YTOP(K)
      YBOT(J)=YBOT(K)
   30 RT(J,JT)=A(K)
      JT=JT+1
   40 K1=K1+NT(KT)
      RETURN
      END
      SUBROUTINE CALCUL (F,NBTRA,LISTRA,JTOT,NT,CT,RT
     & ,CTAU ,P ,T ,G ,YTOP,YBOT,YY,NDIM,MDIM)
      DIMENSION RADA(1),IMPLE(1),KJK(1),LISTRA(1),NT(1)
     & ,CT(NDIM,MDIM),RT(NDIM,MDIM),CTAU(1),P(1),
     & G(NDIM,NDIM),YY(MDIM,MDIM)
      COMMON/DONNEE/NU,RZERO,NTOT,NTTOT,NTE,NTS ,NREF
     & ,FZERO,DF,DELTA,AK2,DB,MINAL
      CHARACTER TITRE*72
      REAL T(1),YTOP(1),YBOT(1)
      COMPLEX G,YY,CT,CTAU
      DATA PI/3.1415927/
      OMEGA=2.*PI*F
      DO 5 J=1,JTOT
      DO 5 KJ=1,NBTRA
    5 CT(J,KJ)=RT(J,KJ)
      DO 10 J=1,JTOT
      TETA=OMEGA*T(J)
      SIGMA=TETA*DB
      CO=COS(TETA);SI=-SIN(TETA)
      EX=EXP(-SIGMA)
   10 CTAU(J)=CMPLX(CO,SI)*EX
      DO 100 I=1,JTOT
      G(I,I)=P(I)*CMPLX(1.,AK2)
      IF(I.EQ.JTOT)GO TO 100
```

```
          DO 90 J=I+1,JTOT
          TIJ=2.*ABS(T(I)-T(J))*OMEGA
          AA=AMIN1(YTOP(I),YTOP(J))-AMAX1(YBOT(I),YBOT(J))
          AA=AK2*AMAX1(0.,AA)
          IF(T(I)-T(J))20,30,30
    20    G(I,J)=CMPLX(0.,AA)*CTAU(J)/CTAU(I);GO TO 40
    30    G(I,J)=CMPLX(0.,AA)*CTAU(I)/CTAU(J)
    40    IF(NU.NE.2)GO TO 90
          G(I,J)=G(I,J)/SQRT(TIJ)*CMPLX(1.,-1.)
    90    G(J,I)=G(I,J)
   100    CONTINUE
*Use system routine HECSEQ to solve linear system
*[G] X = CT
          CALL HECSEQ(G,JTOT,CT,NBTRA,$105)
          GO TO 106
   105    PRINT:"<<<<   HEMP ERROR IN TSSFOS   >>>>"
   106    CONTINUE
          DO 110 J=1,NBTRA
          DO 110 I=J,NBTRA
   110    YY(I,J)=0.
          J=0
          DO 200 JJ=1,NBTRA
          DO 130 K=1,NT(LISTRA(JJ))
          J=J+1;IF(J.GT.JTOT)STOP"<CALCUL>"
          DO 130 II=JJ,NBTRA
   130    YY(II,JJ)=YY(II,JJ)+RT(J,JJ)*CT(J,II)
          DO 140 II=JJ,NBTRA
   140    YY(II,JJ)=YY(II,JJ)*CMPLX(0.,OMEGA)
          IF(JJ.EQ.NBTRA)GO TO 200
          DO 150 II=JJ+1,NBTRA
   150    YY(JJ,II)=YY(II,JJ)
   200    CONTINUE
          RETURN
          END
          SUBROUTINE LOAD(NBTRA,SELF,RESIST,LISTRA,JADA,QADA
        & ,FADA,RG,A,NT,CT,RT,NDIM,MDIM,TAU,YTOP,YBOT,T,P,G
        & ,CTAU,YY,RADA,IMPLE,SEUIL,KJK)
          DIMENSION RADA(1),IMPLE(1),KJK(1),G(NDIM,NDIM),
        & CTAU(1),YY(MDIM,MDIM),JADA(1),NT(1),LISTRA(1)
        & ,A(1),CT(NDIM,MDIM),RT(NDIM,MDIM)
          COMPLEX CT,G,CTAU,YY
          REAL SELF(1),RESIST(1),FADA(1),QADA(1),RG(1),
        & TAU(1), YTOP(1),YBOT(1),T(1),P(1)
          COMMON/DONNEE/NU,RZERO,NTOT,NTTOT,NTE,NTS,NREF
        & ,FZERO,DF,DELTA,AK2, DB,MINAL
          DATA PI/3.1415927/
*References NR ignore open/short circuits
          ND1=NDIM;MD1=MDIM
**Resistances computation,
*Input
          IAM=1;KT=1;NTR=NTE;NR=0
          GO TO 100
    10    CONTINUE
*Output
          IAM=2;KT=NTE+1;NTR=NTS
          IF(NTS.EQ.0)GO TO 20
          GO TO 100
    20    CONTINUE
*Reflectors
          IAM=3;NTR=1
          IF(NREF.EQ.0)GO TO 500
          DO 30 JKT=NTE+NTS+1,NTTOT
          KT=JKT
          IF(JADA(KT).GT.0)GO TO 100
          IF(JADA(KT).NE.(-2))GO TO 30
          NR=NR+1;RESIST(NR)=0.
    30    CONTINUE
          GO TO 500
   100    NR=NR+1
```

```
      IF(JADA(KT).EQ.999)GO TO 120
      GO TO (110,110,130,120,135),JADA(KT)
  110 RESIST(NR)=RG(KT);GO TO 150
  120 RESIST(NR)=2.*RZERO/NTR;GO TO 150
  130 IF(NTR.EQ.1)GO TO 140
  135 CONTINUE
      RESIST(NR)=RZERO/NTR;GO TO 150
  140 CONTINUE
      NBTRA=1;LISTRA(1)=KT
      CALL SELECT(KJK,IMPLE,NBTRA,LISTRA,JTOT,A,NT,CT,RT,
     & ND1,MD1,TAU,YTOP,YBOT,T,P)
      F=FADA(KT)
      CALL CALCUL (F,NBTRA,LISTRA,JTOT,NT,CT,RT,CTAU,P,T,
     & G,YTOP,YBOT,YY,ND1,MD1)
      RESIST(KT)=REAL(1./YY(1,1))
  150 CONTINUE
      GO TO (10,20,30),IAM
  500 NBTRA=NTTOT
      DO 510 KT=1,NTTOT
  510 LISTRA(KT)=KT
      CALL SELECT(KJK,IMPLE,NBTRA,LISTRA,JTOT,A,NT,CT,RT,
     & ND1,MD1,TAU,YTOP,YBOT,T,P)
*Compute values of inductances
*Input
      NR=1
      K2=0;CAPA=0
      SELF(1)=0.
      DO 530 KT=1,NTE
      K1=K2+1;K2=K2+NT(KT)
      DO 520 K=K1,K2
  520 CAPA=CAPA+P(K)
  530 CONTINUE
*Save results for S21
      WRITE(11)CAPA/2.,RESIST(1)
      IF(JADA(1).LE.1)GO TO 600
      OMEGA=2.*PI*FADA(1)
      SELF(1)=1./CAPA/OMEGA**2
  600 CAPA=0.;IF(NTS.EQ.0)GO TO 700
*OUTPUT
      SELF(2)=0.
      NR=2
      DO 630 KT=NTE+1,NTE+NTS
      K1=K2+1;K2=K2+NT(KT)
      DO 620 K=K1,K2
  620 CAPA=CAPA+P(K)
  630 CONTINUE
*Results saved for S21
      WRITE(11)CAPA/2.,RESIST(2)
      IF(JADA(NTE+1).LE.1)GO TO 700
      OMEGA=2.*PI*FADA(NTE+1)
      SELF(2)=1./CAPA/OMEGA**2
  700 IF(NREF.EQ.0)RETURN
*REFLECTORS
      DO 750 KT=NTE+NTS+1,NTTOT
      CAPA=0
      K1=K2+1;K2=K2+NT(KT)
      IF(JADA(KT).EQ.0)GO TO 750
      IF(JADA(KT).EQ.(-1))GO TO 750
      NR=NR+1
      SELF(NR)=0.
      IF(JADA(KT).EQ.1)GO TO 750
      DO 720 K=K1,K2
      CAPA=CAPA+P(K)
  720 CONTINUE
      OMEGA=2.*PI*FADA(KT)
      SELF(NR)=1./CAPA/OMEGA**2
      RESIST(NR)=RESIST(NR)+SELF(NR)*OMEGA*QADA(KT)
  750 CONTINUE
      RETURN
```

```
      END
      SUBROUTINE ECRETE(KJK,IMPLE,RADA,SEUIL,A,TAU,P,T,
     & YTOP, YBOT, NT)
      DIMENSION RADA(1),IMPLE(1),KJK(1),A(1),TAU(1),P(1)
     &,T(1),YTOP(1),YBOT(1),NT(1)
      COMMON/DONNEE/NU,RZERO,NTOT,NTTOT,NTE,NTS,NREF,
     & FZERO,DF,DELTA,AK2,DB,MINAL
   10 K2=0
      DO 100 KT=1,NTTOT
      K1=K2+1;K2=K2+NT(KT)
      DO 50 K=K1,K2
   50 IF(ABS(A(K)).LT.SEUIL)GO TO 200
  100 CONTINUE
      RETURN
  200 K2=K;IF(K.EQ.NTOT)GO TO 220
      DO 210 K1=K+1,NTOT
      A(K2)=A(K1);TAU(K2)=TAU(K1)
      YTOP(K2)=YTOP(K1);YBOT(K2)=YBOT(K1)
      P(K2)=P(K1);T(K2)=T(K1)
  210 K2=K2+1
  220 NT(KT)=NT(KT)-1;NTOT=NTOT-1
      GO TO 10
      END
      SUBROUTINE PARAL(YY,CT,G,MDIM,NDIM,NBA)
      DIMENSION RADA(1),IMPLE(1),KJK(1),G(NDIM,NDIM),
     & YY(MDIM,MDIM),CT(NDIM,MDIM)
      COMPLEX G,YY,CT
      COMMON/DONNEE/NU,RZERO,NTOT,NTTOT,NTE,NTS,NREF,
     & FZERO,DF,DELTA,AK2,DB,MINAL
      NBA=NTE+NTS+NREF
      IF(NTE.EQ.1.AND.NTS.LE.1)RETURN
      DO 10 I=1,NTTOT
      DO 10 J=1,NTTOT
      G(I,J)=YY(I,J)
      YY(I,J)=0.
   10 CT(I,J)=0.
      NBA=1
      DO 20 I=1,NTE
   20 CT(I,1)=1.
      IF(NTS.EQ.0)GO TO 40
      NBA=NBA+1
      DO 30 I=NTE+1,NTE+NTS
   30 CT(I,2)=1.
   40 IF(NREF.EQ.0)GO TO 60
      DO 50 I=NTE+NTS+1,NTTOT
      NBA=NBA+1
   50 CT(I,NBA)=1.
   60 CONTINUE
      DO 70 I=1,NBA
      DO 70 J=1,NBA
      DO 70 L1=1,NTTOT
      DO 70 L2=1,NTTOT
   70 YY(I,J)=YY(I,J)+G(L1,L2)*CT(L1,I)*CT(L2,J)
      RETURN
      END
      SUBROUTINE FERME(F,NBA,YY,RESIST,SELF,TAMPON
     &,JADA,MDIM)
      COMPLEX CDELTA,YY
      DIMENSION RADA(1),IMPLE(1),KJK(1),YY(MDIM,MDIM),
     & RESIST(1),SELF(1),TAMPON(1),JADA(1)
      DATA PI/3.1415927/
      COMMON/DONNEE/NU,RZERO,NTOT,NTTOT,NTE,NTS,NREF
     &,FZERO,DF,DELTA,AK2,DB,MINAL
      MD1=MDIM; OMEGA=2.*PI*F
      NA1=2;IF(NTS.EQ.0)NA1=1
      IF(NBA.EQ.NA1)GO TO 10
*Open circuit
      JVIEN=1;JSUP=0
      GO TO 100
```

```
   10 CONTINUE
*Short circuit
*Use system routine HECINV to inverse matrix YY
      CALL HECINV(YY,NBA,TAMPON,CDELTA)
      JVIEN=2;JSUP=-1
      IF(NBA.EQ.NA1)GO TO 200
      GO TO 100
  100 KBA=NA1+1
      DO 120 KT=NTE+NTS+1,NTTOT
      IF(JADA(KT).NE.JSUP)GO TO 110
      CALL SUPRIM(YY,NBA,KBA,MD1)
      NBA=NBA-1
      GO TO 120
  110 KBA=KBA+1
  120 CONTINUE
      GO TO (10,200),JVIEN
  200 IF(NBA.EQ.NA1)GO TO 300
*Reflector inductances
      DO 210 IA=NA1+1,NBA
  210 YY(IA,IA)=YY(IA,IA)
     &+CMPLX(RESIST(IA),SELF(IA)*OMEGA)
      CALL HECINV(YY,NBA,TAMPON,CDELTA)
      CALL HECINV(YY,NA1,TAMPON,CDELTA)
  300 CONTINUE
* Save results for S21
      IF(NTS.GT.0)WRITE(11)F,YY(1,1),YY(2,2),YY(1,2)
      IF(NTS.EQ.0)WRITE(11)F,YY(1,1),(0.,0.),(0.,0.)
* Matching network
      DO 310 IA=1,NA1
  310 YY(IA,IA)=YY(IA,IA)+CMPLX(0.,SELF(IA)*OMEGA)
* Normalised coefficients
      DO 320 IA=1,NA1
      DO 320 IB=1,NA1
  320 YY(IA,IB)=YY(IA,IB)
     &/SQRT(RESIST(IA))/SQRT(RESIST(IB))
      IF(JADA(NTE+1).EQ.999)YY(1,2)=YY(1,2)*SQRT(F/FZERO)
      RETURN
      END
      SUBROUTINE SUPRIM(A,N,K,NDIM)
      COMPLEX A(NDIM,NDIM)
      IF(K.GE.N)RETURN
      DO 10 I=K+1,N
      I1=I-1
      DO 10 J=1,N
   10 A(I1,J)=A(I,J)
      DO 20 J=K+1,N
      J1=J-1
      DO 20 I=1,N-1
   20 A(I,J1)=A(I,J)
      RETURN
      END
*Compute exact size of electrodes
      SUBROUTINE CALPEI(LT,KJK,IMPLE,K1,TAU,A,N,YTOP,YBOT
     &,SIG,ITYPE,W,E)
      REAL TAU(1),A(1),YTOP(1),YBOT(1)
      INTEGER IMPLE(1), KJK(1)
      T1=TAU(K1);TMAX=T1;TMIN=T1;DTMIN=1.E20
      IF(N.LE.1)GO TO 3
      DO 2 L=2,N
      K=K1+L-1
      T2=TAU(K)
      TMAX=AMAX1(T2,TMAX)
      TMIN=AMIN1(T2,TMIN)
      DTMIN=AMIN1(DTMIN,T2-T1)
    2 T1=T2
    3 T0=0.5*(TMAX+TMIN)
      ITYPE=1
      IF(DTMIN.GT.1.)GO TO 500
      IF(IMPLE(LT).GT.1)GO TO 500
```

```
      AA=A(K1)/2.;BA=ABS(AA)
      J=0;YK=-BA;YK1=-BA
      YTOP(K1)=BA
      YBOT(K1)=-BA
      IS=-1;KJK(K1)=0
      IF(SIG.GT.0.)GO TO 8
      YK=BA;YK1=BA;IS=1
    8 CONTINUE
      IF(N.LE.1)GO TO 35
      DO 30 L=2,N
      K=L+K1-1
      IF(A(K)*AA.GE.0.)GO TO 10
      J=J+IS
      GO TO 20
   10 IS=-IS
   20 YK=YK+IS*ABS(A(K))
      KJK(K)=J
      YTOP(K)=AMAX1(YK,YK1)
      YBOT(K)=AMIN1(YK,YK1)
      AA=A(K)
   30 YK1=YK
   35 NBITER=20
      YMAX=BA;YMIN=-BA
      DELTA=E*(YMAX-YMIN)
      DO 50 ITER=1,NBITER
      YMAX=BA;YMIN=-BA
      DELTA1=DELTA
      DO 40 L=1,N
      K=L+K1-1
      YMAX=AMAX1(YMAX,YTOP(K)+KJK(K)*DELTA)
      YMIN=AMIN1(YMIN,YBOT(K)+KJK(K)*DELTA)
   40 CONTINUE
      DELTA=E*(YMAX-YMIN)
   50 IF(ABS((DELTA1-DELTA)/DELTA1).LT.1.E-4)GO TO 100
      PRINT:"<<<<<<<<   ERROR : gap too big   >>>>>>>>"
  100 YMOYEN=0.5*(YMAX+YMIN)
      R=W/(YMAX-YMIN)
      DELTA=R*DELTA;YMOYEN=R*YMOYEN
      DO 110 L=1,N
      K=L+K1-1
      YTOP(K)=YTOP(K)*R-YMOYEN+KJK(K)*DELTA
      YBOT(K)=YBOT(K)*R-YMOYEN+KJK(K)*DELTA
  110 CONTINUE
      GO TO 600
  500 YMAX=ABS(A(K1))
      ITYPE=2
      IF(N.LE.1)GO TO 515
      DO 510 L=2,N
      K=L+K1-1
      YK=ABS(A(K))
  510 YMAX=AMAX1(YMAX,YK)
  515 R=W/YMAX
      DO 520 L=1,N
      K=L+K1-1
      YTOP(K)=ABS(A(K))*R/2.
      YBOT(K)=-ABS(A(K))*R/2.
  520 CONTINUE
  600 S=-1.
      IF(A(1).LT.0.)S=-S
      DO 610 L=1,N
      K=L+K1-1
      S=-S
      A(K)=S*R*A(K)
  610 CONTINUE
      RETURN
      END
      SUBROUTINE ARCTA(Z,ANGLE)
      COMPLEX Z
      X=REAL(Z)
```

```
      Y=AIMAG(Z)
      PI=3.14159265
      IF(X) 10,30,20
   10 ANGLE=ATAN(Y/X)+PI*SIGN(1.,Y)
      RETURN
   20 ANGLE=ATAN(Y/X)
      RETURN
   30 IF(Y)40,60,50
   40 ANGLE=-PI/2.
      RETURN
   50 ANGLE=PI/2.
      RETURN
   60 ANGLE=0.
      RETURN
      END
      SUBROUTINE SUPCAPA(TAU,A,YTOP,YBOT,P,
     & JADA,IMPLE,NT,SEUIL,T,RT,MDIM,NDIM)
      DIMENSION NT(1), TAU(1),A(1),YTOP(1),YBOT(1),P(1)
     &,JADA(1),IMPLE(1),T(1),RT(NDIM,MDIM)
      COMMON/DONNEE/NU,RZERO,NTOT,NTTOT,NTE,NTS,NREF
     &,FZERO,DF,DELTA,AK2,DB,MINAL
      JNT=0;K2=0;KN=NTOT
      DO 200 KT=1,NTTOT
      N=NT(KT);K1=K2+1;K2=K2+N
      IF(IMPLE(KT).LE.0)GO TO 200
      DO 190 IC=1,2
      IFAI=0;KN1=KN
      DO 180 K=K1,K2
      GO TO (30,40),IC
   30 AA=0.5-YTOP(K);GO TO 50
   40 AA=YBOT(K)+0.5
   50 IF(ABS(AA).LT.SEUIL)GO TO 100
      IF(IFAI.EQ.0)JNT=JNT+1;IFAI=1
      KN=KN+1;TAU(KN)=TAU(K);P(KN)=ABS(AA);A(KN)=AA
      T(KN)=TAU(KN);RT(KN,NTTOT+JNT)=A(KN)
      GO TO (60,70),IC
   60 YTOP(KN)=0.5;YBOT(KN)=YTOP(K);GO TO 100
   70 YBOT(KN)=-0.5;YTOP(KN)=YBOT(K)
  100 IF(IMPLE(KT).LE.1)GO TO 180
      IF(K.EQ.K2)GO TO 190
      YH=AMAX1(YTOP(K),YTOP(K+1))
      YB=AMIN1(YTOP(K),YTOP(K+1))
      L=1-MOD(K-K1,2)
      IF(A(K1).LT.0)L=1-L
      IVA=1+MOD(IC+L,2)
      GO TO (110,120),IVA
  110 AA=0.5-YB;GO TO 130
  120 AA=0.5+YH
  130 IF(ABS(AA).LT.SEUIL)GO TO 190
      KN=KN+1
      IF(IFAI.EQ.0)JNT=JNT+1;IFAI=1
      TAU(KN)=0.5*(TAU(K)+TAU(K+1))
      A(KN)=AA;P(KN)=ABS(AA)
      T(KN)=TAU(KN);RT(KN,NTTOT+JNT)=A(KN)
      GO TO (140,150),IC
  140 YTOP(KN)=0.5;YBOT(KN)=0.5-AA;GO TO 180
  150 YTOP(KN)=AA-0.5;YBOT(KN)=-0.5
  180 CONTINUE
      IF(IFAI.EQ.0)GO TO 190
      NKT=NTTOT+JNT
      NT(NKT)=KN-KN1
      JADA(NKT)=-1
      IMPLE(NKT)=0
  190 CONTINUE
  200 CONTINUE
      NTOT=KN
      NREF=NREF+JNT
      NTTOT=NTTOT+JNT
      RETURN
      END
```

Appendix H

S_{21}

Computation of the transfer function of SAW delay lines.

```
*#RUN *;/LIBRARY/TEMPS,R;/LIBRARY/COUVIS,R;
*#/LIBRARY/ATAFIC,R=(ULIB)SERVICE/YT4010,R
*Computation of the transfert function of SAW delay lines
*This programme needs additional routine COUVIS for
graphics
*and ATAFIC to manage files
*TEMPS is used to monitor time processor and memory
      COMPLEX Z(2),Y(2),Z12,Y12,S21
      COMPLEX DELTA
      REAL C(2),RP(2),CP1(2),CP2(2),LP(2),RG(2)
      REAL Q(2)
      REAL X(61),YY(61)
      CHARACTER REP
      PI=3.141592654
      CALL TEMPS
    1 PRINT:"   ***    TRANSFER FUNCTION OF A SAW DELAY"
     &," LINE  ***"
      IFAI=0
      PRINT:"---   Description :"
      PRINT:"   0 = STOP"
      PRINT:"   1 = Single regular transducer"
      PRINT:"   2 = Regular delay line"
      PRINT:"   3 = Output file from routine MAREFOS"
      PRINT:"   4 = Consistent outputs from "
     &,"MAREFOS1+MAREFOS2"
      NTS=1
      READ:ICAS;IF(ICAS.LE.0)GO TO 999
      IF(ICAS.GE.3)GO TO 300
   10 PRINT:"Frequency (MHz) ?"
      READ:F ; IF (F.LE.0.)GO TO 1
      F=1.E6*F ; OMEGA0=2.*PI*F
      IF(ICAS.NE.2)GO TO 20
      PRINT:"Distance between transducers (in LAMBDAs) ?"
      READ:D
   20 PRINT:"Radiation resistance R0 (OHMS) ?"
      READ:R0
      IF(R0.LE.0.)GO TO 10
   30 PRINT:"---    Active capacitances:"
      IF(ICAS.LT.3)GO TO 32
      IF(IFAI.GE.1)GO TO 35
      C(1)=RZERO*2.*C1*FZERO/R0/F
      C(2)=RZERO*2.*C2*FZERO/R0/F
      PRINT:"C1=",C(1)*1.E12," pF"
      CC=C(1)
      PRINT:"Matching for L=",1./CC/OMEGA0**2*1.E9," nH"
      IF(JADA2.EQ.999)GO TO 35
      IF(NTS.LE.0)GO TO 35
      PRINT:"C2=",C(2)*1.E12,"  pF"
      CC=C(2)
      PRINT:"Matching for L=",1./CC/OMEGA0**2*1.E9," NH"
      GO TO 35
   32 CONTINUE
      PRINT:"Port 1 : C1 (pF) ?"
      READ:C(1) ; IF(C(1).LE.0.)GO TO 20
      C(1)=C(1)*1.E-12
      CC=C(1)
      PRINT:"Matching for L=",1./CC/OMEGA0**2*1.E9," NH"
      IF(ICAS.EQ.1)GO TO 35
```

```
      PRINT:"Port 2 : C2 (pF) ?"
      READ:C(2);IF(C(2).LE.0.)GO TO 30
      C(2)=C(2)*1.E-12
      CC=C(2)
      PRINT:"Matching for L=",1./CC/OMEGA0**2*1.E9," nH"
   35 PRINT:" "
      DO 50 I=1,2
      CP1(I)=0.;CP2(I)=0.;RP(I)=0.;LP(I)=0.;Q(I)=1.E6
   50 CONTINUE
   40 PRINT:"---   ADDITIONAL OR PARASITIC COMPONENTS"
     &," (yes/no) ?"
      READ:REP;IF (REP.EQ."yes")REP="YES"
      IF(IFAI.EQ.1.AND.REP.NE."YES")GO TO 1
      IF(ICAS.GE.3)IFAI=1
      IF(REP.NE."YES")GO TO 105
      I1=2
      IF(ICAS.EQ.1)I1=1
      IF(JADA2.EQ.999)I1=1
      IF(NTS.EQ.0)I1=1
      DO 100 I=1,I1
      IF(I1-I.EQ.1)PRINT:"---    Port 1   ---"
      IF(I.EQ.2)PRINT:"---    Port 2   ---"
      PRINT:"Finger resistance (OHMS) ?"
      READ:RP(I)
      PRINT:"Shunt capacitance (pF) ?"
      READ:CP1(I);CP1(I)=CP1(I)*1.E-12
      PRINT:"Series inductance (nH) ?"
      READ:LP(I);LP(I)=1.E-9*LP(I)
      PRINT:"Q coefficient ?"
      READ:Q(I);IF(Q(I).LE.0.)Q(I)=1.E4
      PRINT:"Last shunt capacitance (pF) ?"
      READ:CP2(I);CP2(I)=1.E-12*CP2(I)
  100 PRINT:" "
  105 CONTINUE
      PRINT:"---   Load and generator resistances :"
      PRINT:"Port 1 : RG1 (OHMS) ?"
      READ:RG(1)
      RG(2)=2.*R0
      IF(ICAS.EQ.1)GO TO 106
      IF(JADA2.EQ.999)GO TO 106
      IF(NTS.EQ.0)GO TO 106
      PRINT:"Port 2 : RG2 (OHMS) ?"
      READ:RG(2)
  106 PRINT:"========================================="
      IF(ICAS.EQ.2)PRINT 9002,
      IF(ICAS.GE.3)PRINT 9003,
      IF(ICAS.EQ.1)PRINT 9003,
      IF(ICAS.EQ.1)NP=1
      IF(ICAS.EQ.2)NP=21
      IF(ICAS.EQ.1)DDF=1.
      IF(ICAS.EQ.2)DDF=0.5/D/(NP-1)*F
      IF(ICAS.GT.2)DDF=DF*F/FZERO
      DO 200 K=1,NP
      IF(ICAS.GE.3)GO TO 115
      OMEGA=OMEGA0
      TETA=0
      IF(NP.GT.1) TETA=PI*(K-1)/(NP-1)
      CO=COS(TETA);SI=-SIN(TETA)
      IF(ICAS.EQ.1)GO TO 111
      Z12=R0*CMPLX(CO,SI)
      DO 110 I=1,2
  110 Z(I)=R0+1./CMPLX(0.,C(I)*OMEGA)
      GO TO 116
  111 Z(1)=2.*R0+1./CMPLX(0.,C(1)*OMEGA)
      Z(2)=2.*R0 ; Z12=2.*R0
      GO TO 116
  115 READ(11)FRE,Z(1),Z(2),Z12
      OMEGA=(FRE/FZERO)*OMEGA0
      Z(1)=Z(1)*R0/RZERO;Z(2)=Z(2)*R0/RZERO
```

```
      Z12=Z12*R0/RZERO
      IF(ICAS.GT.3)GO TO 114
      IF((JADA2.NE.999).AND.(NTS.NE.0))GO TO 114
      Z(2)=R0*FZERO/FRE
      RG(2)=2.*R0*FZERO/FRE
      IF(NTS.EQ.0)Z12=SQRT(REAL(Z(1)*Z(2)))
      Y12=Z(1)*Z(2)-Z12*Z12
      Z(1)=2.*Z(1)-Y12/Z(2)
      Z(2)=2.*Z(2)
      Z12=2.*Z12
  114 IF(ICAS.LT.4)GO TO 116
      READ(12)FRE,Z(2),Y(1),Y12
      Z(2)=Z(2)*R0/RZERO1
      Z12=Z12*Y12/RZERO1*(OMEGA/OMEGA0)
  116 Z(1)=Z(1)+RP(1)
      X(K)=OMEGA
      Z(2)=Z(2)+RP(2)
      CALL INV(Z,Z12,Y,Y12)
      DO 120 I=1,2
  120 Y(I)=Y(I)+CMPLX(0.,CP1(I)*OMEGA)
      CALL INV(Y,Y12,Z,Z12)
      DO 130 I=1,2
      XX=LP(I)*OMEGA
      RR=XX/Q(I)
  130 Z(I)=Z(I)+CMPLX(RR,XX)
      CALL INV(Z,Z12,Y,Y12)
      DO 140 I=1,2
  140 Y(I)=Y(I)+CMPLX(0.,CP2(I)*OMEGA)
      CALL INV(Y,Y12,Z,Z12)
      DO 150 I=1,2
  150 Z(I)=Z(I)/RG(I)
      Z12=Z12/SQRT(RG(1)*RG(2))
      DELTA=(Z(1)+1.)*(Z(2)+1.)-Z12**2
      S21=2.*Z12/DELTA
      CALL ARCTA(S21,FASE)
      IF(K.EQ.1)FASE1=FASE
      IF(NTS.EQ.0)GO TO 170
  160 IF(FASE1.LT.FASE)FASE1=FASE1+2.*PI
      IF(FASE1.LT.FASE)GO TO 160
  170 TPG=(FASE1-FASE)/DDF/2./PI
      FASE1=FASE
      FASE=FASE*180./PI
      S21L=CABS(S21)
      S21DB=20.*ALOG10(S21L)
      IF(ICAS.EQ.2) DF=TETA/2./PI/D*F*1.E-6
      IF(ICAS.EQ.1)DF=F*1.E-6
      IF(ICAS.GE.3)DF=FRE/FZERO*F*1.E-6
      YY(K)=S21DB
  200 PRINT 9001,DF,S21L,S21DB,FASE,1.E9*TPG
      PRINT:"========================================="
      IF(ICAS.GE.3)REWIND(11)
      IF(ICAS.GE.4)REWIND(12)
      PRINT:" "
      IF(ICAS.GE.3)GO TO 210
      GO TO 30
  210 PRINT:"Plot of the graphical response (yes/no) ?"
      READ:REP;IF (REP.EQ."yes")REP="YES"
      IF(REP.NE."YES")GO TO 310
*Use the graphical routine "COUVIS"
      CALL COUVIS(X,YY,NP)
      GO TO 310
  999 CALL TEMPS;STOP"Bye"
  300 IF(ICAS.GT.3)PRINT:"MAREFOS 1"
      CALL ATAFIC(11,1)
      IFAI=0
  310 READ(11)NP,FZERO,DF,RZERO,JADA1,JADA2,NTS
      READ(11)C1,RG1
      IF(NTS.GT.0)READ(11)C2,RG2
      IF(ICAS.LT.4)GO TO 400
```

```
        IF(IFAI.EQ.1)GO TO 320
        IF(JADA2.NE.999)GO TO 500
        PRINT:"MAREFOS 2"
*Open file 12
        CALL ATAFIC(12,1)
        IFAI=0
  320 READ(12)NP1,FZERO1,DF1,RZERO1,JADA11,JADA12,NTS1
        READ(12)C2,RG2
        READ(12)CC1,RRG1
        JADA2=0
        IF(NP1.NE.NP)GO TO 600
        IF(ABS(FZERO-FZERO1).GT.1.E-6)GO TO 600
        IF(ABS(DF1-DF).GT.1.E-6)GO TO 600
  400 IF(IFAI.EQ.1)GO TO 35
        IF(JADA2.EQ.999)PRINT:"Acoustical output"
        IF(NTS.EQ.0)PRINT:"Single transducer"
      &," / Acoustical output"
        PRINT:"F=",FZERO
        GO TO 10
  500 PRINT:"ILLEGAL FILE"
        GO TO 1
  600 PRINT:"Non consistent files"
        GO TO 1
 9001 FORMAT(2F10.4,3F10.2)
 9003 FORMAT(4X," F (MHZ)",4X,"S21",4X,
      &"S21 (dB)    DEGRES      nS")
 9002 FORMAT(4X,"DF (MHZ)",4X,"S21",4X,
      &"S21 (dB)    DEGRES      nS")
        END
        SUBROUTINE INV(Z,Z12,Y,Y12)
        COMPLEX Z(2),Z12,Y(2),Y12
        COMPLEX D
        D=Z(1)*Z(2)-Z12*Z12
        Y(1)=Z(2)/D
        Y(2)=Z(1)/D
        Y12=-Z12/D
        RETURN
        END
        SUBROUTINE ARCTA(Z,ANGLE)
        COMPLEX Z
        X=REAL(Z)
        Y=AIMAG(Z)
        PI=3.14159265
        IF(X) 10,30,20
   10 ANGLE=ATAN(Y/X)+PI*SIGN(1.,Y)
        RETURN
   20 ANGLE=ATAN(Y/X)
        RETURN
   30 IF(Y)40,60,50
   40 ANGLE=-PI/2.
        RETURN
   50 ANGLE=PI/2.
        RETURN
   60 ANGLE=0.
        RETURN
        END
```

Appendix I

AMPLIF

Computation of acousto-electric gain & saturation.

```
*Computation of acousto-electric gain & saturation
      COMMON/CGA/AMU,VA,OMEGA,EPSS,EPSI,EPSP,EPS,K
     &,SIGMA,T1,T2,N,GL,AK2,ETA
      COMMON/CSA/SIGMAD,EPS0,PSAT,AA,DBKV,VV,PP
      COMMON/LIKI/ATEN
      COMPLEX CMPLX,ZEPS,Z1,ZK
      REAL K
      CHARACTER REPONSE
      TH(X)=1.-2.*EXP(-2.*X)/(1.+EXP(-2.*X))
   10 PRINT:"Frequency (MHz) ?"
      READ:F
      IF(F.LE.0.)STOP
      F=F*1.E6
      PRINT:"Acoustic velocity (m/s) ?"
      READ:VA
      PI=3.141592653
      EPS0=1./4/PI/9.E9
      OMEGA=2.*PI*F
      K=OMEGA/VA
      PRINT : "--- DESCRIPTION OF THE DEVICE ---"
      PRINT:" "
      PRINT:" External medium:"
      PRINT:"Relative dielectric constant ?"
      READ:EPS
   20 PRINT:" "
      PRINT:"Next layer :"
      PRINT:"Relative dielectric constant ?"
      READ:EPS1
      IF(EPS1.LE.0.)GO TO 30
      PRINT:"Thickness (ANGSTROEM) ?"
      READ:H
      H=H*1.E-10
      T=TH(K*H)
      EPS=EPS1*(EPS+EPS1*T)/(EPS*T+EPS1)
      GO TO 20
   30 PRINT:" "
      PRINT:"External permittivity =",EPS
      PRINT:" "
      PRINT:"***   SEMI-CONDUCTOR:"
      PRINT:"Dielectric constant ?"
      READ:EPSS
      PRINT:"Product SIGMA*D (MICRO-MHO) ?"
      READ:SIGMAD
      IF(SIGMAD.GT.0.)GO TO 35
      PRINT:"RESISTIVITY (OHM CM) ?"
      READ:RAU
      PRINT:"D (MM) ?"
      READ:D
      D=0.1*D
      SIGMAD=D/RAU
      PRINT:"SIGMA.D=",SIGMAD*1.E6," MICRO-MHO"
      D=1.E-2*D
      GO TO 42
   35 CONTINUE
      PRINT:"D (ANGSTROEM) ?"
      READ:D
      D=D*1.E-10
      SIGMAD=SIGMAD*1.E-6
```

```
 42 CONTINUE
    PRINT:"MOBILITY (CM2/VS) ?"
    READ:AMU
    AMU=AMU*1.E-4
    SIGMA=SIGMAD/D/EPSO
    PRINT:" "
    PRINT:"Intermediate layer:"
    PRINT:"Dielectric constant ?"
    READ:EPSI
    PRINT:"H (ANGSTROEM) ?"
    READ:H
    H=H*1.E-10
    PRINT:" "
    PRINT:"***   Piezoelectric substrate:"
    PRINT:"Dielectric constant ?"
    READ:EPSP
    PRINT:"Coupling K2 (%) ?"
    READ:AK2
    AK2=AK2/100.
    PRINT:"Decay coefficient  (DB/LAMBDA) ?"
    READ:ATTE
    ATEN=ATTE*F/VA
    PRINT:"=",ATEN*1.E-2," DB/CM"
    ATEN=ATEN*ALOG(10.)/20.
    PRINT:"RAYLEIGH (1)  OR  BLEUSTEIN (2) ?"
    READ:N
 55 CONTINUE
    PRINT:"GAIN (yes/no) ?"
    READ:REPONSE;IF(REPONSE.EQ."yes")REPONSE="YES"
    IF(REPONSE.EQ."YES")PRINT:" "
    IF(REPONSE.EQ."YES")PRINT:"   ***   GAIN VERSUS"
   &," ELECTRICAL FIELD   ***"
    IF(REPONSE.EQ."YES")PRINT:"  KV/CM"
   &,"            DB/CM"
    T1=TH(D*K)
    T2=TH(H*K)
    GSSD=N*OMEGA*EPSP*EPSO*AK2*AMU/SIGMAD/2./VA
    GSSDB=GSSD*1000.*20./ALOG(10.)
    DO 100 I=1,11
    E=(I-6.)/2.5
    LL=1
    IF(I.EQ.5.OR.I.EQ.6)LL=4
    DE=0.4/LL
    E=E-DE
    DO 100 J=1,LL
    E=E+DE
    VOLT=1000.*E
    GL=1.E-2
    GAIN=GAINP(VOLT)
    GAIN=GAIN*20./ALOG(10.)
    IF(ETA.GT.0..OR.ETAR.LT.0.)GO TO 50
    DBKV=(GR-GAIN)/(E-ER)
 50 CONTINUE
    ETAR=ETA
    ER=E
    GR=GAIN
    IF(REPONSE.EQ."YES")PRINT 1,E,-GAIN
100 CONTINUE
    EC=VA/AMU*1.E-5
    PRINT:"***"
    AK2E=AK2*DBKV/GSSDB
    PRINT:"EFFECTIVE K2 =",AK2E*100.," %"
    PRINT:"GAIN= ",DBKV," DB/KV"
    PRINT:"CRITICAL FIELD = ",EC," KV/CM"
    PRINT:" "
110 CONTINUE
    PRINT:"SATURATION (yes/no) ?"
    READ:REPONSE;IF(REPONSE.EQ."yes")REPONSE="YES"
    IF(REPONSE.EQ."YES")CALL SATURE
```

```
      IF(ABS(EPSI-1.).GT.0.)GO TO 10
      PRINT:"New air gap :"
      PRINT:"H (ANGSTROEM) ?"
      READ:H
      IF(H.LE.0.)GO TO 10
      H=H*1.E-10
      GO TO 55
    1 FORMAT(1X,F8.3,F16.1)
      END
      FUNCTION GAINP(VOLT)
      COMMON/CGA/AMU,VA,OMEGA,EPSS,EPSI,EPSP,EPS,
     &K,SIGMA,T1,T2,N,GL,AK2,ETA
      COMMON/LIKI/ATEN
      COMPLEX CMPLX,ZEPS,Z1,ZK
      REAL K
      V0=AMU*VOLT/GL
      ETA=1.-V0/VA
      OMEGAD=OMEGA*ETA
      ZEPS=EPSS+CMPLX(0.,SIGMA/OMEGAD)
      Z1=ZEPS*(EPS+ZEPS*T1)/(EPS*T1+ZEPS)
      ZEPS=EPSI*(Z1+EPSI*T2)/(Z1*T2+EPSI)
      ZK=AK2/(1.+EPSP/ZEPS)**N/2.
      GAINP=AIMAG(ZK)*K*GL
      GAINP=GAINP+ATEN*GL
      RETURN
      END
      SUBROUTINE SATURE
      COMMON/CGA/AMU,VA,OMEGA,EPSS,EPSI,EPSP,EPS,K,
     &SIGMA,T1,T2,N,GL,AK2,ETA
      COMMON/CSA/SIGMAD,EPS0,PSAT,A,DBKV,V,P
      LOGICAL OK
      EXTERNAL EQ
      REAL K,L,DB(7,36)
      PRINT:"Length of the layer (CM) ?"
      READ:GL
      GL=GL/100.
      PRINT:"Width (MM) ?"
      READ:L
      L=L/1000.
      V0=VA*GL/AMU
      PRINT:"V0=",V0," V"
      R=GL/L/SIGMAD
      PRINT:"OHMIC RESISTANCE OF THE LAYER = ",R," OHMS"
      A=R*AMU/VA/GL
      PRINT:"VAE=",A," V/W"
      GAE=DBKV*A/1000.
      PRINT:"GAE=",GAE," DB/W"
      PRINT:" New GAE ?"
      READ:GAEM
      IF(GAEM.GT.0.)A=1000.*GAEM/DBKV
      PSAT=(SIGMAD/AMU)**2*L*VA**2/AK2/EPSP/EPS0/OMEGA/N
      PSATDB=10.*ALOG10(1000.*PSAT)
      PRINT:"PSAT=",PSATDB," DBM"
      PRINT:"New PSAT ?"
      READ:PS1
      IF(PS1.GT.0.)PSAT=0.001*10.**(PS1/10.)
*
      PRINT:"Initial voltage ? (VOLTS)"
      READ:VD
      IERR=0
      DO 200 J=1,7
      V=100.*(J-1)
      V=VD+V
      DO 100 I=1,36
      DBM=-52.+2.*I
      P=1.E-3*10.**(DBM/10.)
      G1=-10.
      G2=0.5*ALOG(PSAT/P)
      G2=G2-1.E-4
```

```
      IF(G2.LE.0.)G1=G2-10.
      G=SOLX(EQ,G1,G2,1.E-6,1.E-6,50,OK)
      IF(.NOT.OK)IERR=IERR+1
  50  PAC=P*EXP(2.*G)
      DBM1=10.*ALOG10(PAC*1000.)
 100  DB(J,I)=DBM1
 200  CONTINUE
      PRINT:"Computation completed : ",IERR," ERRORS"
      PRINT:"                        DBM(OUTPUT) "
     &,"FOR V=(KV)"
      VD=VD/1000.
      PRINT 2,(VD+(I-1)/10.,I=1,7)
      PRINT 1,(((-52.+2.*I),(DB(J,I),J=1,7)),I=1,36)
      RETURN
  1   FORMAT(8F8.2)
  2   FORMAT("   DBMO ",7F8.2)
      END
      FUNCTION EQ(G)
      COMMON/CSA/SIGMAD,EPSO,PSAT,A,DBKV,V,P
      X=P*EXP(2.*G)
      DP=X/(1.-X/PSAT)
      VOLT=V-A*DP
      GAIN=GAINP(VOLT)
      EQ=G+GAIN
      RETURN
      END
      REAL FUNCTION SOLX(FONC,XIN,XSU,XEPS,YEPS,ITER,OK)
      REAL Z(3),F(3),D(3),ZN,ZD,FONC
      REAL A(3)
      LOGICAL OK
      EXTERNAL FONC
      OK=.TRUE.
      Z(1)=(2.*XIN+XSU)/3.
      Z(2)=(XIN+2.*XSU)/3.
      Z(3)=(XIN+XSU)/2.
      ZG=(Z(1)+Z(2)+Z(3))/3.
      DO 10 I=1,3
      F(I)=FONC(Z(I))
  10  A(I)=ABS(F(I))
      DO 100 JTER=1,ITER
      K=1
      X=Z(K)
      GF=0.
      DO 40 I=1,3
      IF(A(I).LT.GF)GO TO 20
      GF=A(I)
      K=I
  20  GO TO (25,30,35),I
  25  I1=2
      I2=3
      GO TO 40
  30  I1=3
      I2=1
      GO TO 40
  35  I1=1
      I2=2
  40  D(I)=(Z(I1)-Z(I2))*F(I1)*F(I2)
      ZN=0.
      ZD=0.
      DO 50 I=1,3
      ZN=ZN+D(I)*Z(I)
  50  ZD=ZD+D(I)
      IF(ABS(ZD).LE.0..AND.DY.LT.YEPS)GO TO 200
      IF(ABS(ZD).LE.0.)GO TO 60
      ZN=ZN/ZD
      X=ZN
  60  CONTINUE
      IF(X.GT.XSU)X=XSU
      IF(X.LT.XIN)X=XIN
```

```
      Z(K)=X
      F(K)=FONC(Z(K))
      A(K)=ABS(F(K))
      DY=A(K)
      IF(DY.LE.0.)GO TO 200
      DX=ABS(ZG-Z(K))
      ZG=Z(K)
  100 IF(DX.LT.XEPS.AND.DY.LT.YEPS)GO TO 200
      SOLX=0.
      OK=.FALSE.
      RETURN
  200 SOLX=Z(K)
      RETURN
      END
```

Appendix J

SURFTSS

Computation of piezoelectric velocities in arbitrary orientation and temperature.

```
*#RUN *;/LIBRARY/SURBINSP,R;/LIBRARY/CONVER,R;
*#SERVICE/POLRTS,R;/LIBRARY/TEMPS,R=
*#(ULIB,BCD)/MF/SPPSI,R;SERVICE/HEMP,R#
*#/LIBRARY/MATERIAU"05",R;06
************** SURFTSS **********************
* Computation of SAW/BAW velocities of various crystals
*Table of characteristic constants are stored in file
*/LIBRARY/MATERIAU
*User library routines are stored in files SURBINSP,
* CONVER, TEMPS, SPPSI
*Two additionnal system routines are used :
* POLRTS to extract real roots from polynomials
* and HEMP to solve linear complex systems
      CHARACTER REP
      REAL GAM(3,6),ET(3,3),EP(3),P0(5,6)
     & ,Q(5,6),CL(4,4),DL(4,4)
     & ,R(3,3),EINI(3,6),CINI(6,6),EPSINI(3,3),VV(3)
     & ,XC(3),XD(3),XT(3),V2(2,9)
      REAL XX1(4,2),XX2(4,2),XXZ(4,2)
      REAL EPS2(2),RES2(2)
      REAL VVV(4,2),DBDB(4,2),VVV2(4),BBB(4),KAPA2(4)
      REAL WW(10)
      INTEGER NM(2),IINDIC(4,2)
      INTEGER LL(2)
      EXTERNAL PHI,PSI
      COMPLEX PHI,Z,Z1,ZSU,ZIN,CSOLZ
      COMPLEX PSI,RESIDU,ZRAC(4,2),XZERO
      COMPLEX CMPLX,IMPED,ADMIT
      COMMON R,EINI,CINI,EPSINI,RAU,ALINI
      COMMON/MATERIAU/MATER
      COMMON/COMPHI/P0,Q,GAM,ET,EP,CL,DL,METAL,DECOUP
      COMMON/IMPRI/TEST,VV1,DAC,ESSAI,LENT,PIEZO,KRAC
      COMMON/COMY/KY,EPSTBF,EPSBF,VVV,DBDB,MODIF
     &,XX1,XX2,AM
      COMMON/JAC/EPSHF,VVV2,BBB,KAPA2
      COMMON/TAMP1/OK,META,PRECIS,EPZERO,IVOL,PI,INTERV
      COMMON/TAMP2/VOU,AOU,IOU,DBOU,AK2,COUPLA,VCC
     &,ACC,ICC,DBCC,SIGMA,VV
      COMMON/TAMP3/BI,BS,ITER,XEPS,YEPS,NBMODE ,PSEUDO
     & ,PSESLT,NBPSEU
```

```
        COMMON/TAMP3/ VMIN,VMAX ,EPSI,JTER
        COMMON/TAMP4/JSOR
        COMMON /TAMP5/WW
        COMMON/DECAPSI/YDECA
        LOGICAL TEST,DAC,ESSAI,LENT,PIEZO
        LOGICAL PSEUDO,PSESLT,EOR
        LOGICAL DAC1,DAC2,DAC3,EC,RC,ECROIT,RCROIT
        INTEGER DECOUP
        LOGICAL META(2),METAL,OK
        LOGICAL RCRT(2),ECRT(2)
        DATE=0
        OK=.FALSE.
        BI=0.6
        BS=1.
        INTERV=1
        ITER=20
        XEPS=1.E-6
        YEPS=1.E-4
        PSEUDO=.TRUE.
        PSESLT=.FALSE.;NBPSEU=10
        VMIN=0.6
        VMAX=1.3
        PIEZO=TEST
        PI=3.141592653
        AM=40.*PI/ALOG(10.)
        EPZERO=0.
        PRECIS=.1E-6
        EPSI=.1E-4
        JTER=ITER*2/3
        META(1)=.TRUE.
        META(2)=.FALSE.
        CALL TEMPS
        PRINT:
       &"    ***    COMPUTATION OF SAW/BAW VELOCITIES    ***"
        PRINT:
      1 PRINT:"CRYSTAL NAME   ?"
        NPTO=1
        READ 9041,MATER
*Read the data file MATERIAU
        CALL LECTT(MAT)
        PRINT:"Number of branches to be computed ?"
        PRINT:"or RETURN for bulk waves"
        READ:NBMODE
*Surface waves: IVOL=0 ; Bulk waves: IVOL=1
        IVOL=0
        YDECA=0
        IF(NBMODE.EQ.0)IVOL=1
        JSOR=1
        PRINT:
       &"CENTER TEMPERATURE OF COMPUTATION (DEGREES C)?"
        READ:TTZ
        PRINT:"VARIATION OF TEMPERATURE"
       &," +dT TO -dT: dT (DEGREES C) ?"
        NBTT=0.;READ:DTT;IF(DTT.LE.0.)GOTO 10
        PRINT:"TOTAL NUMBER OF SAMPLES ?"
        READ:NBTT
     10 NBTT=(NBTT/2)*2+1
        NPTO=NPTO*NBTT
        PRINT:" "
        PRINT:"Nominal orientation as reference ----------"
        CALL CONVER(XC,XD)
        PRINT:"Defining the orientation set to be computed"
        PRINT:"--- Exploring the cut plane ---"
        PRINT:"Departure from the reference (DEGREES) ?"
        READ:TETAI
        PRINT:"Half angle to be explored (DEGREES) ?"
        READ:ANGLE
        PRINT:"Total number of samples ?"
        READ:MIPT;MIPT=MIPT/2
```

```
      NPTO=NPTO*(2*MIPT+1)
      PRINT:" "
      PRINT:"--- Rotating the cut plane ---"
      PRINT:"Departure from the reference (DEGREES) ?"
      READ:TETA0
      PRINT:"Half angle to be explored (DEGREES) ?"
      READ:TTETA
      PRINT:"Total number of samples ?"
      READ:NBNRC;NBNRC=(NBNRC/2)*2+1
      NPTO=NPTO*NBNRC
      PRINT:" "
      PRINT:"--- Rotating the normal ---"
      PRINT:"Departure from the reference (DEGREES) ?"
      READ:TETAN
      PRINT:"Half angle to be explored (DEGREES) ?"
      READ:DTN
      PRINT:"Total number of samples?"
      READ:NBN;NBN=(NBN/2)*2+1
      NPTO=NPTO*NBN
      TEST=.FALSE.;IF(NPTO.EQ.1)TEST=.TRUE.
      PIEZO=TEST
      NB PT=2*MI PT+1
 9001 FORMAT(1X,22HCUT            (X,Y,Z,) )
 9002 FORMAT(3G13.6)
 9003 FORMAT(1X,12HPROPAGATION )
 9004 FORMAT(1X,5HTHANK )
 9005 FORMAT(1X,11HHALF ANGLE )
 9006 FORMAT(G13.6)
 9007 FORMAT(1X,23HHALF NUMBER OF SAMPLES )
 9008 FORMAT(I2)
      CALL NORMA(XC)
      CALL PVEC(XC,XD,XT)
      CALL NORMA(XT)
      CALL PVEC(XT,XC,XD)
      XC1=XC(1)
      XC2=XC(2)
      XC3=XC(3)
      XD1=XD(1)
      XD2=XD(2)
      XD3=XD(3)
      XT1=XT(1);XT2=XT(2);XT3=XT(3)
      YC1=XC1;YC2=XC2;YC3=XC3
      YD1=XD1;YD2=XD2;YD3=XD3
      YT1=XT1;YT2=XT2;YT3=XT3
      DTETA=TTETA*PI/90./MAX0(1,NBNRC-1)
      DDTT=2.*DTT/MAX0(1,NBTT-1)
      TETA0=TETA0-TTETA
      TETA0=TETA0*PI/180.
      TT1=TTZ-DTT
      IF(IVOL.EQ.1)PRINT:"   ***   BULK WAVES   ***"
      IF(IVOL.NE.1)PRINT 9011,
      PRINT 9041,MAT
      IF(IVOL.NE.1)PRINT 9014,
      DO 6000 KTT=1,NBTT
      TTZ=TT1+DDTT*(KTT-1)
      IF(NBTT.GT.1)PRINT:"----- TEMPERATURE=",TTZ,"-----"
      DO 6000 NRC=1,NBNRC
      TETA=TETA0+(NRC-1)*DTETA
      IF(NBNRC.GT.1)PRINT:"##########"
      VTETA=TETA
      CO=COS(TETA)
      SI=SIN(TETA)
      XC(1)=YC1*CO+YD1*SI
      XC(2)=YC2*CO+YD2*SI
      XC(3)=YC3*CO+YD3*SI
      XD(1)=-YC1*SI+YD1*CO
      XD(2)=-YC2*SI+YD2*CO
      XD(3)=-YC3*SI+YD3*CO
      CALL NORMA(XC)
```

```
          CALL PVEC(XC,XD,XT)
          CALL NORMA(XT)
          CALL PVEC(XT,XC,XD)
          XC1=XC(1)
          XC2=XC(2)
          XC3=XC(3)
          XD1=XD(1)
          XD2=XD(2)
          XD3=XD(3)
          XT1=XT(1);XT2=XT(2);XT3=XT(3)
          CONVT=PI/180.
          IF(MIPT.NE.0)GO TO 3010
          PAS=0.
          GO TO 3020
 3010     CONTINUE
          PAS=ANGLE/FLOAT(MIPT)
 3020     CONTINUE
          TETA=0.
          DO 6000 NRN=1,NBN
          TN=-DTN+TETAN+(NRN-1)*DTN*2./MAX0(1,NBN-1)
          IF(NBN.GT.1)PRINT:"+++++++++++ NORMAL=",TN,
        & "+++++++++++++++"
          TN=TN*PI/180.
          CO=COS(TN);SI=SIN(TN)
          XC(1)=XC1*CO+XT1*SI
          XC(2)=XC2*CO+XT2*SI
          XC(3)=XC3*CO+XT3*SI
          XT(1)=-XC1*SI+XT1*CO
          XT(2)=-XC2*SI+XT2*CO
          XT(3)=-XC3*SI+XT3*CO
          DO 5000 NRPT=1,NBPT
          TEST=PIEZO
          IF(MIPT.EQ.0)GO TO 3030
          TETA=ANGLE*FLOAT(NRPT-MIPT-1)/FLOAT(MIPT)
 3030     TETA=TETA+TETAI
          IF(NBPT.GT.1)PRINT 9017,TETA
          A=COS(TETA*CONVT)
          B=SIN(TETA*CONVT)
          DO 4010 I=1,3
          R(2,I)=XC(I)
          R(1,I)=XD(I)*A+XT(I)*B
 4010     R(3,I)=-XD(I)*B+XT(I)*A
          PRINT:"CUT    ",(R(2,I),I=1,3)
          PRINT:"DIR    ",(R(1,I),I=1,3)
          PIEZO=.F.
          CALL INIPAR(TTZ)
          CALL CALCUL
          IF(IVOL.NE.1)GO TO 4995
          DO 4990 I=1,DECOUP
          KAPA2(I)=(VV(I)-WW(I))/VV(I)
          VV(I)=SQRT(1.E11*VV(I)/RAU)
          WW(I)=SQRT(1.E11*WW(I)/RAU)
 4990     CONTINUE
          PRINT:" VELOCITIES=" ,(VV(I),I=1,DECOUP)
          PRINT:" K2         =",(KAPA2(I),I=1,DECOUP)
          GO TO 5000
 4995     CONTINUE
          XCC=1.E-11*RAU*VCC**2
          XOU=1.E-11*RAU*VOU**2
          IF(.NOT.OK)XOU=VV(DECOUP)
          PRINT 9026,EPSBF,EPSHF
          SIG=SIGMA/(1.+0.01*SIGMA)
          PRINT 9027,SIGMA,SIG
 5000     CONTINUE
 6000     PRINT:"----------------------------------------"
          REWIND(05)
          PRINT:" "
          PRINT:"================================="
          PRINT:" "
```

```
      IF(IVOL.EQ.1)GO TO 1
      IF(.NOT.TEST)GOTO 1
      DEL=0.1
      IF(OK)DEL=2.*AK2
      DEL=AMAX1(0.01,DEL)
      DEL=AMIN1(1.,DEL)
      DEL=DEL/20.
      PD1=1.-DEL/2.
      PD2=DEL
      PRINT:"SURFACE PERMITTIVITY FUNCTION (YES/NO) ?"
      READ:REP;IF(REP.EQ."yes")REP="YES"
      IF(REP.NE."YES")GOTO 7010
      PIEZO=.T.
      IMAX=41
      DO 7000 I=1,IMAX
      X=(PD1+PD2*(I-1.)/(IMAX-1.))*XOU
      XZERO=AIGMIT(X)
7000  CONTINUE
7010  STOP
9011  FORMAT("   ***   SAW VELOCITIES   ***")
9013  FORMAT(1X,"DATE   ",A6,/,1X,
     & "SUBSTRATE       ",A6,
     & /,1X,"CENTER CUT        (",3(G10.3,2X,1H,),1H),
     & /,1X,"CENTER PROPAGATION DIRECTION ",            '
     & /,1X,"         (",3(G10.3,2X,1H,),1H),
     & /,1X,"ANGLE TO BE EXPLORED (+,-) ",G10.3,
     & /,1X,"STEP          ",G10.3)
9014  FORMAT(" CAPTION  1=BLEUSTEIN;2=RAYLEIGH;",
     & "3=GENERAL")
9020  FORMAT(1X,F5.1,52X)
9015  FORMAT(2(F6.3,1X),1I1,1X,1L1)
9016  FORMAT(I2,2(1X,E8.1),1X,I1)
9017  FORMAT(1X,5X,4H*** ,5HTETA=,F7.3,4H ***)
9018  FORMAT(60X,F10.4,2X,F10.5,I4,4X,E10.3,4X,E10.3)
9019  FORMAT(2L1,I3,1X,F6.3,1X,F6.3)
9021  FORMAT(1X,2(I2,1X,F6.1,1X,F6.2,1X,F5.2,2X),F7.3)
9022  FORMAT(90X,E10.3,4X,E10.3)
9023  FORMAT(1X,2HJ=,I2,4X,6HECROIT,
     & 2X,1L1,2X,6HBORNES,2(2X,F6.1))
9024  FORMAT(1X,2HJ=,I2,4X,6HRCROIT,
     & 2X,1L1,2X,6HBORNES,
     & 2(2X,F6.1))
9025  FORMAT(1X,7HROOT = ,F6.1)
9026  FORMAT(1X,11HEPSILON LF=,F7.2,5X,
     & 11HEPSILON HF=, F7.2)
9027  FORMAT(1X,12HKAPA2 TOTAL= ,F8.2,1H%,
     & 4X,9HK2TOTAL= , F8.2,1H%)
9028  FORMAT(1H0,4HOPEN  ,F10.1,F10.4,I4,F6.2,
     & /,35X,F6.2,1H%,
     & F6.2,1H%,/,1X,4HSHOR  ,F10.1,F10.4,I4,F6.2,/)
9029  FORMAT(1X,16HK2 TOTAL      = ,F6.2,1H%,//)
9032  FORMAT(80X,18HNOT OK USING SOLZ )
9033  FORMAT(80X,13HOK USING SOLZ )
9034  FORMAT(1X,15HOK USING MODULE )
9035  FORMAT(1X,9HBORNE INF,2X,F12.9)
9036  FORMAT(15H * LOCATION      )
9037  FORMAT(1H1)
9038  FORMAT(80(1H*))
9039  FORMAT(2E15.8)
9040  FORMAT(5E15.8)
9041  FORMAT(A6)
      END
```

SURBINSP

Library routines SURBINSP used for execution of SURFTSS.

```
*#RUN *=:/LIBRARY/SURBINSP(BCD,NOGO)
      SUBROUTINE CALCUL
*SURFONDE
      REAL GAM(3,6),ET(3,3),EP(3),PO(5,6),Q(5,6),CL(4,4),
     & DL(4,4),R(3,3),EINI(3,6),CINI(6,6),EPSINI(3,3)
     &,VV(3),XC(3),XD(3),XT(3),V2(2,9)
      REAL XX1(4,2),XX2(4,2),XXZ(4,2)
      REAL EPS2(2),RES2(2)
      REAL VVV(4,2),DBDB(4,2),VVV2(4),BBB(4),KAPA2(4)
      REAL WW(10)
      INTEGER NM(2),IINDIC(4,2)
      INTEGER LL(2)
      EXTERNAL PHI,PSI
      COMPLEX PHI,Z,Z1,ZSU,ZIN,CSOLZ
      COMPLEX PSI,RESIDU,ZRAC(4,2),XZERO
      COMPLEX CMPLX,IMPED,ADMIT
      COMMON R,EINI,CINI,EPSINI,RAU,ALINI
      COMMON/COMPHI/PO,Q,GAM,ET,EP,CL,DL,METAL,DECOUP
      COMMON/IMPRI/TEST,VV1,DAC,ESSAI,LENT,PIEZO,KRAC
      COMMON/COMY/KY,EPSTBF,EPSBF,VVV,DBDB,
     & MODIF,XX1,XX2,AM
      COMMON/JAC/EPSHF,VVV2,BBB,KAPA2
      COMMON/TAMP1/OK,META,PRECIS,EPZERO,IVOL,PI,INTERV
      COMMON/TAMP2/VOU,AOU,IOU,DBOU,AK2,COUPLA,VCC,
     & ACC,ICC,DBCC,SIGMA,VV
      COMMON/TAMP3/BI,BS,ITER,XEPS,YEPS,NBMODE,
     & PSEUDO,PSESLT,NBPSEU
      COMMON/TAMP3/ VMIN,VMAX ,EPSI,JTER
      COMMON/TAMP4/JSOR
      COMMON/TAMP5/WW
      LOGICAL TEST,DAC,ESSAI,LENT,PIEZO
      LOGICAL PSEUDO,PSESLT,EOR
      LOGICAL OK1
      LOGICAL DAC1,DAC2,DAC3,EC,RC,ECROIT,RCROIT
      INTEGER DECOUP
      LOGICAL META(2),METAL,OK
      LOGICAL RCRT(2),ECRT(2)
      NCAL=1;IF(IVOL.EQ.1)NCAL=2
      DO 4099 ICAL=1,NCAL
      DO 4020 I=1,9
      DO 4020 J=1,2
 4020 V2(J,I)=0.
      GAM(1,1)=C(6,6)
      GAM(1,2)=C(2,2)
      GAM(1,3)=C(4,4)
      GAM(1,4)=C(2,4)
      GAM(1,5)=C(4,6)
      GAM(1,6)=C(2,6)
      GAM(3,1)=C(1,1)
      GAM(3,2)=GAM(1,1)
      GAM(3,3)=C(5,5)
      GAM(3,4)=C(5,6)
      GAM(3,5)=C(1,5)
      GAM(3,6)=C(1,6)
      GAM(2,1)=2.*GAM(3,6)
      GAM(2,2)=2.*GAM(1,6)
      GAM(2,3)=2.*C(4,5)
      GAM(2,4)=GAM(1,5)+C(2,5)
      GAM(2,5)=GAM(3,4)+C(1,4)
      GAM(2,6)=GAM(1,1)+C(1,2)
      IF(ICAL.EQ.2)GO TO 4097
```

```
           ET(1,1)=E(2,6)
           ET(1,2)=E(2,2)
           ET(1,3)=E(2,4)
           ET(3,1)=E(1,1)
           ET(3,2)=E(1,6)
           ET(3,3)=E(1,5)
           ET(2,1)=E(2,1)+ET(3,2)
           ET(2,2)=E(1,2)+ET(1,1)
           ET(2,3)=E(1,4)+E(2,5)
           GO TO 4098
     4097  DO 4096 I=1,3
           DO 4096 J=1,3
     4096  ET(I,J)=0.
     4098  CONTINUE
           EP(1)=EPS(2,2)
           EP(2)=2.*EPS(1,2)
           EP(3)=EPS(1,1)
           COUP=.0
           DO 30 J=1,3
       30  COUP=COUP+ET(J,3)**2
           IF(COUP.GT.PRECIS)GO TO 300
           DECOUP=2
           GO TO 400
      300  COUP=.0
           DO 60 J=1,3
       60  COUP=COUP+ET(J,1)**2+ET(J,2)**2
           IF(COUP.GT.PRECIS)GO TO 500
           DECOUP=1
      400  VERIF=.0
           DO 70 J=1,3
       70  VERIF=VERIF+GAM(J,4)**2+GAM(J,5)**2
           IF(VERIF.LT.PRECIS)GO TO 600
           WRITE(6,3100)VERIF
     3100  FORMAT(1X," electrical decoupling not meaningful ;"
          &," eps= ",E15.8)
      500  DECOUP=3
      600  GO TO(700,620,700),DECOUP
      620  CONTINUE
           TAP=E(1,4)**2
           IF(TAP.LT.PRECIS)GO TO 700
           DECOUP=3
      700  CONTINUE
           DO 10 K=1,3
           L=K+3
           CALL CODE(L,M,N)
           DO 10 JJ1=1,5
           J=JJ1
           PO(J,K)=-POLPRO(GAM(1,M),GAM(1,N),2,2,J)+
          & POLPRO(GAM(1,L),GAM(1,L),2,2,J)
           ML=M+3
           NL=N+3
           PO(J,L)=POLPRO(GAM(1,L),GAM(1,K),2,2,J)-
          & POLPRO(GAM(1,ML),GAM(1,NL),2,2,J)
           IF(K.GT.1)GO TO 11
           Q(J,K)=POLPRO(EP,GAM(1,1),2,2,J)+POLPRO(ET(1,1),
          & ET(1,1),2,2,J)
           Q(J,L)=2.*POLPRO(ET(1,M),ET(1,N),2,2,J)
           GO TO 10
       11  Q(J,K)=POLPRO(ET(1,K),ET(1,K),2,2,J)
           Q(J,L)=2.*POLPRO(ET(1,M),ET(1,N),2,2,J)+
          & POLPRO(EP,GAM(1,L),2,2,J)
       10  CONTINUE
           DO 20 I=1,3
           N=2*I
           CL(I,1)=C(1,N)
           CL(I,2)=C(6,N)
           CL(I,3)=C(5,N)
           CL(I,4)=E(1,N)
           DL(I,1)=CL(I,2)
```

```
      DL(I,2)=C(2,N)
      DL(I,3)=C(4,N)
  20  DL(I,4)=E(2,N)
      CL(4,1)=E(2,1)
      CL(4,2)=E(2,6)
      CL(4,3)=E(2,5)
      CL(4,4)=-EPS(2,1)
      DL(4,1)=ET(1,1)
      DL(4,2)=ET(1,2)
      DL(4,3)=ET(1,3)
      DL(4,4)=-EP(1)+EPZERO
      IF(ICAL.EQ.1)CALL VOLOND(VV)
      IF(ICAL.EQ.2)CALL VOLOND(WW)
4099  CONTINUE
      IF(IVOL.EQ.1)RETURN
      VV1=VV(1)
      NM(1)=0
      NM(2)=0
      MODIF=0
      EPSHF=SQRT(EP(1)*EP(3)-.25*EP(2)**2)*.36*PI
      EPSTBF=AIGMIT(0.)
      EPSBF=EPSTBF*EPSHF
      SIGMA=EPSTBF-1.
      ESSAI=.TRUE.
      JALI=MIN0(DECOUP,NBMODE)
      CALL LOCALI(VV,WW,JALI,XEPS,NBRA)
      ESSAI=.FALSE.
      IF(.NOT.TEST)GO TO 23
      WRITE(6,9036)
      DO 22 I=1,DECOUP
      XZERO=CMPLX(VV(I),0.)
  22  CALL VALEUR(XZERO,VOU,DBOU)
      WRITE(6,9035)
      DO 24 I=1,NBRA
      XZERO=CMPLX(WW(I),0.)
  24  CALL VALEUR(XZERO,VOU,DB)
  23  CONTINUE
      JREF=7;IF(DECOUP.EQ.1)JREF=1
      CVXY=0.5
      OK1=.TRUE.
      DO 4910 KM=1,2
      IF((DECOUP.EQ.1).AND.(KM.EQ.2))JREF=7
      JREF=ITER
      METAL=META(KM)
      IF(TEST.AND.METAL)WRITE(6,9000)"--- SHORT CIRCUIT"
     &," ---"
      IF(TEST.AND.(.NOT.METAL))WRITE(6,9000)"--- OPEN"
     &," CIRCUIT   ---"
      IF(TEST)WRITE(6,9000)"JREF=",JREF
      KBRA2=NBRA+1
      KINI=1;IF(IVOL.EQ.2)KINI=NBRA
      DO 4900 KBRA=KINI,KBRA2
      KBRA1=KBRA-1
      XINF=0.5*WW(1)
      XSUP=4.*WW(NBRA)
      IF(KBRA.GT.1)XINF=WW(KBRA1)
      IF(KBRA.LT.KBRA2)XSUP=WW(KBRA)
      DO 4600 KMOD=1,INTERV
      XIN=XINF+(XSUP-XINF)*FLOAT(KMOD-1)/FLOAT(INTERV)
      XSU=XINF+(XSUP-XINF)*FLOAT(KMOD)/FLOAT(INTERV)
      YSU=(XSU-XIN)/10.*CVXY
      YIN=-CVXY*(XSU-XIN)
      IF(KBRA.GT.1)GO TO 4100
      YIN=0.
      YSU=0.
4100  CONTINUE
      FYEPS=YEPS
      IF(DECOUP.EQ.1)FYEPS=10.*YEPS
      IF(KBRA.GT.1)FYEPS=30.*YEPS
```

```
          XZERO=CSOLZ(PSI,XIN,XSU,YIN,YSU,XEPS,FYEPS
        &,ITER,OK,JREF)
 4200 CONTINUE
          IF(.NOT.OK)GO TO 4550
          NM(KM)=NM(KM)+1
          KLM=NM(KM)
          ZRAC(KLM,KM)=XZERO
          IF(TEST)WRITE(6,9033)
          IINDIC(KLM,KM)=DECOUP+10*KRAC
          NRMODE=NM(KM)
          IF(NRMODE.GE.NBMODE)GO TO 4910
 4550 IF(.NOT.OK.AND.TEST)WRITE(6,9032)
 4600 CONTINUE
 4900 CONTINUE
          OK1=OK1.AND.OK
 4910 IF(TEST)WRITE(6,9038)
 4950 CONTINUE
          NRMODE=MAX0(NM(1),NM(2))
          BK2=0.
          DO 4960 I=1,NRMODE
          CALL VALEUR(ZRAC(I,1),VCC,DBCC)
          ACC=1./VCC*1.E4
          CALL VALEUR(ZRAC(I,2),VOU,DBOU)
          AOU=1./VOU*1.E4
          AK2=(VOU**2-VCC**2)/VOU**2*100.
          IOU=IINDIC(I,2)
          ICC=IINDIC(I,1)
          BK2=BK2+COUPLA
          IF(JSOR.NE.1)GO TO 4960
          PRINT
 9028,VOU,VOU/ALINI,IOU,DBOU,AK2,VCC,VCC/ALINI,ICC,DBCC
 9028 FORMAT(1HO,"VACUUM"," V=",F10.1," V/L=",F10.4,
        &" Type=",I2," IL(dB)=",F6.2,/,55X,"K2=",F6.2,1H%,
        & /,1X,"METAL "," V=",F10.1," V/L=",F10.4,
        &" Type=",I2,"  IL(dB)=",F6.2,//)
 4960 CONTINUE
          SIGMA=100.*SIGMA
          SIG=SIGMA/(1.+0.01*SIGMA)
          OK=OK1
          RETURN
 9000 FORMAT(V)
 9032 FORMAT(80X,"NOT OK USING SOLZ")
 9033 FORMAT(80X,"OK USING SOLZ")
 9035 FORMAT(1X,9HBORNE INF,2X,F12.9)
 9036 FORMAT(1X,"* LOCATING")
 9038 FORMAT(80(1H*))
          END
          SUBROUTINE INIPAR(TZ)
          COMMON R(3,3),EINI(3,6),CINI(6,6),EPSINI(3,3)
        &,RAU,ALINI
          COMMON/CONSTA/EREF(3,6),CREF(6,6),EPSREF(3,3)
        &,RAUREF,ET1(3,6)
        & ,ET2(3,6),CT1(6,6),CT2(6,6),EPST1(3,3),
        & EPST2(3,3),AT1(3),AT2(3),TTT
          DT=TZ-TTT
          DT2=DT**2
          DO 50 I=1,6
          DO 40 J=1,6
   40 CINI(I,J)=CREF(I,J)*(1.+CT1(I,J)*DT+CT2(I,J)*DT2)
          DO 50 J=1,3
   50 EINI(J,I)=EREF(J,I)*(1.+ET1(J,I)*DT+ET2(J,I)*DT2)
          ALINI=0.;RAU=RAUREF
          DO 60 I=1,3
          AINI=1.+AT1(I)*DT+AT2(I)*DT2
          ALINI=ALINI+(AINI*R(1,I))**2
          RAU=RAU/AINI
          DO 60 J=1,3
   60 EPSINI(I,J)=EPSREF(I,J)*(1.+EPST1(I,J)*DT
        &+EPST2(I,J)*DT2)
```

```
      ALINI=SQRT(ALINI)
      RETURN
      END
      SUBROUTINE LECTT(NOM)
      CHARACTER TYPE
      COMMON/MATERIAU/MATER
      COMMON/CONSTA/EREF(3,6),CREF(6,6),EPSREF(3,3)
     &,RAUREF,ET1(3,6)
     & ,ET2(3,6),CT1(6,6),CT2(6,6),EPST1(3,3)
     &,EPST2(3,3),AT1(3),AT2(3),TTT
      PI=3.141592654
      EPZERO=1./.36/PI
  115 READ(5,2002)NOM,RAUREF
      IF(NOM.EQ.MATER)GO TO 130
      GO TO 115
  130 DO 5 I=1,6
      DO 4 J=1,6
      CT1(I,J)=0.
      CT2(I,J)=0.
    4 CREF(I,J)=0.
      DO 5 J=1,3
      ET1(J,I)=0.
      ET2(J,I)=0.
    5 EREF(J,I)=0.
      DO 6 I=1,3
      AT1(I)=0.
      AT2(I)=0.
      DO 6 J=1,3
      EPST1(I,J)=0.
      EPST2(I,J)=0.
    6 EPSREF(I,J)=0.
    1 READ(5,2003)TYPE,I,J,A
      IF(TYPE.EQ."E  ")GO TO 10
      IF(TYPE.EQ."C  ")GO TO 20
      IF(TYPE.EQ."EPS")GO TO 30
      IF(TYPE.EQ."ET1")GO TO 40
      IF(TYPE.EQ."ET2")GO TO 50
      IF(TYPE.EQ."CT1")GO TO 60
      IF(TYPE.EQ."CT2")GO TO 70
      IF(TYPE.EQ."PT1")GO TO 80
      IF(TYPE.EQ."PT2")GO TO 90
      IF(TYPE.EQ."AT1")AT1(I)=A
      IF(TYPE.EQ."AT2")AT2(I)=A
      IF(TYPE.EQ."TTT")TTT=A
      IF(TYPE.EQ."END")RETURN
      GO TO 1
   10  EREF(I,J)=A;GO TO 1
   20 A=A*1.E-11;CREF(I,J)=A;CREF(J,I)=A;GO TO 1
   30 A=A*EPZERO;EPSREF(I,J)=A;EPSREF(J,I)=A;GO TO 1
   40 ET1(I,J)=A;GO TO 1
   50 ET2(I,J)=A;GO TO 1
   60 CT1(I,J)=A;CT1(J,I)=A;GO TO 1
   70 CT2(I,J)=A;CT2(J,I)=A;GO TO 1
   80 EPST1(I,J)=A;EPST1(J,I)=A;GO TO 1
   90 EPST2(I,J)=A;EPST2(J,I)=A;GO TO 1
 2002 FORMAT(4X,A6,3X,E15.8)
 2001 FORMAT(A6)
 2003 FORMAT(4X,A3,1X,I1,1X,I1,2X,E12.6)
      END
*PSI
      COMPLEX FUNCTION PSI(ZZ)
      REAL P0(5,6),P(5,6),Q(5,6),TAMPON(3),CE(4,4),
     & DE(4,4)
     & ,D(9),A(8),B(8),EPSIL(3),G(3,6),H(3,3),X
      REAL DD(9),DP(5,6),DQ(5,6)
      REAL DU(9)
      REAL DDD(9),DDP(5,6)
      REAL CDR(9),CDI(9)
      COMPLEX Z(8),ZETA(3),ZP(3,3),ZV(3),ZU(4,4),
```

```
     & ZT(4.4),ZZERO,ZDET,ZLIM,VPOL
       COMPLEX CMPLX,ZNORM
       COMPLEX DELZ,CSQRT
       COMPLEX ZTM(4,4)
       COMPLEX ZZ,DZ,DDRZ,ZMIN,CVPOL
       COMPLEX ZD,ZGRAD,ZN
       COMPLEX CQ(5,6),CP(5,6),CD(9),CEPSIL(3),CPLPRO
       LOGICAL TEST,METAL,DAC,ESSAI,LENT,PIEZO
       LOGICAL OKRAC
       COMMON/COMPHI/PO,Q,G,H,EPSIL,CE,DE,METAL,KTYP
       COMMON/IMPRI/TEST,VV1,DAC,ESSAI,LENT,PIEZO,KRAC
       COMMON/COMLOC/KRR
       X=REAL(ZZ)
       Y=AIMAG(ZZ)
       DELZ=0.
       IF(Y.EQ.0.)GO TO 5
       X=1./REAL(1./CSQRT(ZZ))**2
       DELZ=ZZ-X
     5 CONTINUE
       DAC=.FALSE.
       IF(TEST.AND.(.NOT.ESSAI))WRITE(6,9004)
       IF(TEST.AND.(.NOT.ESSAI))CALL VALEUR(ZZ,V,DB)
       PSI=1.E12
       NR=KTYP+1
       ND=2*NR
       KD=ND+1
       KP=2*(KTYP-1)
       CALL SETDIM(ZT,4,4)
       DO 40 I=1,3
    40 CEPSIL(I)=EPSIL(I)
       ZZERO=.0
       DO 50 I=1,5
       DO 50 J=1,6
       DP(I,J)=0.
       DDP(I,J)=0.
    50 DQ(I,J)=0.
       IF(KTYP.GT.1)GO TO 99
       DO 1 J=1,3
       DP(J,1)=-FLOAT(J/3)
       DDP(J,1)=0.
     1 P(J,1)=G(J,3)-FLOAT(J/3)*X
       DO 2 J=1,KD
       DDD(J)=0.
       DD(J)=POLPRO(DP(1,1),EPSIL,2,2,J)
     2 D(J)=POLPRO(P(1,1),EPSIL,2,2,J)
      &+POLPRO(H(1,3),H(1,3),2,2,J)
       GO TO 121
    99 DO 100 K=1,3
       TAMPON(K)=Q(K+2,1)
       DQ(K+2,1)=-EPSIL(K)
   100 Q(K+2,1)=Q(K+2,1)-X*EPSIL(K)
       IF(KTYP.NE.3)GO TO 102
       DO 101 K=1,3
       L=K+3
       CALL CODE(L,M,N)
       DO 101 J=1,5
       J1=MAX0(J-2,1)
       J2=J/3
       J3=J/5
       P(J,K)=PO(J,K)+FLOAT(J2)*X*(G(J1,M)
      &+G(J1,N)-FLOAT(J3)*X)
       DP(J,K)=FLOAT(J2)*(G(J1,M)+G(J1,N)-FLOAT(J3)*X)
       DP(J,K)=DP(J,K)-X*FLOAT(J2*J3)
       P(J,L)=PO(J,L)-FLOAT(J2)*G(J1,L)*X
       DP(J,L)=-FLOAT(J2)*G(J1,L)
       DDP(J,K)=-2.*FLOAT(J2*J3)
       DDP(J,L)=0.
   101 CONTINUE
       GO TO 104
```

```
 102 DO 103 J=1,NR
     PJ=FLOAT(J/NR)
     P(J,1)=-G(J,2)+PJ*X
     DP(J,1)=PJ
     P(J,2)=-G(J,1)+PJ*X
     DP(J,2)=PJ
     DDP(J,1)=0.
     DDP(J,2)=0.
     DP(J,6)=0.
     DDP(J,6)=0.
 103 P(J,6)=G(J,6)
 104 CONTINUE
     DO 110 J=1,KD
     D(J)=.0
     CDI(J)=0.
     DD(J)=0.
     DDD(J)=0.
     DO 110 K=1,6
     GO TO(111,112,113),KTYP
 111 WRITE(6,1110)
1110 FORMAT(10H PAS PREVU)
     RETURN
 112 IF(K.LT.6.AND.K.GT.2)GO TO 110
 113 D(J)=D(J)+POLPRO(P(1,K),Q(1,K),KP,4,J)
     DD(J)=DD(J)+POLPRO(DP(1,K),Q(1,K),KP,4,J)
     DD(J)=DD(J)+POLPRO(P(1,K),DQ(1,K),KP,4,J)
     DDD(J)=DDD(J)+POLPRO(DDP(1,K),Q(1,K),KP,4,J)
     DDD(J)=DDD(J)+2.*POLPRO(DP(1,K),DQ(1,K),KP,4,J)
 110 CONTINUE
     DO 120 K=3,5
 120 Q(K,1)=TAMPON(K-2)
 121 DO 123 I=1,KD
 123 DU(I)=D(I)
     CALL POLRTS(DU,A,B,ND,JUSTE)
     IF(ND.EQ.JUSTE)GO TO 200
     IF(TEST)WRITE(6,9010)
     JUSTE=ND
     DO 122 J=1,KD
     CDI(J)=0.
     I=KD-J+1
 122 CDR(J)=D(I)
     CALL CDOWNH(CDR,CDI,ND,A,B)
 200 KRR=0
     DO 125 J=1,ND
     IF(ABS(B(J)).LT.1.E-3)KRR=KRR+1
 125 IF(ABS(B(J)).LT.1.E-5)B(J)=0.
     IF(ESSAI)RETURN
     KR=0.
     KRAC=0
     K=0
     KM=0
     DO 220 L=1,JUSTE
     IF(B(L))203,201,202
 201 KR=KR+1
     IF(ESSAI)GO TO 220
     ZD=DDRZ(D,DD,CMPLX(A(L),0.),ND)
     DA=REAL(ZD)
     IF(DA.LT.0.)GO TO 203
     KRAC=KRAC+1
 202 K=K+1
     Z(K)=CMPLX(A(L),B(L))
     GO TO 220
 203 KM=KM+1
     KKM=NR+KM
     Z(KKM)=CMPLX(A(L),B(L))
 220 CONTINUE
     IF(K.EQ.NR)DAC=.TRUE.
     IF(ESSAI)RETURN
     IF(TEST)WRITE(6,9006)DAC,(Z(I),I=1,K)
```

```
      IF(.NOT.DAC)RETURN
      IF(Y.EQ.0.)GO TO 490
      DO 402 I=1,5
      DO 402 J=1,6
  402 CQ(I,J)=Q(I,J)
      IF(KTYP.GT.1)GO TO 415
      DO 405 J=1,3
      CEPSIL(J)=EPSIL(J)
  405 CP(J,1)=G(J,3)-FLOAT(J/3)*ZZ
      DO 410 J=1,KD
  410 CD(J)=CPLPRO(CP(1,1),CEPSIL,2,2,J)
     &+POLPRO(H(1,3),H(1,3),2,2,J)
      GO TO 470
  415 DO 420 K=1,3
  420 CQ(K+2,1)=Q(K+2,1)-ZZ*EPSIL(K)
      IF(KTYP.NE.3)GO TO 430
      DO 425 K=1,3
      L=K+3
      CALL CODE(L,M,N)
      DO 425 J=1,5
      J1=MAX0(J-2,1)
      J2=J/3
      J3=J/5
      CP(J,K)=P0(J,K)+FLOAT(J2)*ZZ*(G(J1,M)
     &+G(J1,N)-FLOAT(J3)*ZZ)
      CP(J,L)=P0(J,L)-FLOAT(J2)*G(J1,L)*ZZ
  425 CONTINUE
      GO TO 440
  430 DO 435 J=1,NR
      PJ=FLOAT(J/NR)
      CP(J,1)=-G(J,2)+PJ*ZZ
      CP(J,2)=-G(J,1)+PJ*ZZ
  435 CP(J,6)=G(J,6)
  440 CONTINUE
      DO 460 J=1,KD
      CD(J)=.0
      DO 460 K=1,6
      GO TO(445,450,455),KTYP
  445 CONTINUE
      RETURN
  450 IF(K.LT.6.AND.K.GT.2)GO TO 460
  455 CD(J)=CD(J)+CPLPRO(CP(1,K),CQ(1,K),KP,4,J)
  460 CONTINUE
  470 DO 475 I=1,KD
      J=KD-I+1
      CDR(I)=REAL(CD(J))
  475 CDI(I)=AIMAG(CD(J))
      CALL CDOWNH(CDR,CDI,ND,A,B)
      DO 480 I=1,ND
      ZD=DELZ*DZ(D,DD,DDD,Z(I),ND,DELZ)
      ZGRAD=Z(I)+ZD
      Z(I)=ZGRAD
  480 CONTINUE
      IF(TEST)WRITE(6,9005)(Z(I),I=1,NR)
      CALL MAXMIN(Z,A,B,ND,ND)
      IF(TEST)WRITE(6,9006)DAC,(Z(I),I=1,NR)
  490 CONTINUE
      DO 500 K=1,NR
      IF(KTYP.GT.1)GO TO 501
      ZU(1,K)=VPOL(Z(K),EPSIL,2)
      ZU(2,K)=VPOL(Z(K),H(1,3),2)
      DO 502 J=1,2
      ZTM(J,K)=0.
  502 ZT(J,K)=ZZERO
      DO 503 L=1,2
      LZ=L+2
  503 ZT(1,K)=ZT(1,K)+(CE(2,LZ)+Z(K)*DE(2,LZ))*ZU(L,K)
      ZTM(1,K)=ZT(1,K)
      DO 506 L=1,2
```

```
      LZ=L+2
506   ZT(2,K)=ZT(2,K)+(CE(4,LZ)+Z(K)*DE(4,LZ))*ZU(L,K)
504   ZTM(2,K)=ZU(2,K)
      GO TO 500
501   DO 505 I=1,KTYP
      CALL INVCOD(J,1,I)
505   ZV(I)=-VPOL(Z(K),G(1,J),2)
      ZV(1)=ZV(1)+ZZ
      DO 510 I=1,KTYP
      ZETA(I)=VPOL(Z(K),H(1,I),2)
      DO 510 J=1,KTYP
      CALL INVCOD(L,I,J)
      ZP(I,J)=VPOL(Z(K),P(1,L),KP)
      IF(Y.NE.0.)ZP(I,J)=CVPOL(Z(K),CP(1,L),KP)
510   CONTINUE
      DO 520 I=1,KTYP
      ZU(I,K)=ZZERO
      DO 520 J=1,KTYP
520   ZU(I,K)=ZU(I,K)+ZETA(J)*ZP(I,J)
      ZU(NR,K)=ZZERO
      DO 530 J=1,KTYP
530   ZU(NR,K)=ZU(NR,K)+ZV(J)*ZP(1,J)
      DO 545 I=1,3
      ZT(I,K)=ZZERO
      DO 540 J=1,NR
      J4=J+(J/NR)*(4-J)
      ZLIM=CE(I,J4)+Z(K)*DE(I,J4)
540   ZT(I,K)=ZT(I,K)+ZLIM*ZU(J,K)
545   ZTM(I,K)=ZT(I,K)
      IF(KTYP.EQ.3)GO TO 560
      ZT(KTYP,K)=ZT(NR,K)
      ZTM(KTYP,K)=ZTM(NR,K)
560   CONTINUE
      ZT(NR,K)=ZZERO
      DO 550 J=1,NR
      J4=J+(J/NR)*(4-J)
550   ZT(NR,K)=ZT(NR,K)+(CE(4,J4)+Z(K)*DE(4,J4))*ZU(J,K)
600   ZTM(NR,K)=ZU(NR,K)
500   CONTINUE
      DO 710 K=1,NR
710   ZU(NR,K)=ZT(NR,K)
      IF(.NOT.METAL)CALL HECDET(ZT,NR,PSI,$800)
      CALL SETDIM(ZTM,4,4)
      IF(METAL)CALL HECDET(ZTM,NR,PSI,$800)
      CALL SETDIM(ZU,4,4)
      CALL HECDET(ZU,NR,ZNORM,$800)
      IF(CABS(ZNORM).LE.0.)GO TO 800
      PSI=PSI/ZNORM
      GO TO 810
800   PSI=1.E20
810   CONTINUE
      ARGU=ARG(PSI)
      VAL=CABS(PSI)
      IF(TEST)WRITE(6,9009)VAL,ARGU
      RETURN
9001  FORMAT(3(3X,E12.5))
9002  FORMAT(1X,"ROOTS",/,(4X,2(E13.6,4X)))
9003  FORMAT(1X,1HX,4X,F12.9)
9004  FORMAT(2H *)
9005  FORMAT(3X,"ROOT",16F7.3)
9006  FORMAT(1X,1L1,1X,4HRAC ,8F7.3)
9007  FORMAT(5H POLY,9F12.4)
9008  FORMAT(1X,5HDPOLY,9F12.4)
9009  FORMAT(6H /PSI/,F12.4,5H ARG=,F12.4)
9010  FORMAT(" CALCULATION USING DOWNH " )
      END
      COMPLEX FUNCTION CSOLZ(FONC,XIN,XSU,YIN,YSU,XEPS
     &,YEPS,ITER,OK,JREF)
      COMPLEX Z(3),F(3),D(3),ZN,ZD,CMPLX,FONC
```

```
      COMPLEX ZG,CSQRT
      REAL A(3)
      LOGICAL OK
      EXTERNAL FONC
      OK=.TRUE.
      XINF=1./SQRT(XSU)
      XSUP=1./SQRT(XIN)
      Z(1)=(2.*XIN+XSU)/3.
      Z(2)=(XIN+2.*XSU)/3.
      Z(3)=CMPLX((XIN+XSU)/2.,(YIN+YSU)/2.)
      ZG=(Z(1)+Z(2)+Z(3))/3.
      IX=-1
      IY=-1
      IF(ABS(XIN-XSU).LE.0.)IX=-ITER
      IF(ABS(YIN-YSU).LE.0.)IY=-ITER
      DO 10 I=1,3
      F(I)=FONC(Z(I))
   10 A(I)=CABS(F(I))
      DO 100 JTER=1,ITER
      IF(JTER.NE.JREF)GO TO 15
      DO 12 I=1,3
   12 F(I)=F(I)**2
   15 CONTINUE
      DO 40 I=1,3
   20 GO TO (25,30,35),I
   25 I1=2
      I2=3
      GO TO 40
   30 I1=3
      I2=1
      GO TO 40
   35 I1=1
      I2=2
   40 D(I)=(Z(I1)-Z(I2))*F(I1)*F(I2)
      ZN=0.
      ZD=0.
      DO 50 I=1,3
      ZN=ZN+D(I)*Z(I)
   50 ZD=ZD+D(I)
      AZD=CABS(ZD)
      IF(AZD.LE.0..AND.DY.LT.YEPS)GO TO 200
      IF(AZD.LE.0.)ZN=ZG
      IF(AZD.LE.0.)GO TO 51
      ZN=ZN/ZD
   51 CONTINUE
      K=1
      GF=0.
      DO 52 I=1,3
      GF1=CABS(ZN-Z(I))
      IF(GF1.LT.GF)GO TO 52
      K=I
      GF=GF1
   52 CONTINUE
      X=REAL(ZN)
      Y=AIMAG(ZN)
   60 IF(Y.LT.YSU)GO TO 65
      Y=YSU
      IY=IY+1
   65 IF(Y.GT.YIN)GO TO 70
      Y=YIN
      IY=IY+1
   70 CONTINUE
      ZN=CMPLX(X,Y)
      ZD=1./CSQRT(ZN)
      X=REAL(ZD)
      IF(X.LT.0.)ZD=-ZD
      X=REAL(ZD)
      Y=AIMAG(ZD)
      IF(X.LT.XSUP)GO TO 75
```

```
        X=XSUP
        IX=IX+1
   75 IF(X.GT.XINF)GO TO 80
        X=XINF
        IX=IX+1
   80 CONTINUE
        ZD=CMPLX(X,Y)
        ZN=1./ZD**2
        X=REAL(ZN)
        Y=AIMAG(ZN)
        IF(Y.GT.0.)Y=0.
        IF(ABS(YSU-YIN).LE.0.)Y=YIN
        Z(K)=CMPLX(X,Y)
        F(K)=FONC(Z(K))
        A(K)=CABS(F(K))
        DY=A(K)
        IF(JTER.GE.JREF)F(K)=F(K)**2
        IF(DY.EQ.0.)GO TO 200
        DX=CABS(ZG-Z(K))
        ZG=Z(K)
        IF(IX.GT.1.OR.IY.GT.1)GO TO 150
  100 IF(DX.LT.XEPS.AND.DY.LT.YEPS)GO TO 200
  150 OK=.FALSE.
  200 CSOLZ=Z(K)
        RETURN
        END
        SUBROUTINE LOCALI(VV,WW,N,EPS,NB)
        REAL VV(1),WW(1)
        COMPLEX Z,PHI
        COMMON/COMLOC/NR
        NB=0
        M=N+1
        X2=0.5*VV(1)
        N2=0
        XEPS=EPS/4.
        ITER=60
        DO 100 I=1,N
   10 X1=X2
        X2=VV(I)
        N1=N2
        Z=PHI(X2)
        N2=NR
        K=0
        DO 50 J=1,ITER
        X=(X1+X2)/2.
        DX=ABS(X1-X2)/2.
        Z=PHI(X)
        IF(NR.NE.N2)GO TO 20
        X2=X
        GO TO 50
   20 IF(NR.NE.N1)GO TO 30
        X1=X
        GO TO 50
   30 N2=NR
        X2=X
        K=K+1
   50 IF(DX.LT.XEPS/8.)GO TO60
   60 NB=NB+1
        IF(NB.GT.10)STOP"TROP DE BRAS"
        WW(NB)=X2
  100 IF(K.GT.0)GO TO 10
        RETURN
        END
        COMPLEX FUNCTION DZ(D,DD,DDD,Z,NDEGRE,DX)
        DIMENSION D(1),DD(1),DDD(1),P(9)
        COMPLEX A,B,C,ALPHA,BETA,DELTA
        COMPLEX Z,DX,VPOL
        N=NDEGRE
        C=VPOL(Z,DDD,N)/2.
```

```
      DO 10 I=1,N
   10 P(I)=FLOAT(N-I+1)*DD(I)
      B=VPOL(Z,P,N-1)
      M=N-1
      DO 20 I=1,M
   20 P(I)=FLOAT((N-I+1)*(N-I))*D(I)
      A=VPOL(Z,P,N-2)/2.
      BETA=VPOL(Z,DD,N)
      DO 30 I=1,N
   30 P(I)=FLOAT(N-I+1)*D(I)
      ALPHA=VPOL(Z,P,N-1)
      DELTA=A*BETA**2-B*ALPHA*BETA+C*ALPHA**2
      DZ=-(BETA+DELTA*DX/ALPHA**2)/ALPHA
      RETURN
      END
      COMPLEX FUNCTION DDRZ(D,DD,Z,NDEGRE)
      DIMENSION D(1),DD(1),P(9)
      COMPLEX Z,DA,B,VPOL
      N=NDEGRE
      DA=VPOL(Z,DD,N)
      DO 10 I=1,N
   10 P(I)=FLOAT(N-I+1)*D(I)
      B=VPOL(Z,P,N-1)
      IF(CABS(B).LE.0.)RETURN
      DDRZ=-DA/B
      RETURN
      END
*CPLPRO
      COMPLEX FUNCTION CPLPRO(A,B,NA,NB,K)
      COMPLEX A(9),B(9)
      KA=NA+1
      KB=NB+1
      CPLPRO=.0
      KS=MIN0(K,KA)
      KT=MIN0(K,KB)
      KI=K+1-KT
      DO 10 I=KI,KS
      KM=K+1-I
      IF(CABS(A(I)).EQ..0.OR.CABS(B(KM)).EQ..0)GO TO 10
      KEST=-ALOG(CABS(A(I)))-ALOG(CABS(B(KM)))
      IF(KEST.GT.50)GO TO 10
      CPLPRO=CPLPRO+A(I)*B(KM)
   10 CONTINUE
      RETURN
      END
*CVPOL
      COMPLEX FUNCTION CVPOL(Z,COEFF,DEGRE)
      INTEGER DEGRE
      COMPLEX Z
      COMPLEX COEFF(9)
      CVPOL=.0
      I=DEGRE+1
      DO 5 K=1,I
    5 CVPOL=CVPOL*Z+COEFF(K)
      RETURN
      END
      COMPLEX FUNCTION PHI(X)
      COMPLEX PSI,CMPLX
      COMMON/DECAPSI/Y
      PHI=PSI(CMPLX(X,Y))
      RETURN
      END
      COMPLEX FUNCTION RESIDU(ZCC,ZOU)
      REAL P(5,6),Q(5,6),G(3,6),H(3,3),CE(4,4),
     &DE(4,4),V(4),B(4),K(4)
      REAL EPSIL(3)
      COMPLEX Z,ZOU,ZCC,PSI
      LOGICAL METAL
      COMMON/COMPHI/P,Q,G,H,EPSIL,CE,DE,METAL,KTYP
```

```
        COMMON/JAC/EPSHF,V,B,K
        PI=3.141592653
        METAL=.TRUE.
        RESIDU=PSI(ZOU)*EPSHF/0.36/PI
        METAL=.FALSE.
        Z=0.9*ZOU+0.1*ZCC
        RESIDU=10.*RESIDU*(ZCC/ZOU-1.)/PSI(Z)
        RETURN
      1 FORMAT(8H RESIDU=,2F12.4)
        END
        SUBROUTINE VALEUR(Z,V,DB)
        REAL R(3,3),EI(3,6),CI(6,6),EP(3,3),RAU
        LOGICAL TEST,DAC,ESSAI,LENT,PIEZO
        COMPLEX Z,ZA,CSQRT
        COMMON R,EI,CI,EP,RAU
        COMMON/IMPRI/TEST,VV1,DAC,ESSAI,LENT,PIEZO,KRAC
        DB=0.
        V=0.
        IF(CABS(Z).EQ.0.)RETURN
        ZA=1./CSQRT(1.E11*Z/RAU)
        V=1./REAL(ZA)
        DB=54.575052*V*AIMAG(ZA)
        IF(TEST)WRITE(6,1)V,DB
        RETURN
      1 FORMAT(3H V=,F12.3,4X,3HDB=,F12.4)
        END
        SUBROUTINE CDOWNH(A,AI,NARG,RR,CR)
        DIMENSION A(1),AI(1),BR(2),BI(2),QR(101),QI(101)
        DIMENSION RR(1),CR(1)
        BR(2)=1.0
        BI(2)=0.0
      1 J=0
        N=NARG
        NPL1=N+1
        ANPL1=A(NPL1)
        AINPL1=AI(NPL1)
        DEN=ANPL1**2+AINPL1**2
        DO 102 I=1,NPL1
        IF(A(I)**2+AI(I)**2)103,102,103
  102   CONTINUE
  103   C=(A(I)*A(NPL1)+AI(I)*AI(NPL1))/DEN
        CI=(AI(I)*A(NPL1)-A(I)*AI(NPL1))/DEN
        C=SQRT(C**2+CI**2)
        LU=120
        LL=-120
        IF(C-2.**LU)100,100,101
  100   IF(C-2.**LL)101,105,105
  101   NARG=-NARG
        GO TO 5001
  105   II=(LU+LL)/2
        IF(C-2.**II)110,110,109
  109   LL=II
        GO TO 111
  110   LU=II
  111   IF(LU-LL-1)5001,112,105
  112   IB=II/N
        IF(IB)113,120,113
  113   DO 115 I=1,NPL1
        II=I-1
        A(I)=A(I)*(2.**(II*IB))
  115   AI(I)=AI(I)*(2.**(II*IB))
        DEN=A(NPL1)**2+AI(NPL1)**2
  120   DO 121 J1=1,NPL1
        TA=(A(J1)*A(NPL1)+AI(J1)*AI(NPL1))/DEN
        AI(J1)=(AI(J1)*A(NPL1)-A(J1)*AI(NPL1))/DEN
  121   A(J1)=TA
  201   IF(N) 2001,2001,202
  202   IF(A(1)) 301,203,301
  203   IF(AI(1)) 301,211,301
```

```
 211 J=J+1
     RR(J)=0.
     CR(J)=0.
     DO 221 J1=1,N
     A(J1)=A(J1+1)
 221 AI(J1)=AI(J1+1)
     N=N-1
     GO TO 201
 301 IF(N-2) 601,501,401
 401 CALL CGRAD(A,AI,N,X,Y)
 411 J=J+1
     RR(J)=X
     CR(J)=Y
     GO TO 1001
 501 BOT=A(2)**2-AI(2)**2-4.*A(1)
     TOP=2.*A(2)*AI(2)-4.*AI(1)
     CALL ARCTA(BOT,TOP,ARG)
     AMAD=SQRT(BOT**2+TOP**2)
     X=(-A(2)+SQRT(AMAD)*COS(ARG/2.))/2.
     Y=(-AI(2)+SQRT(AMAD)*SIN(ARG/2.))/2.
     GO TO 411
 601 J=J+1
     RR(J)=-A(1)
     CR(J)=-AI(1)
     GO TO 2001
1001 BR(1)=-RR(J)
     BI(1)=-CR(J)
     CALL CDIV(A,AI,BR,BI,N,1,QR,QI)
     DO 1011 J1=1,N
     A(J1)=QR(J1)
1011 AI(J1)=QI(J1)
     N=N-1
     GO TO 201
2001 NPL1=NARG+1
     IF(IB)2002,2005,2002
2002 DO 2000 I=1,NARG
     RR(I)=RR(I)*(2.**IB)
2000 CR(I)=CR(I)*(2.**IB)
2005 DO 2011 I=1,NPL1
     AI(I)=0.0
2011 A(I)=0.0
     A(1)=1.
     NA=0
     J=0
2021 J=J+1
     NB=1
     BR(1)=-RR(J)
     BI(1)=-CR(J)
     CALL CMTALG(A,AI,BR,BI,QR,QI,NA,NB)
     NA=NB+NA
     NAPL1=NA+1
     DO 2031 I=1,NAPL1
     A(I)=QR(I)
2031 AI(I)=QI(I)
     IF(NA-NARG) 2021,3001,3001
3001 DO 3011 J2=1,NPL1
     TA=A(J2)*ANPL1-AI(J2)*AINPL1
     AI(J2)=AI(J2)*ANPL1+A(J2)*AINPL1
3011 A(J2)=TA
5001 RETURN
     END
     SUBROUTINE CPOLY(N,AR,AI,R,C,PR,PC,RHO,PHI)
     DIMENSION AR(9999),AI(9999)
     IF(RHO)10,5,10
   5 R=AR(1)
     C=AI(1)
     PR=AR(2)
     PC=AI(2)
     RETURN
```

```
   10 V1=1.
      V2=0.
      PR=0.
      PC=0.
      R=AR(1)
      C=AI(1)
      W1=RHO*COS(PHI)
      W2=RHO*SIN(PHI)
      NN=N+1
      DO 21 I=2,NN
      T1=W1*V1-W2*V2
      V2=W2*V1+W1*V2
      V1=T1
      IF(ABS(V1)+ABS(V2).LT.1.E-25)GO TO 22
      R=R+AR(I)*V1-AI(I)*V2
      C=C+AI(I)*V1+AR(I)*V2
      PR=PR+(AR(I)*V1-AI(I)*V2)*FLOAT(I-1)
      PC=PC+(AI(I)*V1+AR(I)*V2)*FLOAT(I-1)
   21 CONTINUE
   22 CONTINUE
      PR=PR/RHO
      PC=PC/RHO
 5001 RETURN
      END
      SUBROUTINE CDIV(ARG,AIG,BRG,BIG,NA,NB,QRG,QIG)
      DIMENSION ARG(9999),AIG(9999),BRG(9999),BIG(9999),
     &QRG(9999),QIG(9999)
      I1=NA-NB+1
      DO 61 J1=1,I1
      QRG(J1)=0.
   61 QIG(J1)=0.
  101 KMAX=NA-NB+1
      DO 391 KK=1,KMAX
      K=KK-1
  201 TEMPR=0.
      TEMPI=0.
      IF(K-1) 301,211,211
  211 DO 291 JJ=1,K
      J=JJ-1
      I1=NB-K+J
      IF(I1) 291,221,221
  221 I2=NA-NB-J
      TEMPR=TEMPR+BRG(I1+1)*QRG(I2+1)-BIG(I1+1)*QIG(I2+1)
      TEMPI=TEMPI+BIG(I1+1)*QRG(I2+1)+BRG(I1+1)*QIG(I2+1)
  291 CONTINUE
  301 I1=NA-NB-K
      I2=NA-K
      QRG(I1+1)=ARG(I2+1)-TEMPR
      QIG(I1+1)=AIG(I2+1)-TEMPI
  391 CONTINUE
 5001 RETURN
      END
      SUBROUTINE CMTALG(ARG,AIG,BRG,BIG,CRG,CIG,NA,NB)
      DIMENSION ARG(9999),AIG(9999),BRG(9999),BIG(9999),
     & CRG(9999),CIG(9999)
    1 NAPL1=NA+1
      NBPL1=NB+1
      NCPL1=NA+NB+1
      DO 91 J1=1,NCPL1
      TEMPR=0.
      TEMPI=0.
      DO 81 J2=1,J1
      IF(J2-NAPL1) 61,61,81
   61 N2=J1-J2+1
      IF(N2-NBPL1) 71,71,81
   71 TEMPR=TEMPR+ARG(J2)*BRG(N2)-AIG(J2)*BIG(N2)
      TEMPI=TEMPI+AIG(J2)*BRG(N2)+ARG(J2)*BIG(N2)
   81 CONTINUE
      CRG(J1)=TEMPR
```

```
      CIG(J1)=TEMPI
   91 CONTINUE
 5001 RETURN
      END
      SUBROUTINE ARCTA(X,Y,ANGLE)
      PI=3.14159265
      IF(X) 10,30,20
   10 ANGLE=ATAN(Y/X)+PI*SIGN(1.,Y)
      RETURN
   20 ANGLE=ATAN(Y/X)
      RETURN
   30 IF(Y)40,60,50
   40 ANGLE=-PI/2.
      RETURN
   50 ANGLE=PI/2.
      RETURN
   60 ANGLE=0.
      RETURN
      END
      SUBROUTINE CGRAD(A,AI,N,XZ,YZ)
      DIMENSION A(9999),AI(9999),X(3),Y(3),RP(3),CP(3),
     & RHO(3),PHI(3),ABSP(3),PR(3),PC(3)
      PI=3.14159265
      MTST=1
  101 XZ=0.0
      YZ=1.0
      DZ=2.
      RHOZ=1.
      PHIZ=PI/2.
  201 CALL CPOLY(N,A,AI,RZ,CZ,PRZ,PCZ,RHOZ,PHIZ)
  221 SU=SQRT(PRZ**2+PCZ**2)
      ABSPZ=SQRT(RZ**2+CZ**2)
      U=2.*ABSPZ*SU
      PSI=ATAN(U)
      TOP=RZ*PCZ-CZ*PRZ
      BOT=-(RZ*PRZ+CZ*PCZ)
      CALL ARCTA(BOT,TOP,THETA)
      COSI=COS(THETA+PHIZ)
      SINE=SIN(THETA+PHIZ)
      IF(ABSPZ) 300,5001,300
  300 IF(SU) 301,501,301
  301 IF(RHOZ) 321,401,321
  321 IF(ABSPZ/(RHOZ*SU)-1.E-7) 5001,5001,701
  351 IF(ABSPZ/(RHOZ*SU)-10.**(-MTST)) 801,801,401
  401 DZ=DZ/8.0
      IM=0
      DO 431 I=1,3
      DZ=2.*DZ
      X(I)=XZ+DZ*COSI
      Y(I)=YZ+DZ*SINE
      RHO(I)=SQRT(X(I)**2+Y(I)**2)
      CALL ARCTA(X(I), Y(I), PHI(I))
      CALL CPOLY(N,A,AI,RP(I),CP(I),PR(I),PC(I),
     & RHO(I),PHI(I))
      ABSP(I)=SQRT(RP(I)**2+CP(I)**2)
      IF(ABSPZ-ABSP(I)) 431,431,421
  421 ABSPZ=ABSP(I)
      IM=I
  431 CONTINUE
      IF(IM) 441,441,461
  441 DZ=DZ/8.
      IF(RHOZ) 443,445,443
  443 IF(DZ/RHOZ-1.E-7) 451,451,401
  445 IF(DZ-1.E-7) 451,451,501
  451 IF(SU-ABSPZ) 501,501,5001
  461 DZ=(2.**(IM-2))*DZ
      XZ=X(IM)
      YZ=Y(IM)
      PHIZ=PHI(IM)
```

```
        PRZ=PR(IM)
        PCZ=PC(IM)
        RHOZ=RHO(IM)
        RZ=RP(IM)
        CZ=CP(IM)
        GO TO 221
501     DZ=1.0
        DTHETA=PI/10.
521     THETA=0.0
        DO 561 I=1,20
        THETA=THETA+DTHETA
        XS=XZ+DZ*COS(PHIZ+THETA)
        YS=YZ+DZ*SIN(PHIZ+THETA)
        RHOS=SQRT(XS**2+YS**2)
        CALL ARCTA(XS,YS,PHIS)
        CALL CPOLY(N,A,AI,RS,CS,PRS,PCS,RHOS,PHIS)
        ABSP(1)=SQRT(RS**2+CS**2)
        IF(ABSPZ-ABSP(1))561,561,601
561     CONTINUE
        DZ=DZ/2.
        IF(RHOS) 563,565,563
563     IF(DZ/RHOS-1.E-7) 5001,5001,521
565     IF(DZ-1.E-7) 5001,5001,521
601     XZ=XS
        YZ=YS
        PHIZ=PHIS
        RHOZ=RHOS
        ABSPZ=ABSP(1)
        PRZ=PRS
        PCZ=PCS
        RZ=RS
        CZ=CS
        GO TO 221
701     IF(PSI-1.E-6) 711,711,351
711     IF(SU-ABSPZ) 501,501,351
801     RHO(1)=RHOZ+BOT/SU**2
        IF(RHO(1))901,901,816
816     PHI(1)=PHIZ+TOP/(RHOZ*SU**2)
821     CALL CPOLY(N,A,AI,RZ,CZ,PRZ,PCZ,RHO(1),PHI(1))
        ABSP(1)=SQRT(RZ**2+CZ**2)
        IF(ABSP(1)-ABSPZ)851,901,901
841     XZ=RHOZ*COS(PHIZ)
        YZ=RHOZ*SIN(PHIZ)
        GO TO 5001
851     RHOZ=RHO(1)
        ABSPZ=ABSP(1)
        PHIZ=PHI(1)
        SU=SQRT(PRZ**2+PCZ**2)
        BOT=-(RZ*PRZ+CZ*PCZ)
        TOP=RZ*PCZ-CZ*PRZ
        IF(SU) 855,501,855
855     U=2.*ABSPZ*SU
        PSI=ATAN(U)
        IF(ABSPZ/(RHOZ*SU)-10.**(-MTST)) 861,861,901
861     IF(ABSPZ/(RHOZ*SU)-1.E-7) 841,841,871
871     IF(PSI-1.E-6) 881,881,801
881     IF(SU-ABSPZ) 501,501,901
901     DZ=ABSPZ/SU
        XZ=RHOZ*COS(PHIZ)
        YZ=RHOZ*SIN(PHIZ)
        MTST=MTST+1
        GO TO 201
5001    RETURN
        END
        COMPLEX FUNCTION ADMIT(X)
        REAL P0(5,6),Q(5,6),G(3,6),H(3,3),EPSIL(3)
       &,CE(4,4),DE(4,4)
        REAL V(4,2),DB(4,2),X1(4,2),X2(4,2)
       &,V2(4),B(4),KAPA2(4)
```

```
      REAL R(9),EINI(18),CINI(36),EPSINI(9)
      LOGICAL METAL,TEST,DAC,ESSAI,LENT,PIEZO
      COMPLEX PHI,Z,DADMIT
      COMMON R,EINI,CINI,EPSINI,RAU
      COMMON /COMPHI/PO,Q,G,H,EPSIL,CE,DE,METAL,KTYP
      COMMON/IMPRI/TEST,VV1,DAC,ESSAI,LENT,PIEZO,KRAC
      COMMON /COMY/ KY,EPSTBF,EPSBF,V,DB,MODIF,X1,X2,AM
      COMMON /JAC/EPSHF,V2,B,KAPA2
      METAL=.FALSE.
      ADMIT=PHI(X)
      METAL=.TRUE.
      ADMIT=ADMIT/PHI(X)
      BM=3.141592653
      BM=-BM*.36/EPSHF
      ADMIT=ADMIT*BM
      U=SQRT(1.E11*X/RAU)
      Z=1./ADMIT
      IF(PIEZO)PRINT 1,U,ADMIT,Z
      RETURN
    1 FORMAT(1X,F10.4,1X,"Y=",2(E12.6,2X),
     &" Z=",2(E12.6,2X))
      END
      FUNCTION AIGMIT(X)
      COMPLEX ADMIT
      AIGMIT=AIMAG(ADMIT(X))
      RETURN
      END
      SUBROUTINE MAXMIN(Z,A,B,NR,ND)
      COMPLEX Z(1),CMPLX
      REAL A(1),B(1),DIS(8,8)
      DO 10 I=1,NR
      DO 10 J=1,ND
   10 DIS(I,J)=CABS(Z(I)-CMPLX(A(J),B(J)))
      DO 30 K=1,NR
      DMIN=1.E12
      DO 20 I=1,NR
      DO 20 J=1,ND
      IF(DIS(I,J).GT.DMIN)GO TO 20
      I1=I
      J1=J
      DMIN=DIS(I1,J1)
   20 CONTINUE
      Z(I1)=CMPLX(A(J1),B(J1))
      DO 25 I=1,NR
   25 DIS(I,J1)=1.E12
      DO 30 J=1,ND
   30 DIS(I1,J)=1.E12
      RETURN
      END
```

SPPSI

Library routines SPPSI used by SURFTSS.

```
      SUBROUTINE CODE(I,I1,I2)
*Voigt convention
      IF(I.GT.6)GO TO 10
      GO TO (1,2,3,4,5,6),I
    1 I1=1;I2=1;RETURN
    2 I1=2;I2=2;RETURN
    3 I1=3;I2=3;RETURN
    4 I1=2;I2=3;RETURN
    5 I1=3;I2=1;RETURN
```

```
    6 I1=1;I2=2;RETURN
   10 PRINT:"CODE I=",I
      STOP"ERROR"
      END
      SUBROUTINE INVCOD(I,I1,I2)
*Inverse Voigt convention
      IF(I1.GT.3.OR.I2.GT.3)GO TO 20
      IF(I1.NE.I2)GO TO 10
      I=I1;RETURN
   10 J1=MINO(I1,I2);J2=MAXO(I1,I2)
      IF(J1.NE.2)GOTO 15
      I=4;RETURN
   15 IF(J2.NE.2)GO TO 18
      I=6;RETURN
   18 I=5;RETURN
   20 PRINT:"INVCOD I1 I2 ",I1,I2
      STOP"ERROR"
      END
      FUNCTION EPS(I1,I2)
*Permittivity tensor rotation
      COMMON R,EINI,CINI,EPSINI,RAU,ALINI
      REAL R(3,3),EINI(3,6),CINI(6,6),EPSINI(3,3)
      EPS=0.
      DO 10 K1=1,3
      DO 10 K2=1,3
   10 EPS=EPS+EPSINI(K1,K2)*R(I1,K1)*R(I2,K2)
      RETURN
      END
      FUNCTION E(I1,J)
*Piezoelectric tensor rotation
      COMMON R,EINI,CINI,EPSINI,RAU,ALINI
      REAL R(3,3),EINI(3,6),CINI(6,6),EPSINI(3,3)
      CALL CODE(J,J1,J2)
      E=0.
      DO 10 K1=1,3
      DO 10 L1=1,3
      DO 10 L2=1,3
      CALL INVCOD(L,L1,L2)
   10 E=E+EINI(K1,L)*R(I1,K1)*R(J1,L1)*R(J2,L2)
      RETURN
      END
      FUNCTION C(I,J)
*elastic tensor rotation
      COMMON R,EINI,CINI,EPSINI,RAU,ALINI
      REAL R(3,3),EINI(3,6),CINI(6,6),EPSINI(3,3)
      CALL CODE(I,I1,I2)
      CALL CODE(J,J1,J2)
      C=0.
      DO 10 K1=1,3
      DO 10 K2=1,3
      CALL INVCOD(K,K1,K2)
      DO 10 L1=1,3
      DO 10 L2=1,3
      CALL INVCOD(L,L1,L2)
   10 C=C+CINI(K,L)*R(I1,K1)*R(I2,K2)*R(J1,L1)*R(J2,L2)
      RETURN
      END
      SUBROUTINE VOLOND(VV)
*Computation of bulk acoustic velocities
*VV(i),i=1,3 : RAU*v2 . 1.E-11
      COMMON R,EINI,CINI,EPSINI,RAU,ALINI
      COMMON /BULK/IPIEZO
      REAL VV(1)
      REAL R(3,3),EINI(3,6),CINI(6,6),EPSINI(3,3)
      REAL G(3,3),P(9),Y(4),V2(9),AV(9)
      G(1,1)=C(1,1);G(1,2)=C(1,6);G(1,3)=C(1,5)
      G(2,1)=C(1,2);G(2,2)=C(6,6);G(2,3)=C(6,5)
      G(3,1)=G(1,3);G(3,2)=G(2,3);G(3,3)=C(5,5)
      IF(IPIEZO.EQ.0)GO TO 20
```

```
      Y(1)=E(1,1);Y(2)=E(1,6);Y(3)=E(1,5)
      EPSILON=EPS(1,1)
      DO 10 I=1,3
      DO 10 J=1,3
   10 G(I,J)=G(I,J)+Y(I)*Y(J)/EPSILON
   20 P(1)=1.
      P(2)=-G(1,1)-G(2,2)-G(3,3)
      P(3)=G(1,1)*G(2,2)-G(1,2)*G(2,1)
     &       +G(2,2)*G(3,3)-G(2,3)*G(3,2)
     &       +G(3,3)*G(1,1)-G(3,1)*G(1,3)
      P(4)=-G(1,1)*(G(2,2)*G(3,3)-G(2,3)*G(3,2))
     &       +G(2,1)*(G(1,2)*G(3,3)-G(1,3)*G(3,2))
     &       -G(3,1)*(G(1,2)*G(2,3)-G(1,3)*G(2,2))
*Use system routine POLRTS to compute the real roots VV
*of P(z); Imaginary part VA of the roots vanished
      N=3; CALL POLRTS(P,V2,VA,N,NFOUND)
      VV(1)=V2(1);VV(2)=V2(2);VV(3)=V2(3)
      IF(NFOUND.EQ.N)RETURN
      PRINT:"Error VOLOND : roots not found"
      RETURN
      END
      COMPLEX FUNCTION POLPRO(A,B,NA,NB,K)
      REAL A(9),B(9)
      KA=NA+1
      KB=NB+1
      CPLPRO=.0
      KS=MIN0(K,KA)
      KT=MIN0(K,KB)
      KI=K+1-KT
      DO 10 I=KI,KS
      KM=K+1-I
      IF(ABS(A(I)).LE..0.OR.ABS(B(KM)).LE..0)GO TO 10
      KEST=-ALOG(ABS(A(I)))-ALOG(ABS(B(KM)))
      IF(KEST.GT.50)GO TO 10
      POLPRO=POLPRO+A(I)*B(KM)
   10 CONTINUE
      RETURN
      END
*VPOL
      COMPLEX FUNCTION VPOL(Z,COEFF,DEGRE)
      INTEGER DEGRE
      COMPLEX Z
      REAL COEFF(9)
      VPOL=.0
      I=DEGRE+1
      DO 5 K=1,I
    5 VPOL=VPOL*Z+COEFF(K)
      RETURN
      END
      SUBROUTINE NORMA(X)
*Normalize 3-vector X(i), i=1,3
      REAL X(3)
      A=0.
      DO 10 I=1,3
   10 A=A+X(I)**2
      A=SQRT(A)
      DO 20 I=1,3
   20 X(I)=X(I)/A
      RETURN
      END
      SUBROUTINE PVEC(X1,X2,Y)
*Vector product Y = X1 x X2
      REAL X1(3),X2(3),Y(3)
      Y(1) = X1(2)*X2(3)-X1(3)*X2(2)
      Y(2) = X1(3)*X2(1)-X1(1)*X2(3)
      Y(3) = X1(1)*X2(2)-X1(2)*X2(1)
      RETURN
      END
```

CONVER

Library routine CONVER to translate crystal orientation angles into CUT and DIRECTION coordinates.

```
      SUBROUTINE CONVER(XC,XD)
*CUT = XC (3) ; DIRECTION = XD (3)
*Define crystal orientation : ALPHA, TETA, PHI
      CHARACTER REP
      REAL R(3,3),XC(3),XD(3)
      REAL XT(3)
      PI=3.141592654
   10 PRINT:"ALPHA (DEGREES) ?"
      READ:AL;ALPHA=AL*PI/180.
      PRINT:"TETA (DEGREES) ?"
      READ:TE;TETA=PI/180.*TE
      PRINT:"PHI (DEGREES) ?"
      READ:PH;PHI=PI/180.*PH
      XD(1)=-SIN(TETA)
      XD(2)=COS(TETA)
      XD(3)=0.
      XC(1)=SIN(PHI)*COS(TETA)
      XC(2)=SIN(PHI)*SIN(TETA)
      XC(3)=COS(PHI)
*Normalise unitary vector XC
      CALL NORMA(XC)
*Normalise unitary vector XD
      CALL NORMA(XD)
      CALL PVEC(XC,XD,XT)
      CALL NORMA(XT)
      CALL PVEC(XT,XC,XD)
      CO=COS(ALPHA);SI=SIN(ALPHA)
*Define matrix R for tensor rotation
      DO 90 IX=1,3
      R(1,IX)=CO*XD(IX)+SI*XT(IX)
      R(2,IX)=XC(IX)
   90 R(3,IX)=-SI*XD(IX)+CO*XT(IX)
      PRINT 9002,(R(2,IX),IX=1,3)
      PRINT 9001,(R(1,IX),IX=1,3)
      PRINT:" "
      DO 100 I=1,3
      XC(I)=R(2,I)
  100 XD(I)=R(1,I)
      RETURN
 9001 FORMAT(" DIR  ",3F13.6)
 9002 FORMAT(" CUT  ",3F13.6)
      END
```

MATERIAU

Data file of piezoelectric material constants LiNbO3, Bil2GeO2O(BIGO), LiTaO3, TeO2, Quartz, Banana, PZTs, ADP, PKN, Tl3VS4, Tl3TaSe4, Tl3TaS4, AlPO4, Basito, Selenium, Tellure, AsGa, InP.

```
LINBO3   +4.70000000E+03    E  (3,1)=+.200000E+00    C  (1,4)=+.900000E+10
E  (1,5)=+.370000E+01      E  (3,2)=+.200000E+00    C  (2,2)=+.203000E+12
E  (1,6)=-.250000E+01      E  (3,3)=+.130000E+01    C  (2,3)=+.750000E+11
E  (2,1)=-.250000E+01      C  (1,1)=+.203000E+12    C  (2,4)=-.900000E+10
E  (2,2)=+.250000E+01      C  (1,2)=+.530000E+11    C  (3,3)=+.245000E+12
E  (2,4)=+.370000E+01      C  (1,3)=+.750000E+11    C  (4,4)=+.600000E+11
```

```
C   (5,5)=+.600000E+11
C   (5,6)=+.900000E+10
C   (6,6)=+.750000E+11
EPS(1,1)=+.440000E+02
EPS(2,2)=+.440000E+02
EPS(3,3)=+.290000E+02
ET1(1,5)=+.147000E-03
ET1(1,6)=+.790000E-04
ET1(2,1)=+.790000E-04
ET1(2,2)=+.790000E-04
ET1(2,4)=+.147000E-03
ET1(3,1)=+.221000E-03
ET1(3,2)=+.221000E-03
ET1(3,3)=+.887000E-03
CT1(1,1)=-.174000E-03
CT1(1,2)=-.252000E-03
CT1(1,3)=-.159000E-03
CT1(1,4)=-.214000E-03
CT1(2,1)=-.174000E-03
CT1(2,3)=-.159000E-03
CT1(2,4)=-.214000E-03
CT1(3,3)=-.153000E-03
CT1(4,4)=-.204000E-03
CT1(5,5)=-.204000E-03
CT1(5,6)=-.214000E-03
CT1(6,6)=-.143000E-03
PT1(1,1)=+.323000E-03
PT1(2,2)=+.323000E-03
PT1(3,3)=+.627000E-03
AT1(1)  =+.154000E-04
AT1(2)  =+.154000E-04
AT1(3)  =+.750000E-05
TTT     =+.250000E+02
END
BIGO        +9.20000000E+03
C   (1,1)=+.128000E+12
C   (2,2)=+.128000E+12
C   (3,3)=+.128000E+12
C   (1,2)=+.305000E+11
C   (2,3)=+.305000E+11
C   (3,1)=+.305000E+11
C   (4,4)=+.255000E+11
C   (5,5)=+.255000E+11
C   (6,6)=+.255000E+11
E   (1,4)=+.990000E+00
E   (2,5)=+.990000E+00
E   (3,6)=+.990000E+00
EPS(1,1)=+.387000E+02
EPS(2,2)=+.387000E+02
EPS(3,3)=+.387000E+02
END
LITAO3      +7.45400000E+03
E   (1,5)=+.272000E+01
E   (1,6)=-.167000E+01
E   (2,1)=-.167000E+01
E   (2,2)=+.167000E+01
E   (2,4)=+.272000E+01
E   (3,1)=-.380000E+00
E   (3,2)=-.380000E+00
E   (3,3)=+.109000E+01
C   (1,1)=+.229800E+12
C   (1,2)=+.440000E+11
C   (1,3)=+.812000E+11
C   (1,4)=-.104000E+11
C   (2,2)=+.229800E+12
C   (2,3)=+.812000E+11
C   (2,4)=+.104000E+11
C   (3,3)=+.279800E+12
C   (4,4)=+.968000E+11

C   (5,5)=+.968000E+11
C   (5,6)=-.104000E+11
C   (6,6)=+.929000E+11
EPS(1,1)=+.426000E+02
EPS(2,2)=+.426000E+02
EPS(3,3)=+.429000E+02
ET1(1,5)=-.132000E-03
ET1(1,6)=-.600000E-04
ET1(2,1)=-.600000E-04
ET1(2,2)=-.600000E-04
ET1(2,4)=-.132000E-03
ET1(3,1)=+.870000E-04
ET1(3,2)=+.870000E-04
ET1(3,3)=+.154000E-03
ET2(1,5)=-.717000E-06
ET2(1,6)=-.628000E-06
ET2(2,1)=-.628000E-06
ET2(2,2)=-.628000E-06
ET2(2,4)=-.717000E-06
ET2(3,1)=+.518000E-05
ET2(3,2)=+.518000E-05
ET2(3,3)=+.141000E-06
CT1(1,1)=-.103000E-03
CT1(1,2)=-.341000E-03
CT1(1,3)=-.500000E-04
CT1(1,4)=+.667000E-03
CT1(2,2)=-.103000E-03
CT1(2,3)=-.500000E-04
CT1(2,4)=+.667000E-03
CT1(3,3)=-.960000E-04
CT1(4,4)=-.430000E-04
CT1(5,5)=-.430000E-04
CT1(5,6)=+.667000E-03
CT1(6,6)=-.470000E-04
CT2(1,1)=+.770000E-07
CT2(1,2)=-.118000E-06
CT2(1,3)=+.600000E-06
CT2(1,4)=+.167000E-05
CT2(2,2)=+.770000E-07
CT2(2,3)=+.600000E-06
CT2(2,4)=+.167000E-05
CT2(3,3)=-.321000E-06
CT2(4,4)=+.167000E-06
CT2(5,5)=+.167000E-06
CT2(5,6)=+.167000E-06
CT2(6,6)=+.124000E-06
PT1(1,1)=+.329000E-03
PT1(2,2)=+.329000E-03
PT1(3,3)=+.116000E-02
PT2(1,1)=+.428000E-06
PT2(2,2)=+.428000E-06
PT2(3,3)=+.780000E-05
AT1(1)  =+.161000E-04
AT1(2)  =+.161000E-04
AT1(3)  =+.410000E-05
AT2(1)  =+.700000E-08
AT2(2)  =+.700000E-08
AT2(3)  =-.100000E-07
TTT     =+.250000E+02
END
TEO2        +5.99000000E+03
C   (1,1)=+.557000E+11
C   (1,2)=+.512000E+11
C   (1,3)=+.218000E+11
C   (2,2)=+.557000E+11
C   (2,3)=+.218000E+11
C   (3,3)=+.105800E+12
C   (4,4)=+.265000E+11
C   (5,5)=+.265000E+11

C   (6,6)=+.659000E+11
E   (1,4)=+.021600E+01
E   (2,5)=-.021600E+01
EPS(1,1)=+.201000E+02
EPS(2,2)=+.201000E+02
EPS(3,3)=+.219000E+02
END
QUARTZ      +2.65000000E+03
C   (1,1)=+.867400E+11
C   (1,2)=+.699000E+10
C   (1,3)=+.119100E+11
C   (1,4)=-.179100E+11
C   (2,2)=+.867400E+11
C   (2,3)=+.119100E+11
C   (2,4)=+.179100E+11
C   (3,3)=+.107200E+12
C   (4,4)=+.579400E+11
C   (5,5)=+.579400E+11
C   (5,6)=+.179100E+11
C   (6,6)=+.398800E+11
E   (1,1)=+.171000E+00
E   (1,2)=-.171000E+00
E   (1,4)=-.040600E+00
E   (2,5)=+.040600E+00
E   (2,6)=-.171000E+00
EPS(1,1)=+.450000E+01
EPS(2,2)=+.450000E+01
EPS(3,3)=+.460000E+01
CT1(1,1)=-.443000E-04
CT1(1,2)=-.299300E-02
CT1(1,3)=-.492000E-03
CT1(1,4)=+.980000E-04
CT1(2,2)=-.443000E-04
CT1(2,3)=-.492000E-03
CT1(2,4)=+.980000E-04
CT1(3,3)=-.188000E-03
CT1(4,4)=-.172000E-03
CT1(5,5)=-.172000E-03
CT1(5,6)=+.980000E-04
CT1(6,6)=+.180000E-03
CT2(1,1)=-.407000E-06
CT2(1,2)=-.724500E-05
CT2(1,3)=-.596000E-06
CT2(1,4)=-.130000E-07
CT2(2,2)=-.407000E-06
CT2(2,3)=-.596000E-06
CT2(2,4)=-.130000E-07
CT2(3,3)=-.141200E-05
CT2(4,4)=-.225000E-06
CT2(5,5)=-.225000E-06
CT2(5,6)=-.130000E-07
CT2(6,6)=+.201000E-06
ET1(1,1)=-.160000E-03
ET1(1,2)=-.160000E-03
ET1(1,4)=-.144000E-02
ET1(2,5)=-.144000E-02
ET1(2,6)=-.160000E-03
PT1(1,1)=+.280000E-04
PT1(2,2)=+.280000E-04
PT1(3,3)=+.390000E-04
AT1(1)  =+.980000E-05
AT1(2)  =+.980000E-05
AT1(3)  =+.560000E-05
AT2(1)  =+.204000E-07
AT2(2)  =+.204000E-07
AT2(3)  =+.940000E-08
TTT     =+.200000E+02
END
BANANA      +5.30000000E+03
```

```
C  (1,1)=+.239000E+12        E  (2,5)= .153    E-01        C  (1,3)=+.140000E+11
C  (1,2)=+.104000E+12        E  (3,6)=-.294    E 00        C  (2,3)=+.140000E+11
C  (1,3)=+.500000E+11        EPS(1,1)= .574    E 2         C  (4,4)=+.410000E+10
C  (2,2)=+.247    E+12       EPS(2,2)= .574    E 2         C  (5,5)=+.410000E+10
C  (2,3)= .520    E 11       EPS(3,3)= .141    E 2         C  (6,6)=+.410000E+10
C  (3,3)= .135    E 12       END                          E  (1,4)=+.320000E+00
C  (4,4)= .650    E 11       PKN       +6.14000000E+03     E  (2,5)=+.320000E+00
C  (5,5)= .660    E 11       C  (1,1)=+.166000E+12         E  (3,6)=+.320000E+00
C  (6,6)= .760    E 11       C  (1,2)=+.037000E+12         EPS(1,1)=+.101000E+02
E  (1,5)= .280    E 01       C  (1,3)=+.045000E+12         EPS(2,2)=+.101000E+02
E  (2,4)= .340    E 01       C  (2,2)=+.161000E+12         EPS(3,3)=+.101000E+02
E  (3,1)=-.400    E 00       C  (2,3)=+.041000E+12         CT1(1,1)=-.697000E-03
E  (3,2)=-.300    E 00       C  (3,3)=+.124000E+12         CT1(2,2)=-.697000E-03
E  (3,3)= .430    E 01       C  (4,4)=+.031000E+12         CT1(3,3)=-.697000E-03
EPS(1,1)= .222    E 03       C  (5,5)=+.030000E+12         CT1(1,2)=+.243000E-03
EPS(2,2)= .227    E 03       C  (6,6)=+.063000E+12         CT1(1,3)=+.243000E-03
EPS(3,3)= .320    E 02       E  (1,5)=+.140000E+02         CT1(2,3)=+.243000E-03
CT1(1,1)=-.200000E-03        E  (2,4)=+.150000E+02         CT1(4,4)=+.146000E-03
CT1(1,2)=+.000000E-00        E  (3,1)=+.400000E+00         CT1(5,5)=+.146000E-03
CT1(1,3)=+.000000E-00        E  (3,2)=+.140000E+01         CT1(6,6)=+.146000E-03
CT1(2,2)=-.140000E-03        E  (3,3)=+.690000E+01         AT1(1)  =+.250000E-04
CT1(2,3)=-.800000E-03        EPS(1,1)=+.810000E+03         AT1(2)  =+.250000E-04
CT1(3,3)=-.540000E-03        EPS(2,2)=+.680000E+03         AT1(3)  =+.250000E-04
CT1(4,4)=+.000000E-00        EPS(3,3)=+.810000E+03         TTT     =+.250000E+02
CT1(5,5)=+.000000E-00        END                          END
CT1(6,6)=+.000000E-00        TL3VS4    +6.14000000E+03     TL3TS4    +6.79000000E+03
ET1(1,5)=-.600000E-03        C  (1,1)=+.485000E+11         C  (1,1)=+.491000E+11
ET1(2,4)=-.600000E-03        C  (2,2)=+.485000E+11         C  (2,2)=+.491000E+11
ET1(3,1)=+.387800E-02        C  (3,3)=+.485000E+11         C  (3,3)=+.491000E+11
ET1(3,2)=+.104410E-01        C  (1,2)=+.165000E+11         C  (1,2)=+.113000E+11
ET1(3,3)=-.361000E-03        C  (1,3)=+.165000E+11         C  (1,3)=+.113000E+11
PT1(1,1)=-.200000E-02        C  (2,3)=+.165000E+11         C  (2,3)=+.113000E+11
PT1(2,2)=-.200000E-02        C  (4,4)=+.470000E+10         C  (4,4)=+.320000E+10
PT1(3,3)=+.200000E-04        C  (5,5)=+.470000E+10         C  (5,5)=+.320000E+10
AT1(1)  =+.111111E-04        C  (6,6)=+.470000E+10         C  (6,6)=+.320000E+10
AT1(2)  =+.111111E-04        E  (1,4)=+.550000E+00         E  (1,4)=+.340000E+00
AT1(3)  =+.600000E-05        E  (2,5)=+.550000E+00         E  (2,5)=+.340000E+00
TTT     =+.250000E+02        E  (3,6)=+.550000E+00         E  (3,6)=+.340000E+00
END                          EPS(1,1)=+.348000E+02         EPS(1,1)=+.134000E+02
PZTS    +4.        E+03       EPS(2,2)=+.348000E+02         EPS(2,2)=+.134000E+02
C  (1,1)= .139    E 12        EPS(3,3)=+.348000E+02         EPS(3,3)=+.134000E+02
C  (1,2)= .778    E 11        CT1(1,1)=-.572000E-03         CT1(1,1)=-.583000E-03
C  (1,3)= .743    E 11        CT1(2,2)=-.572000E-03         CT1(2,2)=-.583000E-03
C  (2,2)= .139    E 12        CT1(3,3)=-.572000E-03         CT1(3,3)=-.583000E-03
C  (2,3)= .743    E 11        CT1(1,2)=-.210000E-03         CT1(1,2)=-.204000E-03
C  (3,3)= .115    E 12        CT1(1,3)=-.210000E-03         CT1(1,3)=-.204000E-03
C  (4,4)= .256    E 11        CT1(2,3)=-.210000E-03         CT1(2,3)=-.204000E-03
C  (5,5)= .256    E 11        CT1(4,4)=+.098000E-03         CT1(4,4)=+.570000E-03
C  (6,6)= .306    E 11        CT1(5,5)=+.098000E-03         CT1(5,5)=+.570000E-03
E  (1,5)= .127    E 2         CT1(6,6)=+.098000E-03         CT1(6,6)=+.570000E-03
E  (2,4)= .127    E 2         CT2(4,4)=-.570000E-06         AT1(1)  =+.180000E-04
E  (3,1)=-.520    E 1         CT2(5,5)=-.570000E-06         AT1(2)  =+.180000E-04
E  (3,2)=-.520    E 1         CT2(6,6)=-.570000E-06         AT1(3)  =+.180000E-04
E  (3,3)= .151    E 2         AT1(1)  =+.254000E-04         TTT     =+.250000E+02
EPS(1,1)= .730    E 3         AT1(2)  =+.254000E-04         END
EPS(2,2)= .730    E 3         AT1(3)  =+.254000E-04         ALPO4     +2.62000000E+03
EPS(3,3)= .635    E 3         ET1(1,4)=-.320000E-03         C  (1,1)=+.640100E+11
END                          ET1(2,5)=-.320000E-03         C  (1,2)=+.724000E+10
ADP     1.803     E 3         ET1(3,6)=-.320000E-03         C  (1,3)=+.957000E+10
C  (1,1)= .6877   E 10        PT1(1,1)=-.250000E-04         C  (1,4)=-.123500E+11
C  (1,2)= .406    E 10        PT1(2,2)=-.250000E-04         C  (2,2)=+.640100E+11
C  (1,3)= .2038   E 11        PT1(3,3)=-.250000E-04         C  (2,3)=+.957000E+10
C  (2,2)= .6877   E 11        TTT     =+.250000E+02         C  (2,4)=+.123500E+11
C  (2,3)= .2038   E 11        END                          C  (3,3)=+.857600E+11
C  (3,3)= .3402   E 11        TL3TSE    +7.28000000E+03     C  (4,4)=+.431700E+11
C  (4,4)= .862    E 10        C  (1,1)=+.419000E+11         C  (5,5)=+.431700E+11
C  (5,5)= .862    E 10        C  (2,2)=+.419000E+11         C  (5,6)=-.123500E+11
C  (6,6)= .601    E 10        C  (3,3)=+.419000E+11         C  (6,6)=+.283800E+11
E  (1,4)= .153    E-01        C  (1,2)=+.140000E+11         E  (1,1)=-.300000E+00
```

```
E   (1,2)=+.300000E+00
E   (1,4)=+.130000E+00
E   (2,5)=-.130000E+00
E   (2,6)=+.300000E+00
EPS(1,1)=+.588000E+01
EPS(2,2)=+.588000E+01
EPS(3,3)=+.588000E+01
CT1(1,1)=-.757813E-04
CT1(1,2)=-.148611E-02
CT1(1,3)=-.395833E-03
CT1(1,4)=+.717742E-04
CT1(2,2)=-.757813E-04
CT1(2,3)=-.395833E-03
CT1(2,4)=+.717742E-04
CT1(3,3)=-.217949E-03
CT1(4,4)=-.156713E-03
CT1(5,5)=-.156713E-03
CT1(5,6)=+.717742E-04
CT1(6,6)=+.102817E-03
ET1(1,1)=-.260000E-03
ET1(1,2)=-.260000E-03
ET1(1,4)=-.561000E-03
ET1(2,5)=-.561000E-03
ET1(2,6)=-.260000E-03
PT1(1,1)=+.280000E-04
PT1(2,2)=+.280000E-04
PT1(3,3)=+.390000E-04
AT1(1) =+.159000E-04
AT1(2) =+.159000E-04
AT1(3) =+.970000E-05
TTT    =+.250000E+02
END
BASITO   +4.45000000E+03
C   (1,1)=+.140000E+12
C   (1,2)=+.360000E+11
C   (1,3)=+.240000E+11
C   (2,2)=+.140000E+12
C   (2,3)=+.240000E+11
C   (3,3)=+.830000E+11
C   (4,4)=+.330000E+11
C   (5,5)=+.330000E+11
C   (6,6)=+.590000E+11
E   (1,5)=+.600500E+00
E   (2,4)=+.600500E+00
E   (3,1)=+.575700E+00
E   (3,2)=+.575700E+00
E   (3,3)=+.443000E+00
EPS(1,1)=+.150000E+02
EPS(2,2)=+.150000E+02
EPS(3,3)=+.110000E+02
CT1(1,1)=-.340000E-03
CT1(1,2)=-.300000E-03
CT1(1,3)=-.370000E-03
CT1(2,2)=-.340000E-03
CT1(2,3)=-.370000E-03
CT1(3,3)=-.150000E-03
CT1(4,4)=-.740000E-04

CT1(5,5)=-.740000E-04
CT1(6,6)=-.150000E-03
AT1(1) =+.980000E-05
AT1(2) =+.980000E-05
AT1(3) =+.103000E-04
TTT    =+.200000E+02
END
SELENI   +4.80000000E+03
C   (1,1)=+.198000E+11
C   (1,2)=+.660000E+10
C   (1,3)=+.202000E+11
C   (1,4)=+.720000E+10
C   (2,2)=+.198000E+11
C   (2,3)=+.202000E+11
C   (2,4)=-.720000E+10
C   (3,3)=+.836000E+11
C   (4,4)=+.183000E+11
C   (5,5)=+.183000E+11
C   (5,6)=+.720000E+10
C   (6,6)=+.660000E+10
E   (1,1)=+.320000E+00
E   (1,2)=-.320000E+00
E   (1,4)=+.100000E+00
E   (2,5)=-.100000E+00
E   (2,6)=-.320000E+00
EPS(1,1)=+.757800E+01
EPS(2,2)=+.757800E+01
EPS(3,3)=+.203580E+02
TTT    =+.200000E+02
END
TELLUR   +6.21000000E+03
C   (1,1)=+.325700E+11
C   (1,2)=+.845000E+10
C   (1,3)=+.257000E+11
C   (1,4)=+.123500E+11
C   (2,2)=+.325700E+11
C   (2,3)=+.257000E+11
C   (2,4)=-.123500E+11
C   (3,3)=+.717400E+11
C   (4,4)=+.309400E+11
C   (5,5)=+.309400E+11
C   (5,6)=+.123500E+11
C   (6,6)=+.120600E+11
E   (1,1)=+.100000E+00
E   (1,2)=+.100000E+00
E   (1,4)=+.100000E+00
E   (2,5)=+.100000E+00
E   (2,6)=+.100000E+00
EPS(1,1)=+.100000E+02
EPS(2,2)=+.100000E+02
EPS(3,3)=+.100000E+02
TTT    =+.200000E+02
END
ASGA     +5.31600000E+03
C   (1,1)=+.118800E+12
C   (1,2)=+.538000E+11
C   (1,3)=+.538000E+11

C   (2,2)=+.118800E+12
C   (2,3)=+.538000E+11
C   (3,3)=+.118800E+12
C   (4,4)=+.594000E+11
C   (5,5)=+.594000E+11
C   (6,6)=+.594000E+11
E   (1,4)=+.167000E 00
E   (2,5)=+.167000E 00
E   (3,6)=+.167000E 00
EPS(1,1)=+.110044E+02
EPS(2,2)=+.110044E+02
EPS(3,3)=+.110044E+02
CT1(1,1)=-.970000E-04
CT1(1,2)=-.105000E-03
CT1(1,3)=-.105000E-03
CT1(2,2)=-.970000E-04
CT1(2,3)=-.105000E-03
CT1(3,3)=-.970000E-04
CT1(4,4)=-.970000E-04
CT1(5,5)=-.970000E-04
CT1(6,6)=-.970000E-04
AT1(1) =+.530000E-05
AT1(2) =+.530000E-05
AT1(3) =+.530000E-05
TTT    =+.250000E+02
END
INP      +4.78700000E+03
C   (1,1)=+.102200E+12
C   (1,2)=+.576000E+11
C   (1,3)=+.576000E+11
C   (2,2)=+.102200E+12
C   (2,3)=+.576000E+11
C   (3,3)=+.102200E+12
C   (4,4)=+.460000E+11
C   (5,5)=+.460000E+11
C   (6,6)=+.460000E+11
E   (1,4)=+.110000E 00
E   (2,5)=+.110000E 00
E   (3,6)=+.110000E 00
EPS(1,1)=+.123500E+02
EPS(2,2)=+.123500E+02
EPS(3,3)=+.123500E+02
CT1(1,1)=-.970000E-04
CT1(1,2)=-.105000E-03
CT1(1,3)=-.105000E-03
CT1(2,2)=-.970000E-04
CT1(2,3)=-.105000E-03
CT1(3,3)=-.970000E-04
CT1(4,4)=-.970000E-04
CT1(5,5)=-.970000E-04
CT1(6,6)=-.970000E-04
AT1(1) =+.530000E-05
AT1(2) =+.530000E-05
AT1(3) =+.530000E-05
TTT    =+.250000E+02
END
EOF
```

Appendix K

POM

Program for tracing transducer masks
This program is an example of mask drawing of a SAW transducer.
Some simplifications are used for clarity

```
*#RUN *;/LIBRARY/ATAFIC,R=(ULIB)SERVICE/YT4010,R
******* Example of mask drawing
      COMMON/MSC/DA1,DA2,W1,W2,SHIFTX,SHIFTY,CENTRE,
     &MODE,NBSTOP
      COMMON/C3FAZ/GARDE,XVERU,YVERU,EMPA3,INET
      COMMON/COMB/W,LAMBDA,APERTURE,FRAME,
     &TAP,GAP,ISIGN,IDOUBL
      COMMON/ELEC/XELEC,YELEC,SHIFLEFT,SHIFRIGH
      COMMON /FILE/IFICHE
      REAL LAMBDA
      LOGICAL FRAME,TAP,CENTRE
*Define the sizes
      PAS=0.3
      CENTRE=.TRUE.
      LAMBDA=PAS
      W=10.
      APERTURE=1.1*W
      GAP=0.1*W
      FRAME=.TRUE.
      SHIFTY=0.25*W
      YELEC=SHIFTY
      GARDE=4.*LAMBDA;EMPA3=1.05*W
      XVERU=LAMBDA/6.
      YVERU=XVERU
      INET=0
    1 CONTINUE
*Define input transducer file : T(K),A(K),Numb of weights
*IFICHE=0 for regular comb
      IFICHE=19
      IPERME=1
      FILE="/jh/cof;"
      IF(IFICHE.GT.0)
     &CALL ATTACH(IFICHE,FILE,IPERME,0,ISTAT)
      NPHASE=2
      IDOUBL=0
  100 CONTINUE
      CALL POM(NRPLUM,NBELEC)
  200 CONTINUE
*Close drawing file
      CALL PLOT(0.,0.,999)
      REWIND (IFICHE)
      PRINT 9001,
      GO TO 1
 9001 FORMAT(1X,10(/))
      END
*****************************************************
      SUBROUTINE TRACE(X,Y,I)
*Use the relevant program to control the drawing machine
      CALL PLOT(Y,X,I)
      RETURN
      END
      SUBROUTINE POM(NRPLUM,NBELEC)
*Main subroutine to transform the input file into
* plotting orders
      LOGICAL FRAME,TAP
      COMMON/COMB/W,LAMBDA,APERTURE,FRAME,
     &TAP,GAP,ISIGN,IDOUBL
```

```
      COMMON/ELEC/XELEC,YELEC,SHIFLEFT,SHIFRIGH
      REAL A(621),TAU(621),YTOP(621),YBOT(621)
      REAL LAMBDA
      LOGICAL FRAME,TAP
      E=GAP/W
      IF(E.LE.0.)E=0.02
      SIG=ISIGN
      WRITE(6,9011)
 9011 FORMAT(1X,"-----------------------------------")
      WRITE(6,9012)
 9012 FORMAT(1X,"Plot of apodized comb")
      N=NBELEC-1
*Read the input file
      CALL LIFICH(TAU,A,N)
*Compute the sizes of electrodes
      CALL  CALPEI(TAU,A,N,YTOP,YBOT,SIG,ITYPE,W,E)
*Draw the comb
      CALL TRAPEI(TAU,A,N,YTOP,YBOT,SIG,ITYPE,W,LAMBDA,E)
      DO 10 I=1,N
   10 PRINT 9002,I,TAU(I),A(I),YTOP(I)/W,YBOT(I)/W
 9002 FORMAT(1X,I3,4F8.4)
      WRITE(6,9013)N
 9013 FORMAT(1X,"N=",I4)
      WRITE(6,9011)
      RETURN
      END
      SUBROUTINE LIFICH(TAU,A,N)
*Read the input file
      COMMON/FILE/IFICH
      REAL A(1),TAU(1)
      IF(IFICH.LE.0)GO TO 10
      WRITE(6,9014)IFICH
 9014 FORMAT(1X,"FILE :",I2)
      READ(IFICH)N
      READ(IFICH)(TAU(K),K=1,N)
      READ(IFICH)(A(K),K=1,N)
      IF(N.GT.621)STOP"N TOO BIG"
      RETURN
   10 WRITE(6,9015)
 9015 FORMAT(1X,"Regular comb")
      DO 20 K=1,N
      TAU(K)=0.5*K;A(K)=1
   20 CONTINUE
      RETURN
      END
      SUBROUTINE CALPEI(TAU,A,N,YTOP,YBOT,SIG,ITYPE,W,E)
*Compute the electrode sizes
      COMMON/MSC/DA1,DA2,W1,W2,SHIFTX,SHIFTY,CENTRE,
     &MODE,NBSTOP
      COMMON/COMB/WW,AMBDA,APERTURE,FRAME,TAP,GAP,
     &ISIGN,IDOUBL
      LOGICAL CENTRE
      REAL TAU(1),A(1),YTOP(1),YBOT(1)
      INTEGER JJ(621)
      T1=TAU(1);TMAX=T1;TMIN=T1;DTMIN=1.E30
      DO 2 K=2,N
      T2=TAU(K)
      TMAX=AMAX1(T2,TMAX)
      TMIN=AMIN1(T2,TMIN)
      DTMIN=AMIN1(DTMIN,T2-T1)
    2 T1=T2
      T0=0.5*(TMAX+TMIN)
      IF(CENTRE)PRINT:"Central comb"
      IF(.NOT.CENTRE)PRINT:"Non central comb"
      IF(.NOT.CENTRE) T0=TMAX+0.25
      DO 4 K=1,N
    4 TAU(K)=TAU(K)-T0
      ITYPE=1
      IF(ABS(DTMIN).GT.1)ITYPE=2
```

```
      IF(IDOUBL.GT.0)ITYPE=2
      AA=A(1)/2.;BA=ABS(AA)
      J=0;YK=-BA;YK1=-BA
      YTOP(1)=BA
      YBOT(1)=-BA
      IS=-1;JJ(1)=0
      IF(SIG.GT.0.)GO TO 8
      YK=BA;YK1=BA;IS=1
    8 CONTINUE
      DO 30 K=2,N
      IF(A(K)*AA.GE.0.)GO TO 10
      J=J+IS
      GO TO 20
   10 IS=-IS
   20 YK=YK+IS*ABS(A(K))
      JJ(K)=J
      YTOP(K)=AMAX1(YK,YK1)
      YBOT(K)=AMIN1(YK,YK1)
      AA=A(K)
   30 YK1=YK
      NBITER=20
      YMAX=BA;YMIN=-BA
      GAP=E*(YMAX-YMIN)
      DO 50 ITER=1,NBITER
      YMAX=BA;YMIN=-BA
      GAP1=GAP
      DO 40 K=1,N
      YMAX=AMAX1(YMAX,YTOP(K)+JJ(K)*GAP)
      YMIN=AMIN1(YMIN,YBOT(K)+JJ(K)*GAP)
   40 CONTINUE
      GAP=E*(YMAX-YMIN)
   50 IF(ABS((GAP1-GAP)/GAP1).LT.1.E-4)GO TO 100
      PRINT:"<<<<<<<<   ERROR : GAP TOO BIG   >>>>>>>>"
  100 YMOYEN=0.5*(YMAX+YMIN)
      R=W/(YMAX-YMIN)
      GAP=R*GAP;YMOYEN=R*YMOYEN
      DO 110 K=1,N
      YTOP(K)=YTOP(K)*R-YMOYEN+JJ(K)*GAP
      YBOT(K)=YBOT(K)*R-YMOYEN+JJ(K)*GAP
  110 CONTINUE
      RETURN
      END
      SUBROUTINE TRAPEI(TAU,A,N,YTOP,YBOT,SIG,
     &ITYPE,W,LAMBDA,E)
      REAL A(101),TAU(101),YTOP(101),YBOT(101)
      REAL LAMBDA
      COMMON/ELEC/XELEC,YELEC,SHIFLEFT,SHIFRIGH
      COMMON/COMB/WW,AMBDA,APERTURE,FRAME,TAP,GAP,
     &ISIGN,IDOUBL
      COMMON/MSC/DA1,DA2,W1,W2,SHIFTX,SHIFTY,CENTRE,
     &MODE,NBSTOP
      LOGICAL    FRAME,TAP
      LOGICAL CENTRE
      CALL PLOTS(0.1)
      CALL FACTOR(0.95)
      CALL PLOT(15.,8.,-3)
      Y1=APERTURE/2.+LAMBDA
      Y2=-Y1
      Y3=Y1
      Y4=-Y3
      GAP=E*W
      PDOU=0.25
      IF(IDOUBL.GT.0)PDOU=0.125
      PRINT:"IDOUBL=",IDOUBL
      XDEBUT=(TAU(1)-PDOU)*LAMBDA
      XFIN=(TAU(N)+PDOU)*LAMBDA
      IF(ITYPE.EQ.2)GO TO 400
      DTMIN=TAU(2)-TAU(1)
      PRINT:"DTMIN=",DTMIN
```

```
      X=(TAU(1)-PDOU*DTMIN/ABS(DTMIN))*LAMBDA
      K=1;JVIEN=1;JTYP=2
      IF(SIG.LT.0)JTYP=1
      GO TO 200
  150 JVIEN=2
      AA=A(1);BB=AA
      DO 190 K=1,N
      IF(K.LT.N)BB=A(K+1)
      X=(TAU(K)+PDOU*DTMIN/ABS(DTMIN))*LAMBDA
      IF(BB*AA.GE.0.)GO TO 170
      JTYP=3+MOD(JTYP,2)
      GO TO 200
  170 JTYP=1+MOD(JTYP,2)
      GO TO 200
  190 AA=BB
      GO TO 600
  200 GO TO (210,220,230,240),JTYP
  210 YA=Y3;YB=YTOP(K)+GAP
      YC=YTOP(K);YD=Y2;GO TO 300
  220 YA=Y1;YB=YBOT(K)
      YC=YBOT(K)-GAP;YD=Y4;GO TO 300
  230 YA=Y1;YB=YTOP(K)+GAP
      YC=YTOP(K);YD=Y2;GO TO 300
  240 YA=Y1;YB=YBOT(K)
      YC=YBOT(K)-GAP;YD=Y2
  300 CALL FINGER(JTYP,YA,YB,YC,YD,X)
      IF(JTYP.EQ.3)GO TO 301
      IF(JTYP.EQ.4)GO TO 302
      GO TO 303
  301 JTYP=4;GO TO 303
  302 JTYP=3;GO TO 303
  303 GO TO (150,190,600),JVIEN
  400 CONTINUE
      DTMIN=TAU(2)-TAU(1)
      PRINT:"DTMIN=",DTMIN
      JTYP=1;AA=A(1);GAP=E*W
      IF(SIG.LT.0)JTYP=2
      DO 550 K=1,N
      IF(A(K)*AA.LT.0.)JTYP=JTYP+1
      JTYP=1+MOD(JTYP,2)
      X=(TAU(K)-PDOU*DTMIN/ABS(DTMIN))*LAMBDA
      GO TO (530,540),JTYP
  530 YA=Y3;YB=YTOP(K)+GAP
      YC=YTOP(K);YD=Y2
      CALL  FINGER(JTYP,YA,YB,YC,YD,X)
      IF(JTYP.EQ.2)GO TO 545
      X=(TAU(K)+PDOU*DTMIN/ABS(DTMIN))*LAMBDA
  540 YA=Y1;YB=YBOT(K)
      YC=YBOT(K)-GAP;YD=Y4
      CALL FINGER(JTYP,YA,YB,YC,YD,X)
      X=(TAU(K)+PDOU*DTMIN/ABS(DTMIN))*LAMBDA
      IF(JTYP.EQ.2)GO TO 530
  545 IF(ABS(DTMIN).LT.1.)GO TO 550
      IF(K.EQ.N)GO TO 550
      PSUP=2.*PDOU*DTMIN/ABS(DTMIN)
      XS=X+PSUP*LAMBDA
      IF(IDOUBL.GT.0)GO TO 546
      NDSUP=ABS(DTMIN)*2.-2.
      DO 512 KD=1,NDSUP
      CALL FINGER(JTYP,YA,YB,YC,YD,XS)
  512 XS=XS+PSUP*LAMBDA
      GO TO 547
  546 NDSUP=ABS(DTMIN)*4.-2.
      DO 513 KD=1,NDSUP
      CALL FINGER(JTYP,YA,YB,YC,YD,XS)
  513 XS=XS+PSUP*LAMBDA
  547 CONTINUE
  550 AA=A(K)
  600 CONTINUE
```

```
      IF(.NOT.FRAME)RETURN
      IF(.NOT.CENTRE)GO TO 610
      X1=(TAU(1)-1.)*LAMBDA
      X1=AMIN1(X1,-XELEC/2.)
      X2=-X1
      GO TO 620
  610 X1=AMIN1(XDEBUT,XFIN-XELEC)
      X2=XFIN
  620 CONTINUE
      X3=X1+SHIFLEFT
      X4=X2-SHIFRIGH
      Y1=APERTURE/2.
      Y2=-Y1
      Y3=Y1+YELEC
      Y4=-Y3
      Y5=Y1+LAMBDA
      Y6=-Y5
      IF(.NOT.TAP)GO TO 800
      IF(SHIFLEFT+SHIFRIGH.GT.0.)GO TO 900
  700 CONTINUE
      RETURN
  800 CONTINUE
      CALL TRACE(X1,Y1,3)
      CALL TRACE(X1,Y3,2)
      CALL TRACE(X2,Y3,2)
      CALL TRACE(X2,Y1,2)
      CALL TRACE(X1,Y1,2)
      CALL TRACE(X1,Y2,3)
      CALL TRACE(X1,Y4,2)
      CALL TRACE(X2,Y4,2)
      CALL TRACE(X2,Y2,2)
      CALL TRACE(X1,Y2,2)
      RETURN
  900 CONTINUE
      IF(SHIFLEFT+SHIFRIGH.GT.X2-X1)GO TO 1000
      IF(SHIFLEFT.GT.0.)X1=AMIN1(XDEBUT,X3)
      IF(SHIFRIGH.GT.0.)X2=AMAX1(XFIN,X4)
      RETURN
 1000 Y3=Y5;Y4=Y6;GO TO 700
      END
      SUBROUTINE FINGER(JTYP,YA,YB,YC,YD,X)
      COMMON/JJJ/J
 9001 FORMAT(1X,I2,5F8.4)
      IF(ABS(YA+YD).LT.1.E-2)GO TO 5
      NEUTRE=1
      IF(NEUTRE.GT.0)GO TO 5
      CALL FINGR1(YA,YB,YC,YD,X);GO TO 100
    5 CONTINUE
   10 J=J+1
      IF(MOD(J,2).EQ.0)GO TO 20
      IF(YB.GT.YA)GO TO 15
      CALL TRACE(X,YA,3)
      CALL TRACE(X,YB,2)
   15 IF(YD.GT.YC)GO TO 100
      CALL TRACE(X,YC,3)
      CALL TRACE(X,YD,2);GO TO 100
   20 IF(YC.LT.YD)GO TO 25
      CALL TRACE(X,YD,3)
      CALL TRACE(X,YC,2)
   25 IF(YA.LT.YB)GO TO 100
      CALL TRACE(X,YB,3)
      CALL TRACE(X,YA,2)
  100 RETURN
      END
      SUBROUTINE FINGR1(YA,YB,YC,YD,X)
      COMMON/JJJ/J
      ITYP=1
      IF(ABS(YA).GT.ABS(YD))ITYP=2
   10 J=J+1
```

```
      IF(ITYP.EQ.2)GO TO 100
      IF(MOD(J,2).EQ.0)GO TO 20
      CALL TRACE (X,YC,3)
      CALL TRACE (X,YD,2)
      RETURN
  20  CALL TRACE(X,YD,3)
      CALL TRACE(X,YC,2)
      RETURN
 100  IF(MOD(J,2).EQ.0)GO TO 120
      CALL TRACE(X,YA,3)
      CALL TRACE(X,YB,2)
      RETURN
 120  CALL TRACE(X,YB,3)
      CALL TRACE(X,YA,2)
      RETURN
      END
```

Appendix L

PEIGNE

Program of matching of SAW transducers.

```
      PRINT:"    *** MATCHING OF SAW REGULAR TRANSDUCER"
     &," ***"
      CHARACTER TEST
      REAL LAMBDA,K2
      COMPLEX Z
      PI=3.141592653
      EPSO=1./36./PI/1.E9
  10  CONTINUE
      PRINT:"-- Description of the piezoelectric"
     &," substrate --"
      PRINT:"Relative dielectric constant EPS ?"
      READ :EPS
      IF(EPS.LT.1.E-37)STOP
      PRINT:"Piezoelectric coupling K2 (%) ?"
      READ:K2
      PRINT:"Acoustic velocity V (m/s) ?"
      READ:V
      PRINT:"-- Transducer parameters --"
  15  PRINT:"Frequency F (MHz) ?"
      READ:F
      IF(F.GT.1.E-37)GO TO 7
      PRINT:"Wavelength LAMBDA (+m) ?"
      READ:LAMBDA
      IF(LAMBDA .LT.1.E-37)GO TO 10
      F=V/LAMBDA
   7  CONTINUE
      PRINT:" "
      PRINT:"EPS=",EPS
      PRINT:"K2=",K2," %"
      PRINT:"V=",V," m/s"
      PRINT:"F=",F," MHz"
      PRINT:"LAMBDA=",V/F," MICRONS"
      EPST=EPS*EPSO
      OMEGA=2.*PI*F*1.E6
      FF=F*1.E6
      W=1.2*K2*1.E-2/EPST/OMEGA/50.
      X=1./EPST/W/OMEGA
      R=50.
      PRINT:"-- Transducer aperture width W --"
```

```
      PRINT:"W (50 OHMS)=",W*1000.," mm"
      PRINT:"CAPACITANCE=",EPST*W*1.E12," pF per finger"
   &," pair"
      PRINT:"     REACTANCE=",X," OHMS for 1 pair"
      PRINT:" "
 20   PRINT:"New W (mm) ?"
      READ:W
      IF(W.GT.0.)GO TO 17
      PRINT:"Interdigital comb (1) or grating array (2)"
      READ:ITYPE
      PRINT:"Number of fingers ?"
      READ:N
      N=N-1
      X=-X*2./N
      IF(ITYPE.LE.1)GO TO 30
      X=X*N**2
      R=R*N**2
 30   CONTINUE
      PRINT:"Radiation resistance = ",R
      PRINT:"Total reactance = ",X
      PRINT:"*"
      PRINT:"Additional spurious impedances:"
      PRINT:"Ohmic series resistance (OHMS) ?"
      READ:RP
      R=R+RP
      Z=CMPLX(R,X)
      PRINT:"Parallel capacitance (pF) ?"
      READ:CP
      Z=1./(1./Z+CMPLX(0.,1.E-12*CP*OMEGA))
      R=REAL(Z)
      X=AIMAG(Z)
      PRINT:"Series inductance (nH) ?"
      READ:SP
      X=X+1.E-9*SP*OMEGA
      PRINT:"Actual unmatched impedance :"
      PRINT:"R=",R," OHMS"
      PRINT:"X=",X," OHMS"
      Z=CMPLX(R,X)
      RAU=CABS((50.-Z)/(50.+Z))
      TOS=(1+RAU)/(1.-RAU)
      PRINT:"Reflection coefficient on 50-Ohm load"
   &," RAU=",RAU
      PRINT:"RWR=",TOS
      PRINT:"Matching (yes/no) ?"
      READ:TEST;IF(TEST.EQ."yes")TEST="YES"
      IF(TEST.NE."YES")GO TO 15
      CALL ADAPTA(R,X,FF)
      PRINT:" "
      PRINT:"***"
      GO TO 15
 17   CONTINUE
      W=W/1000.
      R=1.2*1.E-2*K2/EPST/W/OMEGA
      X=1./EPST/W/OMEGA
      PRINT:" "
      PRINT:"Radiation resistance = ",R
      PRINT:"Capacitance = ",EPST*W*1.E12," pF"
      PRINT:"     REACTANCE=",X," OHMS per pair"
      PRINT:" "
      GO TO 20
      END
      SUBROUTINE ADAPTA(R,X,F)
      COMPLEX Z,Z1,CMPLX
      Z=CMPLX(R,X)
      R0=50.
      NR=0
      IF(R.GT.R0)GO TO 100
      D=-SQRT(R*(R0-R))
      DO 50 I=1,2
```

```
      D=-D
      NR=NR+1
      PRINT:" "
      PRINT:" ***    SOLUTION NR ",NR
      X1=D-X
      X2=-R*R0/D
      PRINT:" In series with the transducer :"
      CALL IDENTI(X1,F)
      PRINT:" In parallel on the port : "
      CALL IDENTI(X2,F)
      Z=CMPLX(R,X)
      Z1=Z+CMPLX(0.,X1)
      Z=1./(1./Z1+1./CMPLX(0.,X2))
      PRINT:"VERIFICATION: Z=",Z
   50 CONTINUE
  100 D=(R0*X)**2+R0*(R-R0)*(X**2+R**2)
      IF(D.LT.0.)GO TO 200
      D=-SQRT(D)
      DO 150 I=1,2
      D=-D
      NR=NR+1
      PRINT:" "
      PRINT:" ***    SOLUTION NR ",NR
      X2=(X*R0+D)/(R-R0)
      X1=-X2*(R**2+X*(X+X2))/(R**2+(X+X2)**2)
      PRINT:" In parallel on the transducer : "
      CALL IDENTI(X2,F)
      PRINT:" IN SERIES WITH THE PORT :"
      CALL IDENTI(X1,F)
      Z=CMPLX(R,X)
      Z1=1./(1./Z+1./CMPLX(0.,X2))
      Z=Z1+CMPLX(0.,X1)
      PRINT:"VERIFICATION: Z=",Z
  150 CONTINUE
  200 IF(NR.EQ.0)PRINT:"No solution"
      RETURN
      END
      SUBROUTINE IDENTI(X,F)
      PI=3.141592653
      OMEGA=2.*PI*F
      IF(X)100,200,300
  100 VALEUR=1./X/OMEGA
      VALEUR=VALEUR*1.E12
      PRINT 1,-VALEUR
      PRINT 3,X
      PRINT:" "
      RETURN
  200 PRINT:"Short circuit"
      PRINT:" "
      RETURN
  300 VALEUR=X/OMEGA*1.E9
      PRINT 2, VALEUR
      PRINT 3,X
      PRINT:" "
      RETURN
    1 FORMAT(" One capacitance of ",F12.2,"   pF")
    2 FORMAT(" One inductance ",F12.2,"   nH")
    3 FORMAT("(REACTANCE=",F12.4,"  OHMS)")
      END
```

Appendix M

ATAFIC

Miscellaneous library routines used in the previous programs.

Library routine ATAFIC to create/attach files.

```
      SUBROUTINE ATAFIC(IFILE,IPERME)
*IFILE = file code
*IPERME = 1 for reading or 2 for writing
      COMMON/CATAFI/FICHIER
      CHARACTER FICHE*20,FICHIER*21
      CHARACTER CARA*1(20)
      CHARACTER FIC*8,FIC1*9
      DATA IAPL/0/
      PRINT:"FILE NAME ?"
      IF(IAPL.NE.0) GOTO 19
      PRINT:"(EXAMPLE: /CATA/FICHE)"
   19 IAPL=1
      READ:FICHE
      IF(FICHE.EQ." ")STOP"bye "
      ENCODE(FICHIER,9001)FICHE
*This system programme is used to attach files
      CALL ATTACH(IFILE,FICHIER,IPERME,0,ISTAT)
      IF(ISTAT.EQ.4)GO TO 100
      ISTAT=ISTAT/100000
      IF(ISTAT.EQ.-342758)GO TO 100
      RETURN
  100 CONTINUE
      PRINT:"File cannot be accessed"
      IF(IPERME.EQ.1)RETURN
      DECODE(FICHE,9002)(CARA(I),I=1,20)
      DO 110 I=1,20
      K=21-I
      IF(CARA(K).EQ."/")GO TO 150
  110 CONTINUE
      K1=1;K2=8;GO TO 160
  150 CONTINUE
      K1=K+1;K2=MIN0(K+8,20)
      CARA(I)=" "
  160 CONTINUE
      ENCODE(FIC,9003)(CARA(I),I=K1,K2)
      ENCODE(FIC1,9004)FIC
      PRINT : "A temporary file is to be created"
      PRINT:
*System routine DEFIL to create temporary files
      CALL DEFIL(FIC,12,0,ISTAT)
      CALL ATTACH(IFILE,FIC1,IPERME,0,ISTAT)
      IF(ISTAT.EQ.4)STOP"ERROR"
      PRINT : "Temporary file ",FIC," created"
      RETURN
 9001 FORMAT(A20,";")
 9002 FORMAT(20A1)
 9003 FORMAT(8A1)
 9004 FORMAT(A8,";")
      END
```

COURBE

Library routine COURBE to plot "stars".

```
      SUBROUTINE COURBE(X,Y,NB PT)
*Plotting diagrammes X(I),Y(I),I=1,NBPT with "stars" (*)
*to be used with alphanumeric consoles
*Input : coordinates X(.),Y(.) and number of points NBPT
      INTEGER WORD(32,2)
      CHARACTER IMAGE *1(64)
      REAL X(1),Y(1)
      NBWORD=2
      NBLIN=18
      NBCOL=64
      LINEA=12
      PRINT:""
      XMIN=X(1)
      XMAX=XMIN
      YMIN=Y(1)
      YMAX=YMIN
      DO 20 I=2,NBPT
      XMIN=AMIN1(XMIN,X(I))
      XMAX=AMAX1(XMAX,X(I))
      YMIN=AMIN1(YMIN,Y(I))
   20 YMAX=AMAX1(YMAX,Y(I))
      DX=(XMAX-XMIN)/(NBCOL-1)
      DY=(YMAX-YMIN)/(NBLIN-1)
      DO 30 LIN=1,NBLIN
      DO 30 KWORD=1,NBWORD
   30 WORD(LIN,KWORD)=0
      DO 40 K=1,NBPT
      NX=.5+(X(K)-XMIN)/DX
      LIN=(YMAX-Y(K))/DY+1.5
      KWORD=NX/32+1
      KA=2**(KWORD*32-NX)
      L=WORD(LIN,KWORD)
      IF((L-(L/KA)*KA).GE.(KA/2))GO TO 40
      WORD(LIN,KWORD)=L+KA/2
   40 CONTINUE
      DO 100 LIN=1,NBLIN
      DO 50 KWORD=1,NBWORD
      IMA=1+32*KWORD
      L=WORD(LIN,KWORD)
      DO 50 I=1,8
      N=L-(L/16)*16
      DO 70 K=1,4
      IMA=IMA-1
      IA=N-(N/2)*2
      IF(IA.EQ.1)IMAGE(IMA)="*"
      IF(IA.NE.1)IMAGE(IMA)=" "
   70 N=N/2
   50 L=L/16
      DO 80 I=1,64
      J=65-I
   80 IF(IMAGE(J).NE." ")GO TO 100
  100 PRINT 1000,((IMAGE(NIM)),NIM=1,J)
      PRINT 1100,
      RETURN
 9001 FORMAT(1X,A4)
 1000 FORMAT(1X,1HI,64A1)
 1100  FORMAT(64(1H-))
      END
```

COUVIS

Library routine COUVIS for graphic display.

```
      SUBROUTINE COUVIS(X,Y,NBPT)
*Input : coordinates X(.),Y(.), Number of points NBPT
*Plotting curves on graphic terminal
*Standard Tektronix YT4010
*System routines PLOT PLOTS FACTOR are in system library
      REAL X(1),Y(1)
      XMIN=1.E30 ;YMIN=1.E30 ; XMAX=-1.E30 ;YMAX=-1.E30
      DO 10 I=1,NBPT
      XMIN=AMIN1(XMIN,X(I));YMIN=AMIN1(YMIN,Y(I))
      XMAX=AMAX1(XMAX,X(I));YMAX=AMAX1(YMAX,Y(I))
   10 CONTINUE
      CALL PLOTS(0.1)
      CALL FACTOR(10.)
      CALL PLOT(0.5,0.3,-3)
      DO 20 I=1,NBPT-1
      DX=(X(I)-XMIN)/(XMAX-XMIN)
      DY=(Y(I)-YMIN)/(YMAX-YMIN)
      IF(I.EQ.1)CALL PLOT(DX,DY,3)
      CALL PLOT(DX,DY,2)
   20 CONTINUE
      CALL PLOT(0.,0.,3)
      CALL PLOT (0.,0.,999)
      RETURN
      END
```

TEMPS

Library routine TEMPS to define memory size and processor time.

```
      SUBROUTINE TEMPS
      COMMON/TEMPROC/TPROC1,TPROC2,TPROC3,TPROC,TPROCTOT
     &,ITPROC
*System routine PTIME
      CALL PTIME(TPROC3)
      IF(ITPROC.NE.0)GO TO 5
      TPROC1=TPROC3
      TPROC2=TPROC3
      PRINT:" "
*System routine MEMSIZ
      CALL MEMSIZ(ISIZE)
      PRINT 20,ISIZE
    5 PRINT:" "
      ITPROC=ITPROC+1
      TPROC=TPROC3-TPROC2
      TPROC=TPROC*3600.
      TPROC2=TPROC3
      TPROCTOT=3600.*(TPROC3-TPROC1)
      IF(ITPROC.EQ.1)RETURN
      PRINT 10,TPROC,TPROCTOT
   10 FORMAT(/1X,"Processor time used =",F12.7," seconds"
     & ,1X,"TOTAL=",F12.7," seconds"/)
   20 FORMAT(1X,"Memory size =",I3," K  ")
      RETURN
      END
```

INDEX